FUNDAMENTALS OF HORTICULTURE

FUNDA
of HORTI

MENTALS
CULTURE

Third Edition

A Textbook Designed for Courses
in Basic or General Horticulture

J. B. Edmond
Professor Emeritus of Horticulture
Mississippi State University
Recipient, L. M. Ware Distinguished Teaching Award
Southern Region, American Society for Horticulture Science, 1959

T. L. Senn
Professor of Horticulture
Clemson College

F. S. Andrews
Associate Professor of Horticulture
Virginia Polytechnic Institute

McGraw-Hill Book Company
New York   San Francisco   Toronto   London

Dedicated to the memory of
FREDERICK CHARLES BRADFORD
(1887–1950)
outstanding teacher
of students in horticulture

In 1936 the first courses in fruit production and vegetable gardening at Clemson Agricultural College were combined into one course entitled "General Horticulture," and a mimeographed text was prepared for the use of the students. A second and revised edition of this text was brought out in 1941, and, following the suggestions and encouragement of several colleagues, the material was prepared as a published text in 1951 under the title of *Fundamentals of Horticulture*. Since 1951 *Fundamentals of Horticulture* has been adopted by several junior and senior colleges and universities throughout the country as a basis for the work in the first, or basic, course in horticulture. Thus, the text seems to be meeting a real need and suggests possibilities of going through several more editions.

The purpose of the text is threefold: to provide an opportunity for the student (1) to acquire a working knowledge of the fundamentals of plant growth, (2) to develop the ability to apply the fundamentals to the solution of practical problems, and (3) to obtain an appreciation of the significance of horticulture in human affairs. To meet these objectives, the text discusses the fundamentals, particularly the processes of photosynthesis, respiration, and water absorption and transpiration, and applies the fundamental processes to the growth and development of plants and to the solution of plant-production problems. Thus, the book is primarily a "why" book. As Gardner, Bradford, and Hooker,[1] Gardner,[2] Thompson,[3]

[1] V. R. Gardner, F. C. Bradford, and H. D. Hooker, *Orcharding,* New York, McGraw-Hill Book Company, Inc., 1927.
[2] V. R. Gardner, *Basic Horticulture,* New York, The Macmillan Company, 1942.
[3] H. C. Thompson, *Vegetable Crops,* 2d ed., New York, McGraw-Hill Book Company, Inc., 1931.

and others have pointed out, the primary purpose of a college education is to teach the student to think for himself. For this reason, particular emphasis is placed on teaching the student to understand the fundamentals underlying a given practice rather than to acquire proficiency in any given operation.

In common with other life sciences, horticulture is dynamic. As a result of research, new knowledge is leading to a more complete understanding of plant behavior. Accordingly, the third edition retains the emphasis on the manufacture and disposition of the carbohydrates characteristic of the first and second editions, and in addition it discusses the significance of hormones and related substances in plant growth and development. Further, the text presents the subject matter from the point of view that the green plant is essentially a biochemical factory. From their experience in class, the authors believe that the presentation of the subject matter from this point of view will lead to a more accurate understanding of plant behavior and plant-production problems.

As were the first and second editions, this text is divided into three parts: Part 1, a study of the fundamental processes; Part 2, the application of the fundamental processes to horticultural practices; and Part 3, a discussion of the principal horticultural crops. Within each part, and for the book as a whole, the authors have endeavored to present a well-balanced view of the entire field rather than only the field in which they have been trained or with which they are the most familiar or have had the most experience. Thus, in Parts 1 and 2, as far as research data permit, fruit, vegetable, and ornamental plants have been used to show the effect of environment and practices on the growth, development, and yields of horticultural crops. Further, three chapters in Part 3 have been given over to each of the three main groups: fruits, vegetables, and ornamentals. In other words, *Fundamentals of Horticulture* transcends departmentalization of knowledge within the field of horticulture. Thus, it should appeal to and be equally valuable for students who are interested primarily in the growing of fruits, or vegetables, or ornamentals, or in other phases of crop production.

The use of the book should eliminate the necessity of taking extensive notes in class—always a time-consuming practice—and, as a result, provide more time for discussion and explanation of important points and, if desirable, for a more extended coverage of the field of horticulture. In addition, a study of any given chapter prior to its discussion in class will place the responsibility for fundamentals on the student and afford greater opportunity to the instructor to make local, regional, national, or world-wide application.

Although many factors operate simultaneously on any given process, the text has been developed on the assumption that effective teaching consists, partially at least, in the presentation of the effect of one factor at a time. In general, students at the freshman and sophomore levels can hardly be expected to grasp and understand fully at first the effect of two or more factors interacting on any given process. As their knowledge of the subject matter increases, the relative influence of two or more factors on the same process can be more fully understood and appreciated.

The authors believe that the text is applicable to courses in general horticulture given on either the semester or the quarter basis. To achieve the objectives of the book, not all the chapters need be assigned. This is particularly true of certain chapters in Part 2 and all the chapters in Part 3. For example, since time may not permit a discussion of all the chapters in Part 3, representative chapters may be selected from each of the three main groups of crops: fruits, vegetables, and ornamentals. For example, students in the northeast or middle western regions may be more interested in the apple or potato, whereas those in the southeast region may be more interested in the citrus fruits, pecan, or sweetpotato.

In conclusion, the authors express appreciation to all colleagues and coworkers who have assisted in any way in the preparation of this text. In particular, they are indebted to Dr. Leon C. Snyder of University of Minnesota for reviewing the entire manuscript and making several suggestions for its improvement; to Dr. E. W. McElwee of University of Florida and Professor Ferris S. Batson formerly of Mississippi State University for suggestions on the development of Chapters 23, 24, and 25; to Dr. Jackson B. Hester, Elkton, Maryland, for use of the cuts for Figs. 9.4, 11.1, and 13.1; to Mr. Robert W. Gray of Virginia Polytechnic Institute for making the drawings for Figs. 25.2 and 25.3; to the several coworkers who provided photographs; and to Professor Alex Laurie formerly of The Ohio State University, Dr. William L. Giles and Dr. Walter J. Drapala both of Mississippi State University for their encouragement. The authors also extend thanks to Miss Jacqueline Mullen for assistance in typing the manuscript.

J. B. Edmond
T. L. Senn
F. S. Andrews

CONTENTS

PLANT GROWTH AND DEVELOPMENT 1

FUNDAMENTAL PLANT PROCESSES

*And ye shall know the truth
and the truth shall make you free.*
John 8:32

The fundamental processes in higher plants are (1) photosynthesis, (2) respiration, and (3) water absorption and transpiration. The student should have a working knowledge of these processes in order to acquire the ability to understand plant growth and development.

PHOTOSYNTHESIS

Nature of Photosynthesis. Photosynthesis is essentially a biochemical reaction. Carbon dioxide and water combine through the agency of chlorophyll and enzymes and in the presence of light in the formation of the initial food substances, the soluble carbohydrates and related compounds. In this reaction the kinetic energy of light is transformed to the potential or chemical energy of foods. Thus, the energy that comes from the sun is fixed in usable form in the green tissues of plants, and a supply of energy is made available for almost all living things on the surface of the earth. This fundamental reaction is illustrated as follows:

(chlorophyll and enzymes)
Carbon dioxide + water + light ⎯⎯⎯⎯⎯⎯⎯⎯⎯⎯→
initial food substances + oxygen

Photosynthesis is essentially a manufacturing process. The chloroplasts, small blobs of protoplasm inside the manufacturing cells, are the individual factories. Carbon dioxide and water are the raw materials, and the initial food substances are the first manufactured compounds. Chlorophyll

3

may be considered as the machinery, the enzymes as lubricators of the machinery, and oxygen as the by-product.

Photosynthesis and the Entire Plant.   As previously stated, the initial food substances are made in the green tissues, usually the leaves. From these substances a wide variety of other compounds are made. These compounds may be made in the leaves or in many other parts of the plant. Two examples should suffice: (1) When the meristem of the roots or stems is dividing, it is making protoplasm. Protoplasm requires the formation of proteins, and proteins in turn require the combination of certain sugars and certain compounds containing nitrogen. The sugars are made in the leaves and are translocated to the meristem of the roots or stems where they combine with compounds containing nitrogen in the formation of proteins. (2) When the tubers of the potato are developing, large quantities of starch are stored in the tissues. This starch is made in the tubers from an initial food substance called glucose. Here again, the glucose is made in the leaves and translocated to the storage tissue of the tubers where it is changed to starch. The same situation exists in the formation of many other compounds, such as the hydrophilic colloids, the pigments, fats, cellulose, and compound celluloses. Thus, two facts should be kept in mind: (1) The initial food substances are made in the leaves; and (2) from these substances, a wide variety of other compounds are made not only in the leaves, but also in other parts of the plant. For these reasons, the entire plant should be considered as a chemical factory.

The making of the many manufactured compounds from the initial food substances is illustrated as follows:

Initial food substances ⟶ **foods, fibers, enzymes, hormones, and vitamins**

FOODS

In general, foods supply all living things with a source of energy and compounds for the making and maintenance of living cells and living tissues. They comprise three great groups: (1) the carbohydrates and related substances, (2) the lipides and related substances, and (3) the proteins. From the standpoint of plant growth and development, the carbohydrates are particularly important.

The Carbohydrates and Related Substances.   The carbohydrates contain the elements carbon, hydrogen, and oxygen. In general, they are the principal constituents of all plant tissues; for example, the dry matter of a 56-pound bushel of sweetpotatoes weighs from 19 to 20 pounds. Of these 19 to 20 pounds, 17 to 18 pounds consist of carbohydrates. Important carbohydrates and related substances are sugars, starch and related compounds, pectic substances, hydrophilic colloids, and certain pigments.

Sugars. Important sugars in plants are glucose, fructose, and sucrose. Glucose is considered to be the most commonly transported sugar and the main sugar used in respiration. Thus, glucose is present in all living cells. Fructose is very sweet and as such augments the quality of many fruits. On the other hand, sucrose is a storage form of carbohydrate. Certain crops have the ability to store relatively large quantities of sucrose, e.g., sugar beet and sugarcane.

Starch and Related Compounds. Starch is the most important energy reserve or storage carbohydrate in plants. It is made from glucose. During photosynthesis glucose is made and changed to starch which occurs as grains in the chloroplasts. During the night the starch is changed to glucose and translocated to other parts of the plant where it is either used or stored. For example, if the glucose is translocated to the meristem or cambia, it is used in the making of new cells or in respiration, or if it is translocated to storage tissues, it is changed back to starch or used in respiration. As is well known, certain crops have the ability to store large quantities of starch. In fact, some of these crops develop storage structures for this purpose, such as the tubers of the potato and the fleshy roots of the sweetpotato and carrot. Substances closely related to starch are inulin, the chief storage carbohydrate of the Jerusalem artichoke, and hemicellulose, the chief storage carbohydrate in the tissues of many woody plants and in the endosperm of many seeds.

Pectic Substances. Pectic substances include (1) protopectin, (2) a compound which appears to be a mixture of calcium and magnesium pectate, and (3) pectin. Protopectin is found in abundant quantities in the primary cell wall, particularly in meristem and parenchyma; the mixture of calcium and magnesium pectate is found in the middle lamella; and pectin is formed from protopectin. The function of the protopectin and the mixture of calcium-magnesium pectate is to hold the cellulose chains together in cell wall formation. In this way, the cells of a given tissue are held together and form a compact group.

The rate of change of protopectin to pectin is associated with the ripening of many fruits. For example, the cell walls of the apple, pear, and tomato contain large quantities of protopectin. As these fruits ripen, the protopectin gradually changes to pectin which is soluble. Ripening of these fruits is, therefore, associated with a certain degree of softening or lack of resistance to pressure.

Hydrophilic Substances. Hydrophilic substances include pectins, pentosans, and perhaps certain proteins. These substances are colloidal in nature; that is, an individual colloidal particle consists of numerous molecules acting together as a unit. These particles possess a large surface in proportion to their size. This surface attracts large quantities of water, hence the name "hydrophilic," meaning "water loving." The adsorbed water is called bound water. Bound water acts more like a solid than a liquid and cannot be frozen at ordinary temperatures. Thus, the making of the hydrophilic colloids by the protoplasm is the basis for hardiness and particularly for resistance to low winter temperatures.

Pigments. Pigments are chemical compounds which stimulate the retina of the eye and give the sensation of color. In other words, they provide for distinctive color. In general, there are two kinds: (1) plastid and (2) sap. Plastid pigments occur in the surface of plastids—small blobs of protoplasm within certain cells. Principal plastid pigments are (1) chlorophyll, (2) carotene, (3) xanthophyll, and (4) lycopene. Chlorophyll is the green pigment of higher plants. Actually it consists of two pigments, chlorophyll a and chlorophyll b. In both pigments magnesium is the center of the molecule, and pyrrole rings containing nitrogen are on the outside. Thus, both magnesium and nitrogen are essential for chlorophyll formation. *The function of chlorophyll is the absorption of light for the combination of carbon dioxide and water in the photosynthetic reaction.* In this way, a source of energy is made available for practically all living things. For this reason, chlorophyll is considered to be the most important organic compound known to man.

Carotene and xanthophyll are yellow pigments. Carotene is associated with chlorophyll and thus occurs in all green tissues. In addition, it is stored in the fleshy roots of carrots, in yellow-fleshed varieties of sweet-potatoes, turnips, and rutabagas and occurs in tomato fruits and yellow-fleshed varieties of peaches. Since carotene is the precursor, or "mother," substance of vitamin A, the compound necessary for normal vision, it is particularly important in human nutrition. Lycopene is one of the pigments of red varieties of tomatoes and peppers and the pigment of red-fleshed varieties of watermelons and pink-fleshed varieties of grapefruit.

The principal sap pigments are (1) the anthocyanins and (2) the anthoxanthins. The anthocyanins are responsible for the reds, blues, and purples of many flowers, fruits, and vegetables; the anthoxanthins are responsible for the yellows and ivories. These compounds are rather complex in chemical constitution and contain, with other groups, one or two molecules of sugar in their molecular structure; hence sugars are necessary for their formation.

The Lipides and Related Substances. Lipides comprise fats, waxes, sterols, and lipins. Fats contain the same elements as the carbohydrates—carbon, hydrogen, and oxygen—only in different proportion. In general, they are relatively high in hydrogen and low in oxygen and have a high energy value per unit weight. Thus, from the standpoint of the plant, fats are excellent reserve energy materials. The formation of fats from carbohydrates is illustrated as follows:

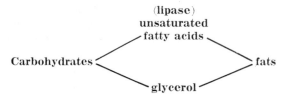

Note that carbohydrates, usually sugars, break down and form unsaturated fatty acids and glycerol, the trihydric alcohol. These combine in the formation of fats.

Waxes occur in the cuticle of the epidermis of plants, and thus they reduce transpiration. They in turn are made from accumulated carbohydrates. Sterols are complex secondary alcohols. An important sterol is ergosterol. When ergosterol is irradiated with ultraviolet light, it is changed into several substances, including calciferol, or vitamin D_2. Lipins are fatty-like substances containing nitrogen and phosphorus. An important lipin is deoxyribonucleic acid, called DNA. This compound is found in all living cells, particularly in the nucleus.

Substances which are usually discussed with the lipides are the essential oils. Essential oils are responsible for the distinctive odors and flavors of plants. They are not oils in the strict sense, but since they are soluble in petroleum ether and similar compounds, they are discussed with the fats. Important essential oils are oil of lemon, wintergreen, cloves, peppermint, menthol, camphor, thymol, and the allylpropyl sulfides characteristic of the onion family.

The Proteins. Proteins are colloids of high molecular weight and of complex chemical composition. All proteins contain the elements carbon, hydrogen, oxygen, and nitrogen. In addition, some proteins contain phosphorus and others contain sulfur. Proteins are made from sugars, usually glucose, combining with certain compounds containing nitrogen. Amino acids are the first substances formed. These then condense in the formation of the complex proteins. Steps in the process are (1) the reduction of nitrate-nitrogen to ammonium-nitrogen, (2) the reaction of sugars with the ammonium compounds in the formation of amino acids, and (3) the condensation of the amino acids in the formation of proteins. The reaction is illustrated as follows:

$$NO_3\text{—}N \xrightarrow{\text{(reductase)}} NH_4\text{—}N + sugar \xrightarrow{\text{(enzymes)}} amino\ acids \xrightarrow{\text{(condensation)}} proteins$$
(nitrate-nitrogen)

Protoplasm, the living substance, consists mostly of proteins.

Fibers. Fibers are long, thick-walled dead cells which dovetail into each other and often occur as continuous strands. In general, their function is to hold stems erect, enabling the stems to bear large crops of flowers and fruit and to withstand the stress and strain due to the wind. Cellulose is the principal constituent of fibers. In fact, cellulose is the chief structural framework material of plants. For example, the primary cell wall consists largely of cellulose and pectic materials which bind the cellulose fibers together. As the cells become older, or more mature, the cellulose fibers become impregnated with other substances, such as lignin, forming lignocellulose which is characteristic of woody plants, or with suberin, a fatty-like material forming adipocellulose which is characteristic of the cork layers or periderm. Certain crops are grown principally for their ability to make large quantities of cellulose fibers, e. g., cotton and flax.

NONFOODS

The principal nonfoods are enzymes, hormones, and vitamins. In general, enzymes, hormones, and vitamins differ from the foods in that they do not supply plants with energy or compounds for the formation and repair of living tissues, but they facilitate the fixation or release of energy in the numerous chemical reactions taking place in plants.

Enzymes. In crop plants thousands of chemical reactions are taking place at the same time. These reactions occur at a relatively low temperature level, and, in a sense, certain substances are necessary to take the place of high temperatures. These substances are the enzymes. In general, enzymes are in the colloidal state; they consist of proteins with or without some other compound; they are effective in minute concentration; and they are specific in action. For example, sucrase is an enzyme which is necessary for the splitting of one molecule of sucrose in the formation of one molecule of glucose and one molecule of fructose, and catalase is an enzyme associated with the splitting of two molecules of hydrogen peroxide into two molecules of water and one molecule of oxygen. In general, *enzymes may be defined as organic catalysts.*

The numerous enzyme systems in plants may be classified as hydrolyzing and desmolyzing in action. Hydrolyzing enzymes are necessary for the breaking down of substances with the fixation of water, and desmolyzing enzymes are necessary for the breaking of linkages between carbon atoms, or the removal of an atom from a given compound, or the removal of a group from one compound and adding it to another. Several examples of enzymes of both types are presented in Table 1.1.

Hormones. Hormones are similar to enzymes in that they are effective in very low concentration, but they differ from enzymes in that they are made in one part of the plant and translocated to another, e.g., the auxins and the so-called florigens. Auxins are made in active meristems and are translocated to the region of cell elongation where they are needed to give the cell walls the ability to stretch. The so-called florigens

Table 1.1.   EXAMPLES OF ENZYME SYSTEMS IN PLANTS

Hydrolyzing		Desmolyzing	
Enzyme	Reaction	Enzyme	Reaction
Amylase	Starch ⟶ dextrin	Catalase	Hydrogen peroxide⟶ water and oxygen
Protopectinase	Protopectin → pectin	Tyrosinase	Phenols ⟶quinones
Lipase	Fats ⟶ glycerol and fatty acids	Ascorbic acid oxidase	Ascorbic acid ⟶ dehydroascorbic acid
Trypsin	Proteins ⟶ polypeptides and amino acids		

are made in young, physiologically active leaves and are translocated to the growing points where they are associated with the changing of vegetative buds to flower buds. Thus, *hormones may be defined as organic substances which are made in one part of the plant and translocated to another part where they are necessary for specific physiologic or biochemical processes.*

Vitamins. Vitamins are enzyme-like or hormone-like in action in plants. For example, thiamin, called vitamin B_1, is part of the enzyme system for respiration of all living tissues of plants. Vitamin B_1 is made in young, physiologically active leaves and is translocated to all living tissues in both the root system and the stem system. Other vitamins associated with respiration are riboflavin, called vitamin B_2, niacin, and pyridoxine, called vitamin B_6. All the vitamins or their immediate precursors needed for human nutrition are made by plants.

RESPIRATION

Nature of Respiration. Respiration, like photosynthesis, is essentially a biochemical reaction. Manufactured food is decomposed to carbon dioxide and water with the liberation of heat and other forms of kinetic energy. In this reaction, the potential chemical energy of food is transformed to various forms of kinetic energy. In this way, the light energy reserve, built up by plants in the formation of foods, becomes available for all crop plants and all animals. In fact, all higher plants and all animals secure energy for their vital needs through this process. In other words, respiration in plants and in animals has exactly the same function —the liberation of energy. Thus, *respiration may be defined as the oxida-*

tion of foods with the liberation of heat and other forms of kinetic energy.
This fundamental reaction is illustrated as follows:

Foods + oxygen $\xrightarrow{\text{(enzymes)}}$ **carbon dioxide + water**
(usually glucose)   **+ heat and other forms of kinetic energy**

Photosynthesis and Respiration Contrasted. The student will note
that, as far as energy relations are concerned, respiration is exactly the
reverse of photosynthesis. A contrast between these processes will help
to clarify the differences between them.

Photosynthesis	Respiration
Takes place in green tissues only	Takes place in all living tissues of both plants and animals
Takes place in light only	Takes place in light and in darkness
Absorbs light and fixes energy (endothermic)	Liberates heat and other forms of kinetic energy (exothermic)
Always increases dry weight of green plants	Always decreases dry weight of green plants (and of all other living things)

These processes, photosynthesis and respiration, are undoubtedly the
most important chemical reactions known to man. Without them no
living things could exist. Without them diamonds, coal beds, vast oil
deposits, soil, and the great forests would never have been formed. Without them the great industries of pulp and paper, nitrocellulose, rayon,
lacquers, dyes, and other great plant and animal industries would be
unknown. In short, photosynthesis and respiration are the foundation of
agriculture and many other great industries. In fact, plant scientists have
estimated that 90 per cent of the world's population are engaged in the
production, processing, and merchandising of the wide variety of plant
and animal products developed by these two fundamental reactions.

The Relation of Photosynthesis and Respiration to Growth and Yield.
Three examples are presented to show the relation of photosynthesis and
respiration to the yield of crops: the production of cotton fibers, of
potato tubers, and of red roses. Cotton is grown primarily for its fibers.
The fibers consist largely of cellulose. Cellulose is made from glucose,
and glucose is made in photosynthesis. Therefore, with other factors
favorable, the greater the rate of photosynthesis, the greater will be the
amount of glucose available for cotton fiber formation. However, glucose is decomposed in respiration. Therefore, the greater the rate of
respiration, the lesser will be the amount of glucose available for cotton
fiber formation. Thus, the difference between the rate of photosynthesis

and the rate of respiration will determine the amount of glucose available for cotton fiber formation and, in general, the yield of the cotton plant.

Potatoes are grown for their tubers. The tubers are primarily structures for the storage of starch. Starch is made from glucose, and glucose is made in photosynthesis. As with the production of cotton fibers, the greater the rate of photosynthesis, the greater will be the amount of glucose available for starch and tuber formation. However, as previously stated, glucose is decomposed in respiration. Therefore, the greater the rate of respiration, the lesser will be the amount of glucose available for starch and tuber formation. Thus, the difference between the rate of photosynthesis and the rate of respiration will determine the amount of glucose available for starch formation and yield of the tubers.

The principal pigment in red roses is an anthocyanin. This substance is made from glucose, and glucose is made in photosynthesis. As with the production of potato tubers, the greater the rate of photosynthesis, the greater will be the amount of glucose available for anthocyanin formation. Here again, glucose is decomposed in respiration. Therefore, the greater the rate of respiration, the lesser will be the amount of glucose available for anthocyanin formation. Thus, the difference between the rate of photosynthesis and the rate of respiration will determine the amount of glucose available for the formation of the red pigment, the market value of the flowers, and the yield of the plant.

In general, this relation of the rate of photosynthesis to the rate of respiration exists for all crops. In other words, the greater the rate of photosynthesis in proportion to the rate of respiration, the greater will be the amount of carbohydrates available for the growth and development of any given crop; and if the plant has been grown according to approved cultural practices, the greater will be the marketable yield. This statement expressed mathematically is as follows: $P - R = Y$. P represents the rate of photosynthesis, R the rate of respiration, and Y the marketable yield. Thus, if the rate of photosynthesis is high and the rate of respiration is also high, or above normal, the yields are likely to be low. However, if the rate of photosynthesis is high and the rate of respiration is normal, the yields are likely to be high. In general, for satisfactory crop production the rate of photosynthesis should be eight to ten times greater than the rate of respiration.

WATER ABSORPTION AND TRANSPIRATION

Water absorption and transpiration are essentially biophysical processes. Water is absorbed in the liquid state in the regions of cell elongation and the root-hair zone, and water is lost in the vapor state from the tissues of plants. This loss, or outgo, of water in the form of vapor is called transpiration. Although any part of a plant exposed to the air may give off water vapor, the leaves, because of their structure, shape, position, and function, give off the most.

Relation to Photosynthesis.   A prime function of water within the plant is to maintain turgor within the guard cells of the leaves. The guard cells are in a state of turgor when they are fully stretched. To maintain turgor the amount of water absorbed must, in general, equal the amount of water transpired. When the rate of absorption is much less than the rate of transpiration, the guard cells lose turgor, the stomates partially or completely close, carbon dioxide cannot rapidly diffuse into the leaves, and photosynthesis slows down or entirely stops while respiration continues. As a result, very few carbohydrates are available for growth and development and growth and yields are low. Thus, when plants are growing in soils with insufficient water, as many of them are for occasional periods in regions of poorly distributed rainfall and lack of irrigation, water absorption and transpiration assume great practical significance.

DIFFUSION AND OSMOSIS

Diffusion and osmosis are processes necessary for the proper functioning of photosynthesis, respiration, and water absorption and transpiration. Both processes are essentially biophysical in character.

Diffusion.   Suppose a vessel is filled with water and crystals of sodium nitrate or cane sugar are dropped into it. The ions of sodium nitrate, or the molecules of sugar, soon become equally distributed or concentrated in all parts of the water. In other words, *the particles of sodium nitrate or sugar have moved from regions of relatively high concentration to regions of relatively low concentration.* In much the same way, mineral substances get into the plant from the soil solution. Consider, for example, the absorption of nitrate or ammonium ions. In the root hairs and leaves, sugars and nitrate or ammonium-nitrogen combine to form proteins. Hence, at the place of protein formation, these nitrogenous materials are constantly taken out of solution to form proteins and the concentration of the nitrate or ammonium ions is reduced. Thus, the relatively greater concentration of nitrate ions or ammonium ions existing in the soil solution enables them to pass from the soil solution into the plant.

Scientists have found that minerals are absorbed independently of each other and independently of the movement of water. In fact, a mineral can move out of the root hair while water moves in. Factors which influence the rate of absorption of any mineral are (1) its relative concentration in the plant sap and in the soil solution, (2) its density, and (3) the temperature of the system. With other factors favorable, the higher the concentration of any mineral in the soil compared with its concentration in the plant sap and the higher the temperature of the soil solution, the faster will be the movement of the mineral from the soil into the plant.

Osmosis.   Suppose a vessel A contains water only, and a vessel B contains both sugar and water. Suppose that a glass tube is joined to the bottom of both vessels and that this tube contains a membrane which allows only the molecules of water to pass through it. Because of the greater concentration of water in vessel A than in vessel B, the water molecules will pass from A to B at a faster rate than from B to A, until the rate of diffusion is the same in both directions. This movement of water from regions of higher concentration of water to regions of lower concentration or from regions of lower concentration of solution to regions of higher concentration is called osmosis.

Water enters the plant by means of osmosis. The plasma membranes of the root hairs behave as semipermeable membranes. They will allow water molecules to diffuse through them more readily than sugar molecules. Since the concentration of water is less within the cell than in the soil, by virtue of the kinetic energy of its molecules, water passes from the soil to the cell and from cell to cell until it reaches the conducting tubes—the xylem. Thus, *osmosis is simply the passage of water through a semipermeable membrane* and the means by which water gets into the plant.

QUESTIONS

1. Set up equations (*a*) for making the initial food substances, (*b*) for making all the manufactured compounds, and (*c*) for respiration.
2. Photosynthesis may be considered a manufacturing process. Explain.
3. What is the function of chlorophyll?
4. Chlorophyll is considered the most important chemical compound known to man. Explain.
5. In general, a plant with a large quantity of chlorophyll (large leaf area) makes more foods in a given time than a plant with a small quantity of chlorophyll (small leaf area). Explain.
6. Investigations have shown that apple trees with dark green leaves make from two to four times more sugar per unit time than trees with light green leaves. Explain.
7. Disease infection and insect infestation of the leaves reduce photosynthesis, growth, and yield. Explain.
8. A lack of magnesium (Mg) in the soil solution markedly decreases growth and yield. Explain.
9. What is meant by the slogans: "A blanket of green for South Carolina," "Every acre continuously at work in Mississippi," "Keep Florida green"?

10. What is the main carbohydrate used in respiration? The main storage carbohydrate? The main structural carbohydrate?
11. Name two horticulture products particularly high in starch, two high in carotene, and two high in fats.
12. Contrast photosynthesis and respiration from the point of view of (*a*) seat of operation, (*b*) time of operation, and (*c*) weight and energy relations.
13. The dry weight of all green plants decreases at night. The dry weight of deciduous perennials decreases during the winter. Explain.
14. What is wrong with the statement, "Plants give off oxygen only in the light and carbon dioxide only in the dark"?
15. If, for some reason, all the animals on the surface of the earth should disappear, the carbon dioxide and oxygen content of the atmosphere would remain practically the same as they are now. Explain.
16. Show the relation of the rate of photosynthesis and the rate of respiration to the yield of crop plants.
17. Define transpiration.
18. When the stomates are closed during the day, the green plant is not making the initial food substances. Explain.
19. Illustrate the law of diffusion by showing how carbon dioxide is absorbed.
20. What is osmosis?

2

PLANT TISSUES AND STRUCTURES

The green plant is the foundation of agriculture—the basic industry.

PLANT TISSUES AND THEIR FUNCTIONS

Crop plants are composed of cells. These cells may be regarded as the structural units of plants in much the same way as bricks are considered the structural units of brick buildings. Cells vary in size, shape, and arrangement. Some cells are small, some large, some boxlike, and others are long and fiberlike. In some parts of the plant they appear to be like stones in a stone wall with air spaces between them; in other parts they appear to be like bricks in a brick building with no air spaces between them.

Cells do not work alone; they work together in groups. For example, the group of cells at the growing points of the roots and stems has the common function of cell division, and the group of cells which contain chlorophyll has the common function of the manufacture of initial food substances. *Groups of cells which have a common function are called tissues.* There are two types: (1) simple and (2) complex.

SIMPLE TISSUES

In simple tissues the individual cells are similar in size, shape, and arrangement. Principal kinds are (1) meristem, (2) parenchyma, (3) collenchyma, (4) sclerenchyma, and (5) cork.

15

Meristem is living tissue. It presents a most active manifestation of life in plants. Individual cells are small and boxlike. They possess thin, pliable walls, dense cytoplasm, very minute vacuoles, and a large, centrally located nucleus. The function of meristem is the making of new cells. In this way the plant increases in size. *Meristem does not make foods; it uses them.* These foods are used in the making of the various constituents of the cells—the walls and the protoplasm—and in providing energy. When plant cells are dividing, they are working and must have a source of energy. Thus, the fundamental process, as far as meristem is concerned, is respiration. In fact, when the meristem is making many cells in a given time, its rate of respiration is quite high. Note the characteristics of the group of meristematic cells in the root tip of onion in Fig. 2.1.

Parenchyma is living tissue also. Although individual cells of parenchyma differ in size, shape, and arrangement according to the work they perform, in general they are larger and more elongated and possess thicker walls, less dense cytoplasm, and smaller nuclei than the meristem. Unlike the meristem, some types of parenchyma contain plastids, small blobs of dense protoplasm, and comparatively large vacuoles between the cytoplasmic strands. The kinds and functions of parenchyma vary greatly. Principal kinds are (1) chlorenchyma, (2) epidermis, (3) cortex, (4) endodermis, (5) pericycle, (6) sieve tubes and companion cells, (7) pith, and (8) nectaries.

Chlorenchyma are relatively thin-walled and possess chloroplasts—the individual food-making factories of the plant. On the surface of the chloroplasts, the carbon dioxide and water combine in the presence of light in the formation of the initial food substances. Thus, *the primary function of chlorenchyma is the manufacture of the initial foods.*

The epidermis is the surface layer of leaves, herbaceous and young woody stems, and fruits and roots not covered with cork. In most plants it is usually one cell thick and varies in structure according to its particular function. In the region of the root-hair zone the cells are of one type. In general, they are all colorless, possess thin walls, and absorb water and solutes in the water. Many of these cells become tubular and are called root hairs. In leaves and green stems the epidermis consists of colorless cells and green cells called the guard cells. The guard cells contain chloroplasts. These chloroplasts possess the ability to make sugars just like the chloroplasts in the chlorenchyma tissue.

The cortex is situated next to the epidermis and consists of round or elongated, thin- or moderately thick-walled cells. The thickness of the walls depends on the function which they perform. *In the root-hair zone, the cortex serves as a diffusion system for the passage of water and essential raw materials in the water from the root-hair zone to the endodermis and the passage of sugars and other manufactured compounds*

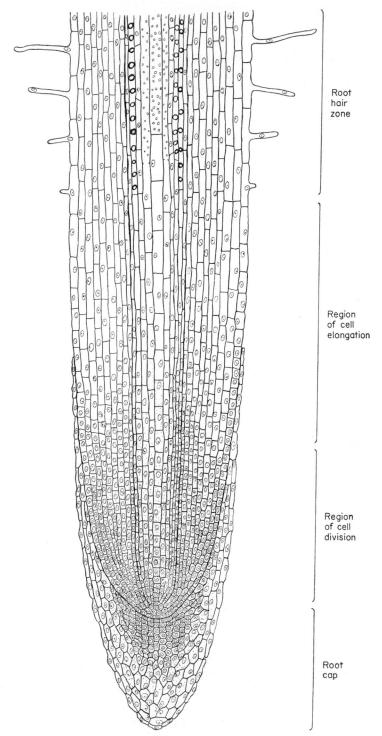

Root
hair
zone

Region
of cell
elongation

Region
of cell
division

Root
cap

Fig. 2.1. Longitudinal section of root tip. (Courtesy, J. F. Locke, Mississippi State University.)

17

from the endodermis to the root-hair zone. In other portions of the plant, particularly in erect stems, the cortex contains fibers—elongated, thick-walled cells—which give strength and rigidity to stems.

The endodermis is a single layer of cells between the cortex and pericycle. Although the exact function of the endodermis in stems is unknown, its function in roots is essential for the growth and well-being of the root system. In the root-hair zone the root hairs and ordinary epidermal cells and cortex contain protoplasm and require sugars for their respiration. Further, when the meristem is dividing, large quantities of sugars are needed for the formation of new cells. The sugars for all these tissues, the root hairs, cortex, and meristem, are made in the leaves and are translocated downward in the phloem of the stem and the root to the root-hair zone. In the root-hair zone the transverse and tangential walls of the endodermis are suberized. The suberization of these walls confines the diffusion of sugars and other substances through the protoplasm only. In this way *the endodermis, in a sense, controls the amount of sugars and other manufactured substances which pass into the cortex and down to the meristem.*

The pericycle consists of one to several layers of cells between the endodermis and conducting vessels. In roots this tissue forms growing points usually just back of the root-hair zone, and each growing point with the making of new cells grows through the endodermis and cortex and becomes a lateral root. Thus, *the function of the pericycle in roots is the formation of growing points which develop into lateral roots.* In stems, particularly those which are erect, certain groups of cells have thick walls to hold the leaves in the light, to support the flowers and fruit, and to withstand stress and strain due to the wind.

Sieve tubes and companion cells are an essential part of the vascular bundles and consist of vertical rows of elongated cells. The side walls of the tubes are thin, but the end walls are thick and minutely perforated. Strands of cytoplasm extend through these perforations from cell to cell. Thus, the living substance of the cells of the tubes is connected. *The primary function of the sieve tubes, together with the companion cells, is the transportation of soluble manufactured food, hormones, and vitamins from the tissues where they are made to the tissues where they are used or stored.*

Pith is found in the central portion of stems and in some roots. This tissue is made up of relatively thin-walled cells frequently with numerous intercellular spaces. The function of the pith is the storage of food, particularly starch—the most important reserve carbohydrate.

Nectaries, or nectar glands, secrete various substances, particularly sugars and essential oils, for the attraction of insects. They are situated in the base of the flowers and in leaves and stems of plants. The form and size of the glands vary greatly. For example, in lilac the glands consist of a single epidermal cell; in geranium they consist of hairs on the surface of the leaves; in the buttercup they form a shallow cavity at the base of the flowers; and in nasturtium they form a deep pouch at the base of the flowers. Figure 2.2 shows various types of parenchyma cells. Note the differences in size, thickness of walls, and arrangement.

Collenchyma is living tissue also. The individual cells usually are elongated and have the same general appearance as those of the parenchyma. Their distinguishing characteristic is the thickened corners of the walls. These thickened walls help the plant to withstand stresses and strains. Collenchyma is usually found in the cortex just beneath the epidermis of young herbaceous stems and petioles, the midrib of leaves, and in pedicels and peduncles of flowers.

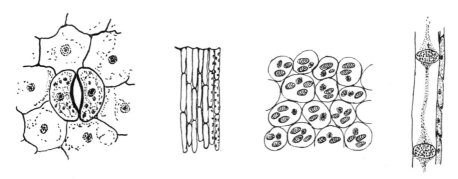

Fig. 2.2. Types of parenchyma. Left to right: guard cells with ordinary epidermal cells, palisade, storage, and food conducting.

Sclerenchyma is dead tissue. The walls of the cells become hard and lignified. There are three types: (1) stone cells, (2) fiberlike cells, and (3) xylem vessels. *Stone cells* are irregular in shape and thick-walled, with exceedingly small cell cavities. They occur mostly in fruits and seeds, e.g., the grit cells in the fruit of certain varieties of pear and the shells of certain nut fruits—pecan, walnut, almond, and coconut. *Fiberlike cells* are extremely long, thick-walled, and tapering. The tapered ends dovetail with each other so that the plant can withstand stresses and strains, as, for example, the forces of the wind. These fibers may occur, as necessity requires, in the cortex, pericycle, phloem, or xylem of stems and roots. *Xylem vessels* are long and pipelike in appearance, and the walls are strengthened according to various patterns and designs. Figure 2.3 shows the three types of sclerenchyma.

Woody plants, the old stems of herbaceous plants, and certain storage structures are covered with a tissue called cork or bark. This tissue takes the place of the epidermis and is formed by the division of the cork cambium. Individual cells are rectangular, with no intercellular spaces. The walls are relatively thin and are impregnated with a fatty-like substance called suberin and with tannin and other substances. The suberin makes the tissue impermeable to water and gases, and the tannin renders the tissue resistant to the attacks of rot-producing organisms. Thus, the function of the cork layer is to protect the stem or root from excessive

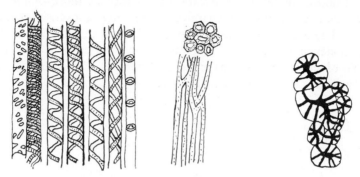

Fig. 2.3. Types of sclerenchyma. Left: xylem vessels. Center: fiberlike cells. Right: stone cells.

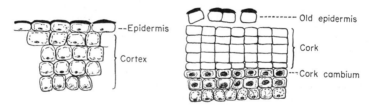

Fig. 2.4. Cross section of primary stem and secondary stem showing replacement of epidermis by layer of cork cells.

loss of water and against the attack of rot-producing organisms. Figure 2.4 shows the replacement of the epidermis by a layer of cork.

COMPLEX TISSUES

In addition to simple tissues which have one kind of cell only, seed-producing plants contain complex tissues which contain more than one kind of cell. The principal complex tissues are (1) phloem and (2) xylem.

Phloem consists of sieve tubes and companion cells. In general, this tissue conducts the manufactured compounds. Thus, *the function of the phloem is the transportation of the manufactured products.*

Xylem consists of long, tubular cells called tracheids in addition to vessels through which water and dissolved essential raw materials pass. Thus, *the function of the xylem is the transportation of water and essential raw materials from the roots to other parts of the plant and in particular to the leaves.*

The student should remember that all tissues work together for the growth and development of the entire plant. In other words, the various tissue systems are interdependent. For example, the food-manufacturing cells depend on the root hairs and conducting tissues for their water supply. The water-absorbing cells depend on the soluble sugars manufactured by and transported from food-manufacturing cells for their osmotic pressure. Without these sugars these water-absorbing cells would not be able to absorb water. Can you think of any other examples of interdependence?

QUESTIONS

1. Do cells work alone? How do they work? Explain fully, giving an example.
2. What is a simple tissue? A complex tissue?
3. Name the principal tissues in plants.
4. Draw a meristematic cell. Label all parts.
5. Why are the walls of meristematic cells thin and pliable?
6. What is the function of the meristem?
7. What is the fundamental process concerned with meristem?
8. How do parenchyma cells differ from meristematic cells?
9. Name the types of parenchyma tissues and state the function of each.
10. Draw from memory an epidermal cell, a carbohydrate-manufacturing cell, and a root hair. Label all parts. Show how the size, shape, and structure of each cell is adapted to its particular function.
11. How does collenchyma differ from parenchyma tissue? What is the primary function of collenchyma?
12. Draw a pipelike cell and a fiberlike cell. Show how each is adapted to its particular function.
13. What is the function of the phloem? The xylem?
14. Photosynthesis is necessary for the absorption of water. Explain.

PLANT STRUCTURES AND THEIR FUNCTIONS

Most horticultural plants are spermatophytes; that is, they produce pollen, which eventually contains sperms, and ovules, which eventually contain, with other cells, an egg. When a sperm and an egg unite, a new individual is formed which, together with nourishing and protecting tissues, constitutes the seed. In other words, spermatophytes produce seed.

Spermatophytes are divided into two groups: (1) gymnosperms and (2) angiosperms. In general, gymnosperms produce neither flowers nor fruit and hence nonenclosed or naked seed, e.g., pine, spruce, fir, yew, hemlock, juniper, and sequoia. On the other hand, angiosperms, with a few exceptions, produce flowers and fruit and hence enclosed seed. They comprise a large group and are divided into two subgroups: (1) monocots and (2) dicots. In general, monocots develop one seed leaf, parallel-veined leaves, closed vascular bundles, and flower parts in groups of three or in multiples of three; whereas dicots develop two seed leaves, net-veined leaves, open vascular bundles, and flower parts in groups of four or five or in multiples of four or five.

The body of spermatophytes is divided into two parts: (1) primary and (2) secondary. The primary body develops from the meristem at the root and stem tips, and the secondary body develops from the cambia. In general, the body of monocots consists of primary tissues only throughout the life cycle of the plant. However, the body of gymnosperms and dicots consists of primary tissues during the first stages of their development and secondary tissues during the later stages.

THE PRIMARY BODY

From the standpoint of structure and function, the primary body is divided into two parts: (1) primary root and (2) primary stem.

The Primary Root System

The primary root system provides for growth in length or extension and consists of four distinct but overlapping regions: (1) cell division, (2) cell elongation, (3) water and essential-element absorption and initial differentiation, and (4) lateral root formation and further differentiation.

The region of cell division consists of a growing point and a root cap. The growth point is a group of meristematic cells. When the root is growing, these cells are dividing, and they are using large quantities of sugars and available nitrogen for the making of the protoplasm. The root cap is a thimble-shaped mass of cells which covers the growing point. Its function is to surround and protect the delicate meristematic cells of the growing point.[1] Obviously, *the primary function of the region of cell division is the making of new cells.*

The region of cell elongation is located just back of the growing point. It consists of meristematic cells which have elongated; that is,

---

[1] The roots of aquatic plants have no root caps or root hairs.

the longitudinal axis has increased more than the transverse axis. These cells absorb large quantities of water and require auxinic (or auxin-like) hormones to give the cell walls the ability to stretch. This abundant absorption increases the turgor pressure within the cells and the walls become permanently stretched. Thus, *the region of cell elongation is responsible for most of the growth in length.*

The region of water and essential-element absorption and of the initial stages of differentiation is located just back of the region of elongation and is often referred to as the root-hair zone. The cells are differentiated into distinct tissues: (1) epidermis, (2) cortex, (3) endodermis, (4) pericycle, and (5) vascular bundles.

The epidermis consists of a single layer of cells, and its function is the absorption of water and the essential raw materials dissolved in the water. To absorb water and these essential materials most effectively, the outer wall of many cells elongates and these cells are called root hairs. In general, their walls are very thin and are made of cellulose and pectin or of pectinaceous material only and they are also short-lived (a few hours to a few weeks). When the meristematic cells of the growing points are dividing, root hairs are forming continuously just back of the region of elongation. In this way, new stores of water and essential raw materials become available to the plant.

The cortex consists of relatively large, nearly rounded, thin-walled parenchyma cells. In the root-hair zone this tissue serves as a system for the diffusion of water and solutes in the water from the root hairs to the endodermis and the diffusion of sugars and other manufactured compounds from the endodermis to the root hairs.

The endodermis consists of a single layer of specified parenchyma cells. In the root-hair zone its radial and transverse walls are impregnated with a layer of oxidized fat called suberin. Suberin, in common with all fatty-like substances, is impervious to water and substances in solution in water, so that the sugars and other foods which pass to the root hairs are under protoplasmic control.

The pericycle consists of one to several layers of cells, and the vascular bundles consist of radially arranged primary phloem and primary xylem. Note that this radial arrangement allows the water and solutes to pass directly to the primary xylem. The phloem provides a channel for the passage or translocation of foods, hormones, and vitamins, and the xylem provides a channel for the transportation of water and essential raw materials. Figure 2.5 is a cross section of the root-hair zone. Note the position, thickness, and structure of the cells of each tissue.

The region of lateral root formation and further differentiation occurs just back of the root-hair zone. In this region the walls of the epidermis, cortex, and endodermis increase in thickness and become impervious to water, but the pericycle remains meristematic and forms growing points. These growing points pass through the endodermis, cortex, and epidermis and into the soil. Thus, *the function of the pericycle in this region is the formation of lateral roots.*

Functions of the Primary Root.   The main functions of the primary root system are (1) providing for growth in extension and (2) absorbing water and essential raw materials in the water. Other functions are holding the plant and soil in place, conducting water and solutes in the water through the xylem, conducting the manufactured compounds through the phloem, and storing carbohydrates.

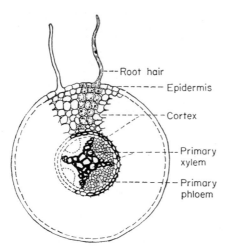

Fig. 2.5. Cross section of a root in the root-hair zone. (Redrawn by permission from M. C. Coulter, "The Story of the Plant Kingdom," Chicago, The University of Chicago Press.)

As previously stated, the root system does not make the initial food substances—the simple carbohydrates. These substances are made in the leaves. Since the initial food substances are the precursors of all other manufactured compounds, the growth and development of the root system of any given plant depend largely on the health and abundance of the leaves. Why are the health and abundance of the leaves so important? Plants with healthy leaves have more chlorophyll per unit area than plants with diseased leaves. Thus, they absorb more light and, with other factors favorable, make more carbohydrates within any given period. As a result, more carbohydrates are available for the growth and development of the root system. Similarly, plants of a given kind with a large leaf area (a large number of leaves) have more chlorophyll than plants with a small leaf area (a small number of leaves). Thus, they absorb more light and, with other factors favorable, make more carbohydrates per unit time. As a result, more carbohydrates are available for growth and development of the root system. This explains why plants with healthy leaves or dark green leaves develop more active and extensive root systems than plants with diseased or light green leaves, why plants with large tops (a large leaf area) develop more extensive root systems than plants with small tops (a small leaf area), and why pruning of the top is likely to reduce the growth and extensiveness of the root system.

Since the root system contains living tissues, it is always respiring. Therefore, the root system is always giving off carbon dioxide and always taking in oxygen. This oxygen supply is present in the atmosphere and diffuses into the pore spaces of the soil. In general, the root systems of most of our crop plants require abundant quantities of oxygen, particularly when the growing points are making new cells and when large quantities of water and essential raw materials are being absorbed. When these processes are taking place, the rate of respiration is usually high and, consequently, large quantities of oxygen are needed. This explains why most crop plants require well-drained soils; why loose, friable, highly colored subsoils provide for deeper root penetration than tight or poorly drained subsoils; and why a layer of clay, if applied on the surface of the soil under a large tree, is likely to retard the growth and development of the tree.

The Primary Stem System

The primary stem system provides for growth in height or extension and consists of three distinct but overlapping regions: (1) cell division, (2) cell elongation, and (3) cell differentiation, or tissue formation.

The region of cell division exists within the buds of stems. These buds are really undeveloped stems. Groups of meristematic cells occur at the terminal portions and at the nodes of these young stems. The mass of cells at the terminal portion or apex is dome-shaped and is surrounded by young developing leaves. When buds are expanding and growing, the meristematic cells are dividing. Thus, *the primary function of this region is the making of new cells.*

The region of cell elongation exists from the base of the buds downward through several nodes and internodes. Like the region of elongation in the root system, individual cells develop large vacuoles for the absorption of abundant quantities of water. This absorption of water, together with the cell-stretching hormones, elongates the cells.

When the buds are expanding, the regions of cell division and cell elongation are centers of intense metabolic activity. In particular, there are high rates of respiration, sugar utilization, and water absorption. Large quantities of sugars are needed for the formation of the walls and protoplasm of the new cells and for the liberation of energy in respiration.

The region of cell differentiation or maturation consists of the remainder of the stem which grows in length. In this region, the cells differentiate into distinct tissues: (1) epidermis, (2) cortex and pericycle, (3) vascular bundles, and (4) pith.

The epidermis consists mainly of cells with thick radial walls and toothed and flanged tangential walls. Usually, the outer wall contains a layer of waxlike material called the cuticle. The thickening and dovetailing of the walls and the cuticle combine to greatly reduce the rate of transpiration of stems. In this way, most of the water absorbed by the roots can get to the leaves. Thus, an important function of the epidermis in stems is to keep the absorbed water within the plant.

The cortex usually contains both living and dead tissues. In general, the living tissue stores carbohydrates, usually as grains of starch; and the dead tissue, the thick-walled, elongated fibers, gives strength and rigidity to stems. In this way, the stems have the ability to hold the leaves in the light and support large crops of flowers and fruit.

The vascular bundles consist of (1) primary phloem and (2) primary xylem. As explained previously, the function of the phloem is the transportation of the many manufactured compounds—the many types of foods, hormones, and vitamins. The function of the xylem is the transportation of water and the essential raw materials in the water. In addition, the xylem tubes or vessels, because of their structure, give strength and rigidity to stems.

The pith is found in the central portion of stems. This tissue is made up of relatively large, thin-walled cells, frequently with numerous intercellular spaces. The function of the pith is the storage of food, particularly starch—the most important reserve carbohydrate.

What is the relative metabolic activity of the region of differentiation? As previously stated, the regions of cell division and elongation are centers of intense metabolic activity, since all the cells in these regions are alive and require a continuous oxygen supply for their respiration. However, the region of cell differentiation contains both living and dead tissues. Since dead tissues do not respire and use foods and since the living tissues do not divide and make new cells, but only keep the protoplasm in good repair, the metabolic activity of the region of differentiation is much lower than that of the regions of division and elongation.

The Stems of Monocots and Dicots.   As previously pointed out, the plant body of monocots is derived from the meristem at the tips, and that of dicots is derived first from the meristem of the tips and finally from the cambia—the vascular cambium and the cork cambium. In other words, the vascular cambium in monocots exists for a short time only, whereas that in dicots exists from the time it is formed until the plant dies. Thus, mature vascular bundles of monocots lack a cambium and are called closed bundles, whereas mature vascular bundles of dicots contain a cambium and are called open bundles. Since monocots contain a vascular cambium for a limited period only, the stems grow in diameter during the development of the primary tissues only; and since dicots contain a vascular cambium throughout the life of the plant, they grow in diameter throughout the life of the plant. Further, in monocots the primary vascular bundles serve as the transportation system throughout the life of the plant, regardless of whether the plant lives for one growing season or for several seasons. However, in dicots the primary bundles serve as the transportation system until the secondary bundles are developed. This period varies with the life of the plant; for annuals it is a relatively long time, and for perennials a

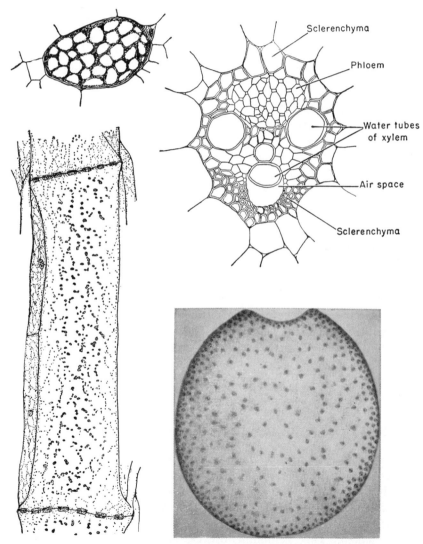

Fig. 2.6. Cross section of stem and vascular bundle of corn—an important monocotyledon. (Courtesy, F. W. Emerson, "Basic Botany," New York, McGraw-Hill Book Company, Inc.)

relatively short time. Note the lack of a cambium and the arrangement of the bundles in corn, an important monocot, in Fig. 2.6 and the cambium and the arrangement of the bundles in a typical dicotyledonous plant in Fig. 2.7.

Functions of the Primary Stem.   The main functions of the primary stem are (1) providing for growth in length, or extension, and (2) serving as the connecting link between the leaves and the roots. Other functions are holding the leaves in the light; supporting flowers, fruit, and seed; and storing manufactured foods, particularly reserve carbohydrates.

As previously stated, the initial food substances and certain hormones and vitamins are made in the leaves. These are needed for the growth of the roots. On the other hand, the leaves require abundant water and

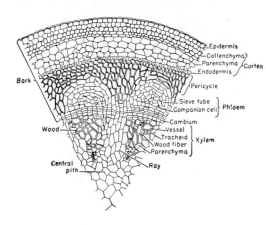

Fig. 2.7. Cross section of stem of dicotyledon. (Courtesy, F. W. Emerson, "Basic Botany," New York, McGraw-Hill Book Company, Inc.)

compounds containing the essential elements for making the initial foods and other manufactured substances. The water and all the compounds containing essential elements, with the exception of carbon dioxide, are absorbed by the roots. Therefore, insect, disease, or mechanical injury to the stems is likely to impair the work of the leaves and the work of the roots as well.

THE SECONDARY BODY

As stated previously, the secondary plant body is limited to gymnosperms and dicots only. In these plants the stems grow in diameter, or thickness. This growth in thickness is due to the activity of (1) the vascular cambium and (2) the cork cambium. The vascular cambium is derived from certain perenchyma cells between the primary phloem and the primary xylem. This cambium divides and forms new cells. These cells differentiate into three distinct tissues: (1) secondary phloem,

(2) secondary xylem, and (3) medullary rays. The secondary phloem and secondary xylem take over the functions of the primary phloem and the primary xylem; and the medullary rays store and translocate foods radially. The cork cambium develops from certain cells in the pericycle or cortex and gives rise to the layer of cork. Since these two cambia develop in the roots and stems of dicots, the anatomy of the secondary root and the secondary stem is similar. Note the arrangement and structure of the tissues in the secondary plant body in Fig. 2.8.

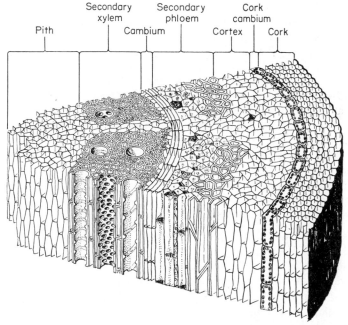

Fig. 2.8. Cross section of a sector cut from a dicot stem. This stem is diagrammatic for a woody plant, showing well-defined cork cambium and vascular cambium.

Functions of the Secondary Plant Body. The main functions of the secondary plant body are (1) providing for growth in thickness, or diameter, and (2) serving as the connecting link between the primary root system and the primary stem system. Other functions are support and the storage of reserve carbohydrates, particularly starch and related substances.

QUESTIONS

1. What are spermatophytes?
2. Distinguish between gymnosperms and angiosperms.

3. Compare monocots and dicots from the standpoint of (*a*) number of seed leaves, (*b*) venation of the leaves, (*c*) type of vascular bundles, and (*d*) number of flower parts.

4. Name the principal plant structures.

5. Name the regions of growth in length of the root system.

6. What is a root hair? What is its function?

7. What is the primary function of the root system?

8. To what extent is the root dependent on the top? The top dependent on the root? Explain.

9. Within the same kind or variety, plants with a large top have a large root system and those with a small top have a small root system. Explain.

10. Name the tissues from which the woody stem arises.

11. What tissue makes up the greater part of the woody stem?

12. A nail partially driven into a young tree soon becomes entirely embedded. Explain.

13. Suppose that when you were 15 years old, you carved your initials on a 15-year-old tree 5 feet from its base. Would your initials be at the same or at a greater height when you and the tree are 30 years old? Explain.

14. Suppose you nail a wire fence to a row of five-year-old trees. Would the fence gradually move upward as the trees increased in height or remain at the original height? Give reasons.

15. The trunks of palm trees and bamboo are as large in diameter when the plants are short (3 to 4 feet high) as when they are tall (50 to 100 feet high). Explain.

16. What is the function of the medullary rays?

THE LEAVES

In general, leaves are modified stems designed primarily for the manufacture of the initial food substances. As is well known, the leaves of crop plants vary greatly in size, shape, and arrangement on the stems. Despite this variation, all leaves have three tissues in common. These tissues and their functions are set forth in Table 2.1.

As shown in Table 2.1, the epidermis consists of two types of cells: (1) the so-called protective cells and (2) the guard cells. In general, the protective cells are colorless and have thick radial, toothed and flanged tangential walls, and a layer of cuticle on the outer walls just like those of the primary stem. As with the epidermis of the primary stem, thickening and dovetailing of these walls, combined with the layer of cuticle, greatly reduces the rate of transpiration through the protective cells. In fact, under conditions of high transpiration, only 1 to 2 per cent of the enormous quantities of water transpired from the leaves is lost through the protective tissue.

The guard cells differ from the protective cells in that they exist in pairs and contain chlorophyll; thus they manufacture food. The walls

Table 2.1. PRINCIPAL TISSUES OF LEAVES AND
            THEIR PRIMARY FUNCTIONS

Tissues	Primary functions

1. Epidermis:
    Protective cells
    Guard cells and stomates
	
	To keep water within the leaf
	To allow CO_2 and O_2 diffusion in photosynthesis and respiration

2. Chlorophyll-containing cells	To manufacture the initial food substances
3. Veins	To translocate water and raw materials to, and manufactured compounds away from, the manufacturing cells

of these cells vary in thickness, and the inner walls are next to an opening, the stomate, through which gases, carbon dioxide, oxygen, and water vapor diffuse. Because of the varying thickness of the walls and because the walls are pliable, changes in shape of these guard cells alter the size of the pore. Thus, since the primary function of the leaf is the manufacture of the initial food substances and since the stomates must be open for the diffusion of carbon dioxide to the manufacturing cells, the behavior of the guard cells and stomates assumes great practical significance. Important environmental factors which influence the shape of these guard cells, which in turn influence the opening and closing of the stomates, are (1) light and (2) the water supply within the plant.

Light. With most crop plants light directly influences the shape of the guard cells and the opening of the stomates. In other words, when light is available and the water supply is favorable, the guard cells are fully stretched and the stomates are usually open. Conversely, when light is absent the guard cells are flaccid and the stomates are closed. How does light influence the shape and turgor of the guard cells? Two explanations are presented herewith. The first and oldest is based on the manufacture of sugars in the guard cells. In the morning just before sunrise the supply of sugars in the guard cells is low and the osmotic pressure is correspondingly low. With sunrise the guard cells begin the manufacture of sugars. This increases the osmotic pressure of these cells, and water is absorbed from the adjacent cells. In this way, the guard cells become turgid and the stomates open. With sunset, because of the decreasing light, sugar manufacture declines, but respiration continues. This decreases the sugar supply, and the osmotic pressure within the cells correspondingly decreases. As a result, water is withdrawn from the guard cells and the stomates close. The second explanation is based on the hydration and dehydration of colloids of the protoplasm within the guard cells. Light causes certain colloids to imbibe water. This in turn induces stretching of the guard cells and the opening of the stomates. During the night these colloids lose their capacity to imbibe water. Thus, the imbibitional capacity of the guard cells decreases and the stomates close.

The Water Supply within the Plant. When a water deficit occurs within the plant, even in the presence of light, the guard cells lose turgor and the stomates close. In general, this deficit occurs when the rate of absorption of water is less than the rate of transpiration. As a result, the water supply within the plant decreases and the guard cells, because of their readily pliable, easily stretched walls, respond to this

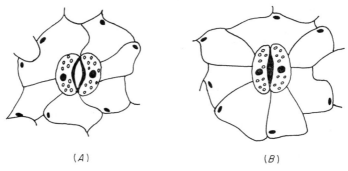

(A)   (B)

Fig. 2.9. Open (A) and closed (B) stomate of apple. (Redrawn from O. F. Curtis and D. G. Clark, "An Introduction to Plant Physiology," New York, McGraw-Hill Book Company, Inc.)

decrease in the water supply. Thus, with a decrease in the supply of water within the plant, the guard cells change in shape, which in turn decreases the size of the stomates. This in turn decreases the amount of water going out of the plant. However, it also decreases the rate of diffusion of carbon dioxide into the plant. With this decrease in rate of diffusion of carbon dioxide, a decrease in the rate of photosynthesis takes place with a corresponding decrease in the rate of sugar manufacture and a corresponding decrease in growth and yield. Figure 2.9 shows an open and closed stomate of apple. Note the differences in shape of the guard cells.

In general, the structure of the epidermis, the position of the guard cells and stomates, and the size, shape, and arrangement of chlorophyll-containing tissues vary with crop plants. Note the differences in these tissues in the leaves of the apple, Kentucky bluegrass, and white pine presented in Figs. 2.10 to 2.12. Note that the apple's guard cells and stomates are on the lower epidermis only, and the chlorophyll-containing

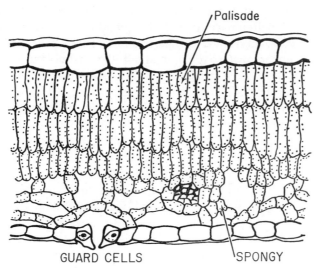

Fig. 2.10. Cross section of leaf of apple. (*Courtesy, A. J. Eames and L. H. Mac-Daniels, "An Introduction to Plant Anatomy," New York, McGraw-Hill Book Company, Inc.*)

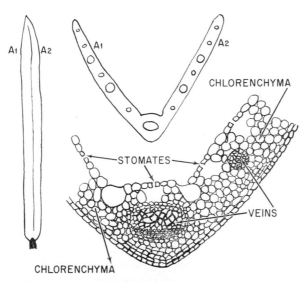

Fig. 2.11. Sections of leaf of Kentucky bluegrass. (*Courtesy, F. W. Emerson, "Basic Botany," New York, McGraw-Hill Book Company, Inc.*)

cells are of two types: the elongated cells at right angles to the upper epidermis, called palisade cells; and the round cells on the lower part, called spongy cells. In Kentucky bluegrass the guard cells and stomates occur on the upper surface only, and all the manufacturing cells are round. In white pine each needle, or leaf, is triangular, and the needles occur in groups of five. The epidermis is very thick, and the guard cells and stomates are situated on the sides facing the adjacent leaves. Can you think of any reason for this?

The veins of leaves are relatively small vascular bundles. They are in close contact with the manufacturing cells and conduct the foods, hormones, and vitamins from, and water and essential raw materials to, these cells. In large veins, in addition to the vascular tissues, there are sheaths of thick-walled cells which give strength and support to the leaves.

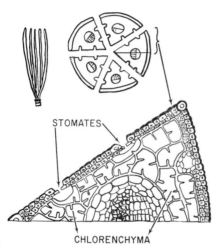

STOMATES

CHLORENCHYMA

Fig. 2.12. Sections of leaf of white pine. (Courtesy, F. W. Emerson, "Basic Botany," New York, McGraw-Hill Book Company, Inc.)

The leaves of many crop plants have petioles. In general, the petiole, or leafstalk, consists mainly of vascular bundles and mechanical tissue. Thus, the petiole serves as a transportation system between the manufacturing cells and the stem and holds the leaf blade in the light. The petioles of some crops are fleshy and form the edible portion, e.g., rhubarb and celery.

The Rate of Translocation of Manufactured Sugars. As previously stated, the initial food substances are soluble in the sap of plants. During the day these soluble carbohydrates are changed into insoluble forms and are stored temporarily in the chloroplasts. During the night these compounds are changed to soluble forms, usually glucose, and are translocated to other parts of the plant. If, for any reason, not all the sugars are translocated from the leaves, the storage capacity of the chloroplasts is decreased and the manufacture of sugar is accordingly decreased. Thus, a slowing down in the growth and development of roots, stems, flowers, or fruit may correspondingly slow down the rate of sugar manufacture. This, you will recall, is a practical application of the law of mass action.

Modified Leaves. Modified leaves are (1) scales, (2) bracts, and (3) tendrils. Scales are usually hard, horny structures which protect the buds of woody plants during the winter. Bracts are either leafy or fleshy. In some plants they take the place of petals, as in dogwood, poinsettia, and bougainvillaea; in others they become fleshy and are used as food, as in Globe artichoke. Tendrils are slender, threadlike structures which possess the ability to twine around objects. For example,

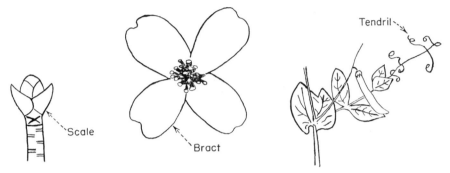

Fig. 2.13. Types of modified leaves.

the upper leaflets of the compound leaves of the garden pea have been modified to form tendrils. Note the modified leaves in Fig. 2.13.

THE FLOWERS

An individual flower consists of groups of modified and highly specialized leaves, arranged concentrically, designed for the purpose of sexual reproduction or reproduction by seed. These groups of modified leaves are (1) sepals, (2) petals, (3) stamens, and (4) pistils. Each group has a specific function.

The sepals, collectively called the calyx, protect the delicate stamens and pistils when the flower is in the bud stage. The petals, collectively called the corolla, also protect the stamens and pistils when the flower is in the bud stage, and large, highly colored petals attract pollinating insects.

An individual stamen consists of a stalk called the filament and a pollen sac called an anther. *The function of the stamen, particularly the anther, is to produce pollen which in due time contains sperms.* For this reason the stamens are called the male organs of the plant.

An individual pistil consists of an ovary, style, and stigma. The ovary is the enlarged portion at the base of the pistil, the stigma is the flattened portion at the apex, and the style is the connecting tissue between the two. *The function of the pistil, particularly the ovary, is to produce one or more ovules, each of which in due time contains, with other cells, an egg.* For this reason the pistils are called the female organs of the plant.[2]

Figure 2.14 shows a longitudinal view of a complete flower. It illustrates the transfer of pollen within the flower, the germination of pollen grains, and the growth of the pollen tube down the style.

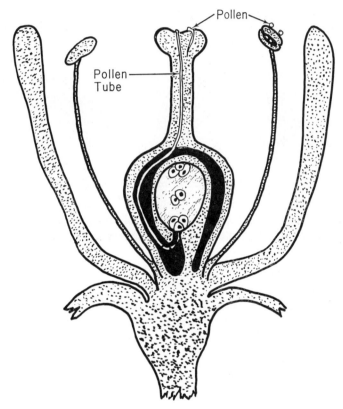

Fig. 2.14. *Longitudinal section of a complete flower. (Courtesy, F. W. Emerson, "Basic Botany," New York, McGraw-Hill Book Company, Inc.)*

Complete and Incomplete Flowers. The flowers of some crops contain all four of the main parts: sepals, petals, stamens, and pistils. This type of flower is called a complete flower. However, the flowers of other crops contain no petals and are called apetalous flowers; others contain

[2] The authors are aware that morphologists regard the *n* generation as "sexual" and the *2n* generation as "nonsexual." In this text both generations are considered one entire life cycle and the stamen is considered the male organ, the pistil the female organ.

functional stamens and nonfunctional pistils and are called staminate flowers; and others contain nonfunctional stamens and functional pistils and are called pistillate flowers. All these types of flowers—apetalous, staminate, and pistillate—are called incomplete flowers.

Sex Expression

The sex expression of plants is based on whether one or both of the sex organs are in the same flower. In general, there are three main types: (1) plants with functional stamens and pistils in the same flower; (2) plants with functional stamens and functional pistils in separate flowers on the same plant; and (3) plants with functional stamens and

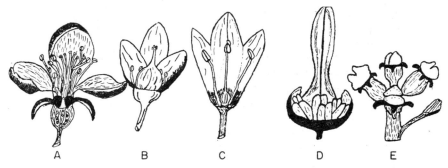

| A | B | C | D | E |

Fig. 2.15. Examples of perfect, staminate, and pistillate flowers. A: perfect flower of apple. B, C: pistillate and staminate flowers of asparagus. D, E: staminate and pistillate flowers of pecan.

functional pistils in separate flowers on different plants. Plants of the first group are called hermaphrodites, those of the second are called monoecious plants, and those of the third are called dioecious plants. Examples of each type follow.

Hermaphrodites.   Apple, pear, peach, plum, labrusca grape (most varieties), raspberry, blackberry, strawberry, gooseberry, cranberry, lemon, orange, grapefruit, avocado, almond, cabbage, radish, carrot, celery, sweetpotato, tomato, pepper, eggplant, bean, pea, okra, rose, chrysanthemum, carnation, violet, sweet pea, and snapdragon.

Monoecious Plants.   Pecan, walnut, filbert, chestnut, tung, cucumber, cantaloupe, pumpkin, squash, watermelon, and sweet corn.

Dioecious Plants.   Persimmon, muscadine grape (certain varieties), date, spinach, asparagus, and holly. Figure 2.15 shows the hermaphroditic flowers of apple and the pistillate (female) and staminate (male) flowers of asparagus and pecan.

QUESTIONS

1. What is the primary function of the leaves?
2. Draw from memory a diagram of the tissues of a leaf showing the upper and lower epidermis, the palisade and spongy tissue, the veins, the guard cells, the stomates.
3. Show how decreasing supplies of sugar and water in the guard cells induce closing of the stomates.
4. In general, the longer the stomates are open during the day, the longer photosynthesis takes place and the greater the yield. Explain.
5. When the stomates are closed, the plant is not making carbohydrates. Explain.
6. In the leaf petiole the corners of certain cells are greatly thickened. Explain.
7. What is the principal function of the flower?
8. Name the four parts of a complete flower and give the function of each.
9. What part of the flower produces pollen? Ovules?
10. Name the different ways in which the sex organs of plants are arranged.
11. What is a hermaphroditic flower, a staminate flower, a pistillate flower?
12. What is the function of staminate flowers? Pistillate flowers?
13. Staminate flowers do not produce fruit, yet they are essential for fruit and seed production. Explain.
14. Monoecious and dioecious crops require pollen-carrying agents for the production of fruit and seed. Explain.

THE FRUIT AND SEED

Pollination

Many plants are grown for their fruits or seeds or for both fruits and seeds. With these plants the development of the fruit and seed depends on the successful union of the sperms and eggs and the subsequent growth of the embryos. Since the egg cells of plants remain within the ovules, the sperms of plants must go to the eggs. With many plants the journey of an individual sperm to an individual egg is not an easy one. Instances are frequent in which the sperm fails to reach the egg. Sometimes the pollen which carries the sperm is not transferred to the stigma of the pistil; sometimes the weather retards or prevents the germination of the pollen; sometimes the rate of growth of the pollen tube down the style is so slow that the egg dies before the sperm arrives. To more fully understand some of the difficulties met by the sperm, its journey to the egg is considered in three stages: (1) the transfer of pollen, (2) time of pollen shedding and pistil receptivity, and (3) growth of the pollen tube down the style to the embryo sac.

The Transfer of Pollen. *The transfer of pollen from the anther of the stamen to the stigma of the pistil is called pollination.* Four general methods of pollen transfer are used: (1) by force of gravity, (2) by contact, (3) by wind, and (4) by insects. Pollen transfer *by the force of gravity* or *by contact* usually takes place when the pistil(s) and stamens are in the same flower. The force of gravity is effective when the flower is in the pendent position and the stigma extends beyond the anthers. Transfer by contact is effected when the stamens, as they elongate, shed their pollen as the anthers come in contact with the receptive stigma. Pollen transferred *by wind* or *by insects* is necessary when the pistil and the stamens are in different flowers or when, for some reason, the stamens fail to pollinate the pistil in the same flower.

Wind- and insect-pollinated crops present somewhat different problems with respect to adequate pollination. Pollen transferred by wind is subject to chance currents of air. Thus, it lacks directness; large quantities of pollen are necessary; and the grower should know how far such pollen is carried. On the other hand, pollen transferred by insects is more direct, and lesser amounts of pollen are necessary. Thus, wind- and insect-pollinated plants have marked differences in adaption to pollination. In general, wind-pollinated plants have inconspicuous flowers, produce small, dry pollen in large quantities, and possess long, branched, or feathery styles in order to catch the pollen grains. On the other hand, insect-pollinated plants have large, highly colored petals or bracts, produce large, sometimes sticky, pollen, and possess well-developed nectaries. These nectaries secrete sugars and other substances for the attraction of insects. They are so situated that, when insects visit the flowers, their bodies which carry the pollen come in contact with the stigma. The principal insects are certain species of bees, most important of which is the honeybee.

THE HONEYBEE. The needs and the physical equipment of honeybees are well adapted for the work of pollination. Their bodies are covered with numerous hairs to which the pollen clings, and their action on the flower is gentle. Thus, the delicate tissues of the pistil are not injured. Important environmental factors affecting the activity of honeybees are (1) the temperature of the air and (2) the food (nectar and pollen) supply. Investigations have shown that honeybees are comparatively inactive at temperatures lower than 50°F and cannot use their wings at temperatures lower than 40°F. Consequently, honeybees do not fly very far in cool weather. To help the bees perform the task of pollination of many crops, growers distribute colonies of bees throughout the orchard, greenhouse, or plantation. Figure 2.16 shows a honeybee visiting a cucumber flower. Cucumbers are monoecious, the pollen is large and sticky, and the honeybee is the chief agent of pollination.

The production of honeybees for pollination purposes in the many

Fig. 2.16. A honeybee visiting a cucumber flower. (Courtesy, W. S. Anderson, Mississippi State University.)

orchards throughout the country is an important industry. For the most part this industry is located in the South where the winter season is comparatively mild. These bees are shipped in small packages, hence the name "package bees." Some authorities have stated that honeybees are about fifty times more valuable for their work of pollination in orchards, gardens, and fields than they are for the honey they make.

Self- and Cross-pollination. In horticulture there are two distinct concepts of self- and cross-pollination. These different concepts are based on differences in the behavior of asexually and sexually propagated crops. In general, the plants of any given variety of an asexually propagated crop, for example, the apple, are descended from a single plant or a single bud, and unless mutations take place, the plants of any particular variety are identical. For example, all the apple trees of the Delicious variety are descendants from one original bud. Since the apple is propagated by using a vegetative structure, the many thousands of Delicious trees in the country are identical to the original tree. Thus, the pollen of all Delicious trees is identical, and in like manner the pollen of any given asexually propagated variety is identical. In other words, in asexually propagated crops the *variety* is considered the unit. Accordingly, *with asexually propagated crops self-pollination is the transfer of pollen from a flower of one variety to a flower of the same variety.* The two flowers may be on the same tree or plant or on different trees or plants of the same variety. *Cross-pollination is the transfer of pollen from a flower of one variety to a flower of another variety.*

On the other hand, the plants of any given variety of a sexually propagated crop, for example, the tomato, are produced from seed, and the plants from the seed may or may not be identical. Thus, the pollen may or may not be identical. In other words, in sexually propagated crops the *plant* is considered the unit. Accordingly, *with sexually propagated plants self-pollination is the transfer of pollen from the stamens to the pistil within the same flower or between flowers of the same plant,* and *cross-pollination is the transfer of pollen from the stamens of a flower of one plant to the pistil of a flower of another plant.* This plant may belong to the same strain or to another variety or even to a related species.

Each type of pollination has its place in horticultural crop production. With asexually propagated plants, many varieties of certain crops produce more fruit when they are cross-pollinated. For example, many varieties of the apple and all varieties of the sweet cherry fail to set complete crops of fruit unless pollen of other varieties is used. Those varieties which are necessary for the pollination of other varieties are called pollinators. Consequently, the choice of a variety for pollination purposes is particularly important. With sexually propagated crops, self-pollination maintains uniformity and reduces variability of any particular strain or variety.[3] On the other hand, cross-pollination introduces new characteristics and increases diversity. A classification of horticultural crops based on type of pollination follows.

SELF-POLLINATED CROPS. Bunch grape (most varieties), peach (most varieties), plum (some European varieties), almond, gooseberry, blackberry, currant, strawberry (most varieties), orange, lemon, and grapefruit (most varieties), cherry (sour), tomato, pepper, eggplant, bean, pea, sweet pea, and snapdragon.

CROSS-POLLINATED CROPS. *By wind:* pecan, walnut, chestnut, filbert, spinach, garden beet, and sweet corn. *By insects:* apple, pear, peach (a few varieties), plum (most Japanese and American varieties), cherry (sweet), cabbage, lettuce, onion, carrot, cucumber, cantaloupe, watermelon, pumpkin, squash, aster, azalea, calceolaria, pansy, and zinnia.

Time of Pollen Shedding and Time of Pistil Receptivity. When the egg is ready to receive the sperm, the pistil becomes receptive. Pistil receptivity is indicated by the secretion of sugars and other food sub-

[3] Some cross-pollination usually takes place in sexually propagated, self-pollinated plants.

stances and hormones on the surface of the stigma. These materials are necessary for the germination of the pollen tube. Obviously, pollen shedding and pistil receptivity should take place at the same time. With some crops these processes do not always take place simultaneously. A notable example is the pecan. Under certain conditions the stamens of the same variety shed their pollen before or after the pistils of the same variety are receptive. This necessitates the planting of at least two varieties in the orchard so that pollen shedding of one variety and pistil receptivity of the other may occur simultaneously.

Growth of the Pollen Tube Down the Style.   On the surface of the stigma the pollen grain germinates; that is, it produces a slender tube which grows down the style. The temperature of the air, the food supplied by the stylar tissue, and the compatibility of the pollen tube and stylar tissues are important to the growth of the tube. Thus, when the weather is cold in the orchard or garden during the pollinating season, the set of fruit is likely to be low. Naturally, if the food supply of the tissues of the style is low, the growth of the tube will be correspondingly slow. Of more importance is the compatibility of the pollen. Compatible pollen possesses the ability to grow down the style in time for the sperm to unite with the egg. Incompatible pollen does not possess this ability; that is, the pollen tube may grow slowly or not at all, even though the temperature and food supply are favorable. With some crops, e.g., apple, sweet cherry, cabbage, and petunia, the pollen of many varieties is self-incompatible. These self-incompatible varieties cannot pollinate their own pistils. Hence, another variety must be used. Such a variety, as previously stated, is known as the pollinator variety.

Fertilization

When the pollen grain germinates, the tube in some plants pushes its way down the style from cell to cell; in others it passes through a channel between the cells; and in either case it finally passes through the micropyle of the ovule and arrives at the embryo sac. Within the embryo sac the tube liberates two sperms. One sperm unites with the egg in the formation of the zygote, or new plant; the other unites with the endosperm nuclei in the formation of the endosperm. This union of the one sperm with the egg and the other sperm with the two endosperm nuclei is called double fertilization.

Immediately after fertilization, the embryo makes new cells and increases in size. At the same time, the ovary increases in size to make room for the rapidly developing embryo(s). During the growth of the embryo(s) and ovary a large amount of sugars, proteins, and water is used for the maturation of the fruit and for the growth of the embryo(s). Later the embryo(s) stops growing, the ovary ripens or becomes mature, and the walls of the ovule(s) become hard and thick. In this way ripe fruit and mature seed are formed.

The fruit of many valuable crops develops without fertilization, e.g., banana, navel orange, seedless grape, pineapple, and certain varieties of cucumber. These fruits are called parthenocarpic fruits irrespective of whether pollination has occurred. Recently, scientists have secured parthenocarpic fruits of crops which normally require pollination and

Grape   Tomato   Orange

SIMPLE FLESHY FRUITS

Pea   Carrot

Pineapple

COMPLEX FLESHY FRUIT   DRY FRUITS

Fig. 2.17. Fleshy and dry fruits. (Redrawn by permission from M. C. Coulter, "The Story of the Plant Kingdom," Chicago, The University of Chicago Press.)

fertilization by applying certain hormone-like chemicals called growth regulators to the stigma of the pistils. Examples of the chemicals used are napthaleneacetic acid and indolebutyric acid.

Classification of Fruits. Fruits of horticultural crops vary greatly in size, shape, color, and chemical composition. In general, they may be classified as fleshy or dry. Fleshy fruits may be further divided into simple and accessory. Simple fruits have developed from ovarian tissue and usually from flowers with superior ovaries, whereas accessory fruits have developed from ovarian and adjacent tissue and from flowers with superior and inferior ovaries. Dry fruits may be further divided as dehiscent and indehiscent. Dehiscent fruits shed their seed when dry; indehiscent fruits do not. Examples of fleshy and dry fruits are presented in Table 2.2 and are illustrated in Fig. 2.17.

Table 2.2.   TYPES OF FRUITS OF SOME
            HORTICULTURAL CROPS

Fleshy, high moisture content when mature		Dry, low moisture content when mature	
Ovary tissue only	Ovary(s) and adjacent tissue	Shedding when mature	Not shedding when mature
Peach, plum, grape, tomato, pepper, eggplant, currant, blueberry, date, gooseberry, olive, orange	Apple, pear, strawberry, fig,* blackberry, pineapple, the cucurbits, dewberry	Peas, beans, okra, larkspur, lily, peony	Celery (seed), carrot (seed), sweet corn

* *Most of the flesh consists of peduncle.*

STORAGE STRUCTURES

Storage structures are modified stems or roots designed primarily for the storage of manufactured food, usually reserve carbohydrates and related compounds. In general, they have the same anatomy as ordinary stems and ordinary roots except that certain tissues, usually the storage parenchyma, have developed many cells and have become greatly enlarged. Thus, storage stems have nodes and internodes and develop buds and shoots at the nodes just like ordinary stems; and storage roots are without nodes and internodes and develop growing points from the pericycle just like ordinary roots. Examples of storage stems are tubers of the potato and Jerusalem artichoke, corms of gladiolus, and rhizomes of canna, iris, lily of the valley, and rhubarb. Examples of storage roots are fleshy roots of dahlia and sweetpotato.

QUESTIONS

1. Define pollination.
2. In general, how do flowers pollinated by wind differ from those pollinated by insects?
3. Growers place bouquets of apple blossoms under the trees during the pollinating season. Explain.
4. Observations have shown that frequently the windward side of apple trees possess less fruit than the leeward side. Can you think of any reason for this?

5. What is meant by self- and cross-pollination of asexually propagated crops? Self- and cross-pollination of sexually propagated crops?
6. What is meant by compatible pollen? Incompatible pollen?
7. What is the main function of a pollinator variety?
8. Pollinator varieties are necessary in apple and sweet cherry orchards. Explain.
9. Large blocks of a single variety of most varieties of peaches can be planted, and large crops can be produced. Explain.
10. A peach orchard may consist of a single variety, but an apple orchard should preferably contain at least two varieties. Explain.
11. Six varieties of muscadine grapes were planted in a vineyard. A very light crop of grapes was produced year after year regardless of cultural practices. What had the grower neglected? Give reasons for your answer.
12. In general, a single and isolated pecan tree fails to produce fruit consistently from one year to the next. Explain.
13. What is double fertilization?
14. Can you think of any advantages of parthenocarpy? Any disadvantages?

3
PHASES OF GROWTH AND THE CARBOHYDRATES

Knowledge is the gold
in the streets of America.

The growth and development of crop plants consist of two distinct, though overlapping, phases: (1) the vegetative and (2) the reproductive.

THE VEGETATIVE PHASE

The Vegetative Phase and Carbohydrate Utilization. The vegetative phase consists essentially in the development of the stems, leaves, and absorbing roots. This phase is associated with three important processes: (1) cell division, (2) cell enlargement, and (3) the initial stages of cell differentiation.

Cell division consists in the making of new cells. These new cells require large quantities of carbohydrates, since the walls are made of cellulose and the protoplasm is made mostly from sugars. Thus, with other factors in favorable supply, the rate of cell division is dependent upon an adequate supply of carbohydrates. As previously stated, cell division takes place within the meristematic tissues, the growing points at the stem and root tips, and the cambia. Therefore, these tissues must be provided with the manufactured foods, hormones, and vitamins in order to form new cells.

Cell elongation consists in the enlargement of the new cells. This process requires (1) abundant supplies of water, (2) the presence of certain hormones which give the cell walls the ability to stretch, and (3) the presence of sugars. As discussed in Chapter 2, the region of

46

cell enlargement occurs just back of the growing points. When the cells in this region begin to enlarge, they develop large vacuoles. These vacuoles absorb relatively large quantities of water. As a result of this absorption of water and the presence of the cell-stretching hormones, the cells elongate. In addition to this increase in cell size, the walls become thicker, owing to the laying down of additional cellulose made from the sugars.

The initial stages of cell differentiation, or tissue formation, consist in the development of the primary tissues. Their development requires carbohydrates, e.g., the thickening of the walls of the protective cells of the epidermis of the stem and the development of the water-conducting tubes of both the root and the stem. Thus, when a plant is making new cells, elongating these cells, and laying down its tissues, it is actually developing its stem, leaf, and root systems. If the rate of cell division and elongation and tissue formation is rapid, growth of the stems, leaves, and roots will be rapid also. Conversely, if the rate of cell division is slow, growth of the stems, leaves, and roots is accordingly slow. Since division, enlargement, and tissue formation require a supply of carbohydrates and since carbohydrates are used in these processes, the development of stems, leaves, and roots requires the utilization of carbohydrates. Thus, *in the vegetative phase of plant development, the carbohydrates are utilized and the plant is using most of the carbohydrates it is making.*

THE REPRODUCTIVE PHASE

The Reproductive Phase and Carbohydrate Accumulation. The reproductive phase consists in the formation and development of flower buds, flowers, fruit, and seed or in the enlargement and maturation of storage structures—fleshy stems and fleshy roots. This phase is associated with several important processes: (1) the making of relatively few cells; (2) the maturation of the tissues; (3) the thickening of the fibers; (4) the formation of hormones necessary for the development of flower-bud primordia; (5) the development of flower buds, flowers, fruit, and seed; (6) the development of storage structures; and (7) the formation of the water-retaining substances—the hydrophilic colloids. The student will note that all these manifestations of the reproductive phase require a supply of carbohydrates. In most cases these carbohydrates are the sugars and the starches. In other words, when a plant is developing its flowers, fruit, seeds, or storage structures, not all the carbohydrates are being used for the development of the stems, leaves, and absorbing roots; some are left for the development of the flowers, fruit, or seed, or for storage structures. For example, the flesh of the apple, the tubers of the potato, and the fleshy roots of the sweetpotato all contain relatively large quantities of starch and sugars. Thus, *in the reproductive phase of plant development, the carbohydrates are stored and the plant is storing most of the carbohydrates it is making.*

THE VEGETATIVE–
REPRODUCTIVE BALANCE

The vegetative and reproductive phases of plant development may be likened to a balance. One side of the balance may be considered the vegetative phase—the development of stems, leaves, and absorbing roots. The other side may be considered the reproductive phase—the development of flowers, fruit, seed, or storage structures. This concept presents three possible cases: (1) The vegetative phase may be dominant over the reproductive; the balance is tipped on the vegetative side. (2) The reproductive phase may be dominant over the vegetative; the balance is tipped on the reproductive side. (3) Neither the vegetative nor the reproductive phase may be dominant; both sides of the balance are practically equal. However, the student should guard against forming the idea that the vegetative phase takes place without the reproductive or that the reproductive phase takes place without the vegetative. If the vegetative phase is dominant with any crop, there is always some reproduction. On the other hand, if the reproductive phase is dominant, there is always some vegetation. For example, cell division is necessary for the development of reproductive and storage structures. However, the number of cells necessary for the development of these structures is small compared with the number necessary for the complete development of the stems, leaves, and absorbing root system of any given plant. Thus, the term "balance" refers to a matter of emphasis rather than to the presence or absence of either phase of plant development.

When the vegetative phase of plant development is dominant over the reproductive, carbohydrate utilization is dominant over accumulation. More carbohydrates are used than are stored. When the reproductive phase is dominant over the vegetative, carbohydrate accumulation is dominant over utilization. More carbohydrates are stored than are used. When the vegetative and reproductive phases are in balance, utilization and accumulation are also in balance. Practically equal amounts of carbohydrates are used and stored.

As an example, take three tomato plants—A, B, and C—each of which has grown for a period of 150 days. In plant A the vegetative phase has been dominant over the reproductive; in plant B the reproductive phase has been dominant over the vegetative; and in plant C both phases have proceeded in practically equal magnitudes.

How would these plants appear? Plant A would be extremely vegetative; that is, there would be an abundant development of stems, leaves, and absorbing roots. The stems would be succulent, the leaves would be large with little development of cuticle—the waxlike substance on the surface. Flowering and fruiting would not occur or would be suppressed, the cell walls would be thin, and the strengthening tissue would be poorly developed. In other words, most of the carbohydrates would be used for the development of the root system, the stem system, and the leaves. As a result, very little of the carbohydrates would be left for the development of flower buds, flowers, fruit, and seed. In this case the vegetative phase was dominant over the reproductive and carbohydrate utilization was dominant over carbohydrate accumulation.

Extreme vigor of the top, combined with a lack of, or reduction in, the growth of flowers, fruit, and seed, generally develops under the following conditions: The plants are in the early stages of growth. They have a rapid rate of photosynthesis. The temperature favors a *rapid rate of cell division*, and water and essential raw materials are abundant. The large quantity of carbohydrates made combines with the nitrogen compounds to form the protoplasm made in the growing points of the stems and roots. As a result vegetative processes are dominant over reproductive processes. Note the plant on the extreme right in Fig. 3.1.

Fig. 3.1. Relation of vegetative vigor to fruitfulness in four tomato plants. (Courtesy, Jackson B. Hester, Elkton, Md.)

Plant B would be poorly vegetative and stunted and would produce some fruit. There would be little development of leaves and stems. The stems would be woody, the internodes would be short, the leaves would be moderately small with the development of a thick cuticle. Flower and fruiting would be evident, the cell walls would be very thick, conducting tissues would be well developed, and storage tissues would be packed with starch. Since stems are necessary to support flowers and fruit and since in plant B there was a relatively low development of stems and leaves, yields would be accordingly low. In this case the reproductive phase was dominant over the vegetative and carbohydrate accumulation was dominant over carbohydrate utilization.

Weak, stunted plants generally result under the following conditions: The plants have a low or moderately low rate of photosynthesis. The temperature or the water supply, or the essential-element supply, or some other factor *is unfavorable for even a moderate rate of cell division.* As a result the carbohydrates accumulate and are used for reproductive processes to a greater extent than for vegetative processes. Note the plant on the extreme left in Fig. 3.1.

Plant C would be moderately vegetative and fruitful. The stems would be moderately succulent, the internodes moderately long, and the leaves moderately large with normal development of cuticle. Flowering and fruiting would proceed simultaneously with the development of stems and leaves and absorbing roots. The cell walls would be fairly thick, and there would be normal development of the conducting tissues. In this case moderate amounts of carbohydrates were used for the development of stems, leaves, and absorbing roots and the remainder was used for the development of flowers and fruit or storage structures. Since both the vegetative and reproductive phases lacked dominance, carbohydrate utilization and accumulation lacked dominance also and each phase proceeded in practically equal magnitudes. Note the two plants in the middle of Fig. 3.1.

Moderate vigor of the top, combined with the development of flowers, fruit, or seed, generally takes place under the following conditions: The plants have a high rate of photosynthesis. The temperature and other environmental conditions favor a *moderately rapid rate of cell division.* As a result not all the carbohydrates are used for the development of stems and leaves; some are left for the development of flowers and fruit. Vegetative and reproductive processes lack dominance and the plants are moderately vegetative and fruitful.

Thus, the growth of stems and leaves is associated with carbohydrate utilization, and the development of flowers, fruit, seed, or fleshy structures is associated with carbohydrate accumulation. The student should also keep in mind (1) that associated with carbohydrate utilization are ex-

Table 3.1.   THE VEGETATIVE-REPRODUCTIVE BALANCE

V-R balance	Disposition of carbohydrates	Appearance of plant
Vegetative processes greater than reproductive processes	Utilization greater than accumulation	Extremely vigorous, vegetative plant. Fruiting suppressed or delayed. Rapid growth of stems and leaves
Reproductive processes greater than vegetative processes	Accumulation greater than utilization	Poorly vigorous, stunted plant. Flowering and fruiting early. Yields low
Vegetative and reproductive processes in equal magnitudes	Accumulation and utilization in equal magnitudes	Moderately vigorous plant. Flower and fruiting nonsuppressed, not delayed. Plant productive

treme succulence, crispness, and juiciness, properties which are highly desirable in some plants, and (2) that associated with carbohydrate accumulation are nonsucculence, woodiness, and resistance to cold and heat, properties which are highly desirable in other plants. Table 3.1 presents a summary of the relation of the disposition of the carbohydrates to plant behavior, and Fig. 3.1 shows the relation of vegetative vigor and fruitfulness in four tomato plants.

The Vegetative-Reproductive Balance and Type of Growth.   As previously stated, (1) the vegetative phase may be dominant over the reproductive phase, (2) the reproductive phase may be dominant over the vegetative phase, and (3) the vegetative and reproductive phases may not show dominance. Some crops require a dominance of vegetative processes during the entire life cycle, and others require a dominance of vegetative processes during the first part of the life cycle and a balance of vegetative and reproductive processes during the latter part. In general, all plants require a dominance of the vegetative phase during the germination stage. Beyond this stage horticultural crops may be divided into three more or less distinct groups: (1) herbaceous crops which require a dominance of the vegetative phase during the first stages of growth and a dominance of the reproductive phase during the later stages, with the former gradually losing dominance over the latter during the intermediate stage; (2) herbaceous crops which require a lack of dominance of both the vegetative and reproductive phases; and (3) woody plants which require a dominance

Table 3.2.   HORTICULTURAL CROPS CLASSIFIED ACCORDING TO TYPE OF GROWTH

Group	Crops
1	Cabbage, celery, potato, onion, carnation, chrysanthemum
2	Tomato, eggplant, okra, cucumber, sweet pea, African violet
3	Apple, peach, pecan, azalea, crepemyrtle

of the vegetative phase during the first part of each growing season and a dominance of the reproductive phase during the latter part. Examples of each group are presented in Table 3.2.

The Vegetative-Reproductive Balance and the Environment.   Since a dominance of the vegetative phase may be desirable in some crops and a dominance of the reproductive phase may be desirable in others, the question arises: Can the vegetative and reproductive phases be controlled by the environment or by cultural methods? As is well known among growers of horticultural crops, certain factors of the environment and certain practices markedly affect the two phases of growth. Principal environmental factors are (1) the water supply, (2) the temperature, (3) the light supply, and (4) the essential-element supply. Since these factors usually limit the growth and development of plants, they are called the limiting factors in growth and development.

LIMITING FACTORS

Meaning of the Limiting Factor.   In general, when a process or group of processes is governed by many factors, *the speed of the process is governed by the factor in the minimum.* For example, the speed of a railway train is dependent on many factors. Some of these are the condition of the track, the type of engine, the load, and the steam pressure. If the track is in poor condition, it is only through improvement in the track that the increase in speed can be obtained. It would be useless to lighten the load, increase the steam pressure, or change the type of engine.

Similarly, the rate of development of stems and leaves is dependent largely on the amount of sugars made and the amount of nitrate or ammonium-nitrogen absorbed and assimilated with the sugars to form proteins. If the supply of available nitrogen in the soil is low, protein formation is accordingly low and the production of leaves and stems is low. In this case the nitrogen supply is the limiting factor, because only through an increase in the available nitrogen supply can an increase be obtained in the growth of stems and leaves. It would be useless to increase the water supply, the light supply, the phosphorus supply, or any other factor except nitrogen.

During the winter months light duration and intensity are usually the limiting factors in growth. For example, crops grown in greenhouses produce greater yields in summer than in winter. In winter it would be useless for the grower to increase the temperature, the water supply, or the fertility of the soil. It is only through an increase of the light supply that an increase in growth can be obtained.

In other words, the growth and ultimate yield of any crop are regulated largely by a limiting factor. This does not mean that any one factor remains the limiting factor throughout the entire life of the plant. Sometimes it may be the carbohydrate supply, sometimes the available nitrogen supply, sometimes the water supply, or sometimes the heat supply. Since the limiting factor largely determines the rate of plant growth and development, an appreciation on the part of the student of the importance of the limiting factor is necessary. In many cases the solving of the grower's problems consists in discovering and dealing with the limiting factor. In the discussion of the principal factors limiting plant growth and development in Chapters 4 through 7, it is assumed that *all factors except the one under discussion are in plentiful supply.*

QUESTIONS

1. Name the two phases of plant development.
2. Carbohydrates and proteins are used in the making of cells. Explain.
3. Abundant water within the plant is necessary for cell enlargement. Explain.
4. Liberal supplies of energy are necessary for the making and enlargement of cells. Explain.
5. When a plant is developing its stems and leaves rapidly, it is using sugars and proteins rapidly. Explain.
6. Thickening of the cell walls and the storage of starch, gums, and mucilages are manifestations of carbohydrate accumulation. Explain.
7. Mild nitrogen deficiency and carbohydrate accumulation frequently go together. Explain.
8. The behavior of green plants is centered around the manufacture of carbohydrates and their utilization and accumulation. Explain.
9. In general, crops in the vegetative phase utilize more available nitrogen in sunny weather than in cloudy weather. Explain.
10. In the growing of spinach and leaf lettuce, what phase of growth should be dominant? Give your reasons.
11. What balance would you maintain during the flowering and fruiting of tomatoes? Give your reasons.
12. Study the tomato plants in Fig. 3.1. Which plants are moderately vigorous? In your opinion, what is the limiting factor in the growth of the plant at the extreme left? Explain.

13. Excessive vegetative growth of young apple trees is likely to delay the time they begin to bear fruit. Explain.

14. Vigorous trees supplied with abundant nitrogen produce fruits which are green longer than those supplied with moderate nitrogen. Explain.

15. Sweet peas growing in the greenhouse in rich soil are likely to produce very long and vigorous vines and long-stemmed flowers late in the season. Explain.

16. The quality of grape juice and wine varies with the nature of the growing season. Explain.

17. With other factors favorable, stem cuttings with large quantities of carbohydrates stored in their tissues produce roots at a greater rate than those with small quantities of carbohydrates. Explain.

18. Name the principal environmental factors influencing the growth of horticultural plants.

19. What is meant by the limiting factor in growth and development of crop plants?

20. If air, water, temperature, light, or essential elements become deficient or unfavorable, high yields of high-quality crops will not materialize. Explain.

21. What environmental factor is likely to be the limiting factor in the growth of a plant during the summer at sunrise? At noon? At sunset? Explain.

4

THE WATER SUPPLY AS THE LIMITING FACTOR

The water supply is a basic and valuable resource.
It should never be wasted.

Water is one of the essential constituents of living things. Life without water is impossible. Large quantities of water are present in plants. In fact, some students of plant life consider the plant as a supported column of water.

Functions of Water. Water has many functions in plant life. This unique compound is the solvent and transportation medium for all foods, hormones, vitamins, and compounds supplying essential elements; it combines with carbon dioxide in the formation of the initial substances in photosynthesis; it combines with starch and related compounds in the formation of glucose in respiration; and more particularly it maintains turgor in living cells.

The Water Supply and Photosynthesis. As previously stated, water is absorbed in the liquid form in the region of the root-hair zone, and water is transpired from any plant surface exposed to the forces of evaporation. For example, roots exposed to the drying effects of air, apples or sweetpotatoes in storage, cut flowers in a room, as well as growing plants give off water in the form of vapor. *This phenomenon, the giving off of water in vapor form, is called transpiration.*

Most of the water vapor is lost through the leaves. There are several reasons for this: (1) The leaves of most crop plants are flat and broad, and as such they present a large external surface to the forces of evaporation. (2) In order for photosynthesis to take place the stomates must be open. (3) When the stomates are open, the moist cells within the leaves

55

are exposed to the forces of evaporation. (4) The area of the internal surface of leaves is several times that of the external surface (see Fig. 4.1). Thus, if photosynthesis is to take place under conditions of high rates of evaporation, high rates of transpiration are inevitable; and if high rates of transpiration take place, high rates of water absorption should take place also. In other words, the amount of water going into a plant per unit of time should, in general, equal the amount going out. When the rate

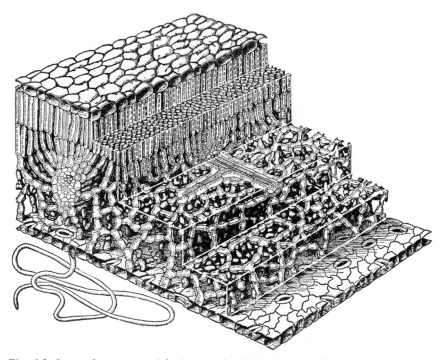

Fig. 4.1. Internal structure of leaf of apple. Note the intercellular spaces below the palisade cells. (Courtesy, A. J. Eames and L. H. MacDaniels, "An Introduction to Plant Anatomy," New York, McGraw-Hill Book Company, Inc.)

of absorption is less than the rate of transpiration, the guard cells lose turgor and thus become flaccid, and the stomates partially or completely close. This results in decreases in the rate of diffusion of carbon dioxide into the chlorophyll-containing cells with resultant decreases in the manufacture of the initial food substances and corresponding decreases in growth and yield. To more fully understand how deficits occur within plants and how this results in unsatisfactory growth and usually low yields, the student should have a working knowledge of the factors which influence the rate of absorption, or the income of water, and of the factors which influence the rate of transpiration, or the outgo of water.

THE ABSORPTION OF WATER

SOIL FACTORS

Amount and Kinds of Water in Soils.   When well-drained soils are saturated with water, as for example after a heavy rain, a certain amount of water percolates through the pore spaces and drains away because of the force of gravity. The water which remains is held against the force of gravity, and when measured it is called the field capacity. Thus, *the field capacity of soils may be defined as the amount of water held against the force of gravity.*[1] The field capacity varies greatly with the type of soil. Study the field capacity of the soils presented in Table 4.1. Note that sand and sandy loams have relatively low field capacities and that silt and clay loams have high field capacities. Since these data are more or less representative of soils as a whole, we can say that, in general, coarse-textured soils have low field capacities and fine-textured soils have relatively high field capacities.

Not all the water held by soils against the force of gravity is available for the use of the plant. Even when the guard cells lose turgor and the leaves droop or wilt, soils still contain some water; thus plants are needed in order to determine the amount of water in the soil which they cannot absorb. In general, this is done by placing samples of soil in standard galvanized cans, each with a hole in the top for the stem of a plant; by planting a seed of a herbaceous plant, usually that of sunflower, in the soil of each can; by bringing the soil to and keeping it at or near the field capacity until the plant has developed three or four leaves and then allowing the leaves to wilt; and finally by placing the plant in a dark chamber with a high relative humidity. When the leaves do not recover from wilting, the amount of water in the soil is measured to determine the permanent wilting percentage. Note that the plants are placed in a dark, moist chamber, a condition which promotes a low rate of transpiration. Thus, *the permanent wilting percentage may be defined as the amount of water in soils when rapidly growing plants fail to recover from wilting under conditions of low transpiration.*

As with the field capacity, the permanent wilting percentage is not the same for all soils. Study the permanent wilting percentage of the soil types presented in Table 4.1. Note the low permanent wilting percentage of the fine sand and the lack of a definite relation of texture to the permanent wilting percentage of the other types. For example, the Yolo fine sandy loam has a somewhat higher permanent wilting percentage

---

[2] The field capacity, as defined, is a rough measure at best, since some soils lose water by drainage over a relatively long period.

Table 4.1.   THE WATER CONTENT OF CERTAIN SOILS

Soil type	Location	Field capacity,* %	Permanent wilting, %	Available water, %	Available water, in./ft
Plainfield fine sand	Ohio	2.4	1.4	1.0	0.2
Yuma sand	Arizona	4.8	3.2	1.6	0.3
Delano sandy loam	California	9.1	4.2	4.9	0.8
Redman sandy loam	Oregon	18.8	6.6	12.2	2.0
Yolo fine sandy loam	California	16.8	8.9	7.9	1.3
Wooster silt loam	Ohio	23.4	6.1	17.3	2.9
Dunkirk silty clay	New York	21.7	5.0	16.7	2.7
Aiken clay loam	California	31.1	25.7	5.4	0.7

* *Determined as moisture equivalent.*
Source: Adapted from Proc. Am. Soc. Hort. Sci. 40:485, 1940.

than the Wooster silt loam and the Dunkirk silty clay loam. Thus, the data indicate that very coarse-textured soils have a low permanent wilting percentage, and no definite or well-defined relation of texture to permanent wilting percentage exists with the other types.

The difference between the field capacity and the permanent wilting percentage is usually called the available water, that is, the water plants can absorb. However, as previously stated, the permanent wilting percentage is determined by placing plants in a dark, moist chamber, a condition which is accompanied by low rates of transpiration. Since the rate of transpiration is relatively high in the light and in dry air, the permanent wilting percentage, as determined by this method, would seem to be too low for crops growing under conditions of high transpiration. Nevertheless, the present method can be used to show the marked variation in the amount of the so-called available water in soil. Here again the student is referred to the data in Table 4.1. Note the low quantities of available water in the Plainfield, Yuma, and Aiken soils and the high quantities in the Redman, Wooster, and Dunkirk soils. Thus, soils with low field capacities necessarily have low quantities of available water, but soils with high field capacities may or may not have high quantities of available water. In general, from the standpoint of the water supply, ideal soils have high field capacities and low permanent wilting percentages, e.g., the Redman sandy loam in Oregon, the Wooster silt loam in Ohio, and the Dunkirk silty clay loam in New York.

Rate of Movement of Available Water.   Important factors are (1) soil temperature and (2) concentration of the soil solution. Temperature affects the movement of available water in three ways. It influences the kinetic energy and viscosity of the molecules and the tension on the surface of the capillary films. In general, rising temperatures increase the kinetic energy and decrease the viscosity and surface tension, and these effects of temperature hold usually between 32 and 95°F. Thus, water moves less rapidly in cold soils than in warm soils. This effect of temperature explains, partially at least, why growers use bottom-heated propagation beds in the greenhouse, why they use warm water in the irrigation of warm-season crops in the greenhouse in winter, why rapidly growing herbaceous crops in the greenhouse may wilt if irrigated with cold water during sunny weather, and why broad-leaved evergreen trees may wilt in winter, especially during periods of intense sunshine.

Concentration of the soil solution refers to the number of solute particles per unit volume of solution. Water has great solvent properties. As a result, the water in the soil contains many substances in solution. The substances in solution, the solutes, naturally get in the way of water molecules and retard their movement. Thus, the greater number of solute particles per unit volume of solution, the greater is the retardation of movement of the water molecules. Usually, the water of soils contains a relatively low concentration of solutes and the available water moves freely to the water-absorbing region. Sometimes, however, the concentration of the solutes becomes so high that the available water moves slowly into the plant and the direction of movement may be reversed. Instead of moving into the plant, the water moves out of the plant and into the soil. Sometimes the grower inadvertantly causes this reversal of water movement when he applies large quantities of soluble fertilizer close to the plant's roots or to the seed.

Depth of Water Table. The water table refers to the surface of the zone in soils which is saturated with water. In this zone, the pore space is entirely filled with water, and as a result insufficient quantities of oxygen are available for the growth and respiration of the root system. In fact, because of capillary movement, insufficient quantities of oxygen are present for a distance of 12 to 18 inches from the water table. Thus, with other factors favorable, the depth of root penetration is limited to a distance which extends from the upper surface of the soil to about 12 inches above the water table. For example, if a water table is 6 feet below the surface, the depth of root penetration would be limited to 5 feet. The question arises: What is the optimum depth of the water table for crop production? In general, soils with a water table close to the surface throughout the period of growth of a crop are unsatisfactory for crop production. For example, studies of the relation of height of the water table to productivity of raspberry plants in a Michigan plantation showed that plants with their root systems confined to the upper 7 inches of the soil, because of a high water table, were small, weakly vigorous, and unproductive. On the other hand, plants with root systems which penetrated to a depth of 14 inches were large, moderately vigorous, and productive. Similar studies have shown that the highbush blueberry requires a water table from 12 to 24 inches from the surface; and onions grown on muck require a water level of 24 to 36 inches from the surface. In fact, many growers of onions and celery on muck regulate the height of the water table by means of dams in the drainage ditches. In this way a uniform supply of moisture to the roots is assured, and excessive oxidation of the muck does not take place. In general, soils with water tables close to the surface, usually 1 to 4 feet, depending on the transpiring surface of the plant and the type of soil, are likely to seriously limit the growth of the root system and the growth and productivity of the plants.

PLANT FACTORS

Rate of Photosynthesis. As previously stated, the water-absorbing region exists just back of the growing points of the root system. Its function is the absorption of water and solutes in the water. In general, the water-absorbing power of this region is conditioned largely by its osmotic pressure. This in turn is determined by differences in the concentration of water on each side of the cytoplasmic membranes of the absorbing cells. These living membranes are semipermeable; that is, they permit some substances to pass through and do not permit others. Usually, these membranes are permeable to mineral solutes and water and impermeable to organic substances, such as sugars and proteins in solution. These sugars and proteins are in solution with water within the aborbing region and are in greater concentration than the minerals in solution with water in the soil. Because of the lower concentration of water in the absorbing cells, water diffuses from the soil into the roots. The relatively low concentration of water in the absorbing region is due largely to the sugars in the cells of the absorbing region. Photosynthesis makes the sugars. These sugars pass down the phloem of the stem into the root system. Consequently, with other factors favorable, plants with high rates of photosynthesis can absorb more water per unit time than can plants with low rates. Thus, plants with dark green leaves or with healthy leaves have the ability to absorb more water per unit time than plants with light green or diseased leaves.

Rate of Respiration. As stated previously, the region of water absorption contains living cells. These cells are constantly respiring. Thus, they are continually giving off carbon dioxide and taking in oxygen. Experiments have shown that if the oxygen of the soil air is displaced by nitrogen or carbon dioxide, water absorption is reduced or entirely stopped. This need of oxygen for the absorption of water emphasizes the importance of adequate drainage. If the pore space of the soil is saturated with water, oxygen for the respiration of the living cells is limited. As a result, the protoplasm dies and the absorption of water ceases. In order to get excess water out of the soil and air with its oxygen into the soil, drainage is necessary. This explains why growers drain relatively low places in crop-growing fields; why they drain soils which would otherwise remain saturated for considerable periods; and why water standing on fields of rapidly growing crops prevents the absorption of water and causes injury, if not death, to the plants. Most fruit, vegetable, and flower crops require well-drained soils.

Depth and Density of the Absorbing Surface. The depth of the absorbing surface refers to the depth of soil penetrated by the roots. In general, depth of penetration varies with the kind of plant and the type of soil. In well-drained soils some plants develop rather shallow root systems, others develop moderately deep root systems, and others develop deep root systems. Naturally, plants with deep root systems can obtain more water than plants with shallow root systems. This is particularly true during conditions of high transpiration. Note the differences in depth of root penetration of the crops presented in Table 4.2.

The density of the absorbing surface refers to the number of root hairs and fine roots which occupy each unit volume of soil. Take two plants, A and B. The root system of plant A has 1 million root hairs for every cubic foot of soil for a depth, width, and length of 10 feet, and the roots of plant B have only 10,000 root hairs for every cubic foot of soil occupied by the roots. Since the capillary water moves for very short distances, plant A, because of its greater root density, will obtain greater quantities of water than plant B. Thus, both depth of root penetration and degree

Table 4.2. EXTENT AND DEPTH OF ROOT SYSTEMS
OF CERTAIN CROPS WHEN GROWN
IN WELL-DRAINED SOILS

Nonextensive and shallow	Extensive and moderately deep	Extensive and deep
Celery, lettuce, onion	Beet, cabbage, carrot, cucumber, lima bean, potato, snap bean, sweet corn, summer squash	Asparagus, cantaloupe, sweetpotato, tomato, watermelon, winter squash

of branching or root ramification are important, particularly during periods of high transpiration. A prime characteristic of drought-resistant crop plants is that they develop deep, extensive, and much-branched root systems.

QUESTIONS

1. Enumerate the functions of water in plant growth.
2. Define transpiration.
3. Most of the water is lost through the leaves. Explain.
4. Under conditions of high transpiration, a high rate of photosynthesis requires a high rate of water absorption. Explain.
5. Distinguish between field capacity, permanent wilting percentage, and available water in soils.
6. What is the relation of texture to the field capacity of soils?
7. From the standpoint of the water supply, ideal soils have high field capacities and low wilting percentages. Explain.
8. Under conditions of high transpiration, plants in full leaf and in cold soils are likely to wilt. Explain.
9. In general, the amount of water available to plants varies inversely with the concentration of soluble salts in the soil solution. Explain.
10. Growers sometimes withdraw water from their growing crops. Explain how they do this.
11. It is largely a matter of the plant roots growing to the water supply rather than the water supply moving to the roots. Explain.
12. A crop plant with a deep root system withstands drought to a better extent than a crop plant with a shallow root system. Explain.
13. Plants with dark green leaves have a greater water-absorbing capacity than plants with light green leaves. Explain.
14. Plants with healthy leaves have a greater water-absorbing capacity than plants with diseased leaves. Explain.
15. Plants growing in well-drained soils have a greater water-absorbing capacity than those growing in saturated soils. Explain.
16. Rapidly growing crops frequently wilt immediately after a heavy rain during the summer. Explain.
17. A heavy sod may limit and eventually prevent the development of root systems of orchard trees. Explain.
18. The presence of a hardpan in the upper level of soils is injurious to fruit trees. Explain.
19. Why does a large deciduous tree decline in growth and finally die after 2 or 3 feet of soil is added to the surface of the original soil?
20. Show how the breaking up of tight subsoils may increase crop yields.
21. In general, farmers should consider the water content, aeration, and fertility of the subsoil. Explain.

THE OUTGO OF WATER, OR TRANSPIRATION

ENVIRONMENTAL FACTORS

Light Intensity. Of the total amount of light energy that impinges on chlorophyll-containing tissues, about 10 per cent is reflected, 10 per cent is transmitted, and 80 per cent is absorbed. Of this absorbed energy only about 1 per cent is used in the union of carbon dioxide and water in the photosynthetic reaction and the remainder is changed to heat. This, in turn, is dissipated by radiation and by transpiration. Radiation is the transfer of radiant energy through space from a relatively hot body to a relatively cold one. In this way, light is transferred from the sun to the earth. In like manner, some of the light energy absorbed by the leaves and green stems is transferred to the environment.

Transpiration involves the changing of liquid water into vapor form. Large quantities of energy are required to effect this change. Since more energy is available at high light intensities than at low light intensities, it follows that, with other factors favorable, the rate of change of liquid water into vapor water varies more or less directly with the light intensity. Thus, the greater the light intensity, the greater is the amount of energy absorbed and the greater is the transpiration rate.

Relative Humidity. As is well known, the atmosphere has the ability to hold water vapor. In general, moist air contains relatively large quantities of water vapor per unit volume, whereas dry air contains small quantities. This ability of the air to hold water in vapor form varies directly with the temperature. Thus, warm air holds more water as vapor than does cold air.

The amount of water vapor in the air compared with the amount when the air is saturated for any particular temperature is known as relative humidity. Thus, when the relative humidity is high, the number of vapor molecules per unit volume of air is high; and when the relative humidity is low, the number of vapor molecules per unit volume of air is also low. Since the outer walls of the manufacturing cells are usually surrounded by films of water, a high relative humidity exists within the chamber of each stomate, and since the air outside the stomates usually has a lower humidity, the molecules of water vapor diffuse from the stomatal chamber to the outside air. Thus, the rate of diffusion depends on the difference in relative humidity of the stomatal chambers and the outside air. In other words, if the outside air contains a small number of water molecules per unit volume (low relative humidity), the vapor molecules will diffuse from the region of the stomates to the outside air at a rapid rate. Conversely, if the outside air contains a large number of molecules of water vapor, the rate of diffusion will be at a slow rate. Therefore, with open stomates and other factors favorable, the rate of transpiration varies inversely with the relative humidity.

Air Temperature.   Since temperature governs the speed of molecules, it governs the rate of diffusion of water vapor from transpiring surfaces to the outside air. A rise in temperature increases the speed of the molecules of water vapor and correspondingly increases the rate of transpiration. Therefore, with constant light intensity and constant relative humidity and in still air, the rate of transpiration will be governed by the temperature.

Air Movement.   When air movement is rapid, the molecules of water vapor immediately above a free water surface are rapidly carried away and the rate of diffusion is accordingly increased. Conversely, when air movement is slow, the molecules are displaced less rapidly and the rate of evaporation is relatively low. Thus, with other factors constant, the rate of evaporation of water is governed by the wind velocity. However, the student should remember that transpiration is biophysical in nature and that the rate of absorption of water and the turgor of the guard cells should be considered. When the rate of absorption becomes less than the rate of transpiration, the guard cells would be expected to lose turgor and change in shape. This would result in partial or entire closing of the stomates and corresponding decreases in the rate of transpiration. In fact, experiments have shown that the rate of transpiration is directly proportional to the wind velocity at very low velocities only, usually up to 3 to 4 miles per hour, and that at high wind velocities the rate of transpiration remains fairly constant. This suggests that winds of moderately high to high velocities bring about partial or complete closing of the stomates, with a resultant decrease in transpiration and, unfortunately, in photosynthesis.

The student should keep in mind that the factors which influence the absorption of water operate together. A warm, moist soil which has low osmotic pressure and which is thoroughly ramified by the plant's roots promotes the absorption of large quantities of water. The warm temperature promotes rapid movement of the capillary water, the moist condition provides abundant quantities of available water and adequate aeration for carbon dioxide and oxygen exchange in the respiration and growth of the roots, and soil water with a low concentration of solutes promotes rapid diffusion of water into the plant. Conversely, a cold or dry soil or a soil saturated with water or a high concentration of soluble salts limits water absorption.

As with the factors that influence the intake of water, those which influence the outgo of water operate together. Thus, high light intensities and high temperatures combined with low relative humidities induce high rates of transpiration; whereas low light intensities and low temperatures combined with high relative humidities promote low rates of transpiration. In like manner, light winds induce higher rates of transpiration than calm or still air. This explains why transpiration is greater during the day as compared with the night, on sunny days as compared with cloudy days, on cloudy days as compared with rainy days, on windy days as compared with calm days, and during the summer months as compared with the spring, fall, and winter months.

THE WATER SUPPLY AND GROWTH AND DEVELOPMENT

The student should bear in mind in this discussion that the water supply is the limiting factor. In other words, all other factors are assumed to be favorable for growth and development: the day and night temperatures and light intensities are within the optimum range, the relative length of the light and dark periods is favorable for the type of growth the plant should be making, and all the essential elements are in favorable supply. With the water supply as the limiting factor, its effect on plant growth and development is discussed from three standpoints: (1) favorable supplies, (2) deficits, and (3) excesses.

Favorable Supplies. In general, with favorable supplies the rate of absorption equals the rate of transpiration. Under these conditions the guard cells and the cells surrounding the guard cells are turgid and the stomates are open. As a result, carbon dioxide diffuses rapidly into the leaves and photosynthesis proceeds at high rates. With high rates of photosynthesis during the day and normal rates of respiration during the day and night, abundant carbohydrates are available for growth and development; and if the plant has been handled properly, particularly with respect to the vegetative and reproductive phases, the marketable yields will be high. Thus, if the environment induces a high transpiration rate by high light intensity, or high temperature, or dry air, or high wind velocity, or any combination of these factors, the supply of available water in the soil, the water-absorbing power of the root-hair zone, and the area of absorbing surface should be correspondingly high. Conversely, if the environment induces a low transpiration rate, relatively low supplies of water in the soil, or a low water-absorbing capacity of the root-hair zone, or a small absorbing surface, or any combination of these factors may be sufficient to supply the plant with abundant water. In other words, whenever the water supply is the limiting factor, the rate of absorption and the rate of transpiration should be considered together. The effect of favorable supplies is diagrammatically represented by the line AB as follows:

A	The rate of absorption = the rate of transpiration	B

The guard cells are turgid.
The stomates are open.
Carbon dioxide diffuses rapidly into the leaves.
The rate of photosynthesis is high.
The rate of respiration is normal.
Abundant carbohydrates are available for growth.

Deficits. Plants do not always receive favorable supplies of water; unfortunately, deficits occur. What are the immediate, subsequent, and extreme effects of water deficits within crop plants? In general, the immediate effect is a reduction in the size of the cells in the region of cell elongation. Thus, the cells which are made are small. This explains why plants grown under mild deficiencies produce stems with short internodes and why their leaves, flowers, and fruits are small.

The subsequent effect is a reduction in the rate of photosynthesis. The rate of absorption is much lower than the rate of transpiration, the guard cells lose turgor and become flaccid, and the stomates either partially or completely close. Consequently, the rate of diffusion of carbon dioxide into the manufacturing cells is low, and the rate of manufacture of the initial food substances is accordingly low. Very few carbohydrates, pigments, fats, proteins, and other substances are made; growth is slow, and the marketable yields are low. Investigations have

Fig. 4.2. Relation of the amount of available water to the growth of young apple trees. (Courtesy, A. L. Kenworthy, Michigan State University.)

shown that the guard cells of many crops—apples, pears, peaches, plums, pecans, and lima beans—are markedly sensitive to water deficits. As soon as moderately severe water deficits occur within the plants, the guard cells lose turgor and the stomates begin to close. When the rate of transpiration is high and the rate of absorption is low, the stomates begin to close in the early afternoon. Under extreme conditions, that is, very low rates of absorption combined with high rates of transpiration, they close in the morning and remain closed for the remainder of the day. The effect of deficits explains why marketable yields are low after a dry spell, why orchard trees and other woody plants become susceptible to winter injury, why low water supplies during the summer in an apple orchard usually mean a crop of small apples with a dull finish, and why water deficits during the summer in a pecan orchard are likely to produce crops of poorly filled nuts. Figure 4.2 shows the effects of varied quantities of water on the growth of young apple trees. Each tree is representative of an experimental group. These trees, from left to right, were given abundant, moderately abundant, and low quantities of available water.

The extreme effect results in wilting. When plants are wilted, the guard cells are fully flaccid and the stomates are closed, and, as a result, photosynthesis practically ceases. Since respiration continues, the plants begin to decrease in dry weight. With continued wilting, plants continue to starve, and finally they die. Note the appearance of the leaves of the wilted corn plant in Fig. 4.3. The effect of water deficits is diagrammatically represented by line XA as follows:

Wilting	Decreasing supplies of water	
X		A

No food manufacture	Decreasing turgor of guard cells
Plants living on reserve	Decreasing size of stomates
substances only	Decreasing rate of food manufacture
	Decreasing growth and yield
	With overwintered plants, decreasing resistance to winter injury

SYMPTOMS OF WATER DEFICIENCY. Since water deficits within plants retard growth and development, a knowledge of the symptoms of water deficiency should be helpful in plant-production practices. In general, the first symptom for plants in the vegetative phase is a reduction in the rate of extension of stems and twigs accompanied with the development of relatively small, healthy, dark green leaves. This is followed by the development of slender stems or twigs, small flowers, and small, poorly colored fruit. With certain crops—lemons, peaches,

Fig. 4.3. A wilted corn plant. Note the rolling of edges of leaves. Photograph taken during period of drought. (Courtesy, F. W. Emerson, "Basic Botany," New York, McGraw-Hill Book Company, Inc.)

and tomatoes—the leaves, under conditions of low rates of absorption and high rates of transpiration, actually draw water from the fruit. This causes a marked decrease in volume of the fruit of lemons and a pathologic condition in tomatoes known as blossom end rot.

How can water deficits be prevented or reduced? Growers avail themselves of various practices depending on the kind of crop and enterprise. For example, florists reduce the light intensity and florists, gardeners, and orchardists transplant and cultivate carefully and apply irrigation water. These practices—reducing light intensity, transplanting, cultivating, and irrigating—are discussed more fully in Chapters 6 and 13.

EXCESSES.   Under certain conditions with certain crops, excessive supplies within the plant produce unfavorable effects. In general, these effects include the development of leggy seedlings and the occurrence of growth cracks. Leggy seedlings usually develop under the following conditions: when the plants are set close together, when the soil is kept warm and moist, when the air temperature is within the optimum range, and when light intensity is relatively low. A warm, moist soil and a well-developed root system ensure abundant absorption; but close planting, favorable temperature, reduced light intensity and wind velocity com-

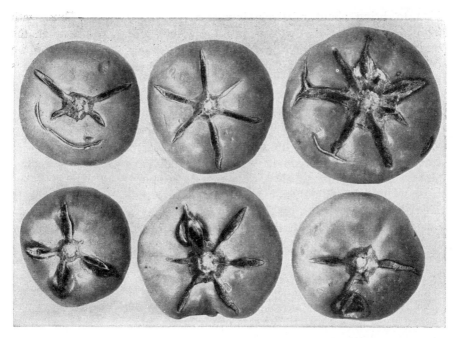

Fig. 4.4. Cracked tomato fruits and sweetpotato roots. (Courtesy, V. R. Boswell, U.S. Department of Agriculture.)

bine to bring about relatively low rates of transpiration. Thus, with high absorption on the one hand and relatively low transpiration on the other, turgor pressure in the region of cell elongation is high and the cells are unduly stretched. This often happens in greenhouses and hotbeds in early spring.

Growth cracks occur under similar conditions of water absorption and transpiration, e.g., the bursting of cabbage heads and the cracking of tomato fruits and carrot and sweetpotato roots. The wet weather provides abundant supplies of available water, which, for plants with an extensive root system, promote a high rate of absorption. The wet weather also, with its comparatively low temperatures, low light intensities, and high relative humidities, causes a low rate of transpiration. Thus, the high absorption of water on the one hand and the low transpiration on the other are associated with the growth cracks. Figure 4.4 shows cracked fruits of the tomato and cracked roots of the sweetpotato. The effect of excess water within the plant is diagrammatically represented by line BC as follows:

The rate of absorption is greater
than the rate of transpiration.

B   **C**

Increasing cell size
Long internodes and leggy growth
Bursting cells
Growth cracks

QUESTIONS

1. Define transpiration.
2. In general, the rate of transpiration is greater during the summer as compared with the winter, during sunny days as compared with cloudy days within the same season, and during the light period as compared with the dark period of any given 24-hour day. Explain.
3. Sweetpotato and cotton plants frequently wilt during the middle of the day in July, August, and September. They become turgid at night. Explain.
4. In general, when the rates of water absorption and transpiration are practically the same, high rates of photosynthesis take place. Explain.
5. During the summer months in the southern United States, a high rate of photosynthesis requires a high rate of water absorption. Explain.
6. What is the immediate effect of a water deficit within growing plants?
7. A continual mild deficiency of water within growing plants results in the development of short internodes and small leaves. Explain.

8. After a drought, yields are low when the plants are grown in nonirrigated soils. Explain.
9. Investigations have shown that temporary wilting of pecan leaves is accompanied by marked reduction in photosynthesis and transpiration. Explain.
10. Show how a severe drought during the latter part of the growing season makes woody plants susceptible to winter injury.
11. A low water supply during the summer in an apple orchard usually means small apples with a dull finish. Explain.
12. A low water supply during the summer in a pecan orchard is likely to produce a crop of small, poorly filled nuts. Explain.
13. When a plant is wilted, it is not making carbohydrates. Explain.
14. In general, with continuous wilting, plants finally die. Explain.
15. Do plants growing in shade (on the floor of a forest or under crowded conditions in a greenhouse) reach for the light? Explain.
16. Tomato seedlings in the center of flats in a greenhouse frequently become more "leggy" than those on the outside. Explain.
17. Cabbage heads burst open and carrot and sweetpotato roots crack during wet weather, particularly when the plants are grown in moderately heavy soils. Explain.
18. The cracking of tomato fruits is severe during a rainy period preceded by drought. Explain.

5

TEMPERATURE AS
THE LIMITING FACTOR

*To every thing there is a season
and a time to every purpose.*
Ecclesiastes 3:1

In our planetary system, the sun is the central body, and nine planets revolve around the sun. The temperature on the surface of all these planets, except that on the surface of the earth, is either too high or too low to support plant and animal life as it is known on the earth. In other words, the temperature which supports plant and animal life as we know it exists only on the surface of the earth. However, the temperature on the surface of the earth is not always favorable for plant growth and development. Within crop-producing areas the temperature is sometimes too low for the manufacture of the initial carbohydrates or for the making of protoplasm, and at other times it may be so high as to induce extremely high rates of transpiration and/or respiration. Extremely high rates of transpiration are likely to result in closing the stomates with a corresponding reduction in the rate of photosynthesis, and extremely high rates of respiration are likely to reduce the supply of carbohydrates for growth and development. In either case, low yields are likely to take place.

To obtain a working knowledge of the influence of temperature on plant growth, temperatures within crop-producing areas are classified as follows: (1) the temperature range favorable for growth and development and (2) the temperature ranges unfavorable for growth and development.

FAVORABLE EFFECTS

The Favorable or Optimum Temperature Range. The favorable temperature range for the growth and development of any particular plant is

72

known as the optimum temperature range. Within this range the two fundamental processes, photosynthesis and respiration,[1] are proceeding in such a way throughout the life cycle of the plant that the highest marketable yields are produced. In other words, from the time the crop is established to the time the product is ready for the harvest, the rate of photosynthesis is high and the rate of respiration is normal. As a result, large quantities of carbohydrates are available for growth and development. Thus, if plants of any given crop are handled properly, particularly with respect to the vegetative and reproductive phases, high marketable yields are obtained. Therefore, *the optimum temperature range may be defined as the range within which maximum photosynthesis and normal respiration take place throughout the life cycle of the plant[2] and within which the highest marketable yields are obtained.*

Not all crops have high rates of photosynthesis combined with normal rates of respiration within the same temperature range. In general, some crops have high rates of photosynthesis combined with normal rates of respiration within a relatively low range, and other crops have high rates of photosynthesis combined with normal rates of respiration at a relatively high range. On this basis, horticultural plants are classified as follows: (1) crops which produce their highest yields within a comparatively low temperature range and (2) crops which produce their highest yields within a comparatively high temperature range. The former are called cool-season crops and the latter are called warm-season crops. Examples of cool-season and warm-season crops are listed in Table 5.1.

The Optimum Night Temperature Range and Phases of Growth. In general, crop plants for the most part make new cells and the protoplasm for these cells during the night. As previously stated, protoplasm is made by sugars, usually glucose, combining with certain compounds containing nitrogen. Thus, the making of new cells is essentially a biochemical reaction; and as in other biochemical reactions, with other factors favorable, temperature directly influences the rate of the process. This effect of temperature on the vegetative and reproductive phases may be illustrated by dividing the optimum night temperature range into two parts: (1) the upper half and (2) the lower half. Since, within the optimum range, the rate of cell division is more or less directly proportional to the temperature, comparatively high rates will take place within the upper half and moderately high rates will take place within the lower half. The high rate of cell division makes for a rapid development of

---

[1] In this chapter it is assumed that the rate of water absorption and the rate of transpiration are practically the same.

[2] As is well known, the time factor should always be considered in any discussion of temperature. In this discussion the time factor is the period of growth of any given crop.

Table 5.1. CLASSIFICATION OF HORTICULTURAL
CROPS BASED ON TEMPERATURE
REQUIREMENTS

Fruit crops	Vegetable crops	Flower and ornamentals
A. Crops Thriving Best within the Cool Temperature Range, 45–60°F*		
Cool-season Crops		
Apple, pear, cherry, plum, gooseberry, currant, strawberry, labrusca grape, raspberry	Asparagus, rhubarb, spinach, lettuce, the cabbages, beet, carrot, pea, potato	Carnation, sweet pea, snapdragon, violet, calendula, geranium, gypsophila, daisy, petunia, larkspur, lupine, pansy, marguerite, mignonette, stevia, scabiosa, schizanthus, zinnia, swainsonia
B. Crops Thriving Best within the Warm Temperature Range, 60–75°F*		
Warm-season Crops		
Peach, apricot, citrus, date, olive, tung, vinifera grape, rotundifolia grape, fig, persimmon, blackberry	Sweetpotato, tomato, pepper, eggplant, cucumber, cantaloupe, watermelon, pumpkin, squash, bean, okra	Rose, poinsettia, gardenia, euphorbia, lily, hyacinth, amaryllis, orchid

* Night temperatures. The day temperature may be 10–20°F higher.

stems, leaves, and absorbing roots and a rapid utilization of carbohydrates; and the moderately high rates make for a moderately rapid development of stems, leaves, and absorbing roots and a moderately rapid utilization of carbohydrates. Thus, with other factors in favorable supply and with high rates of photosynthesis and normal rates of respiration, the maintenance of temperature within the upper half of the optimum range promotes vigorous vegetative growth, whereas the maintenance of temperature on the lower half induces moderately vigorous vegetative growth. Therefore, at temperatures within the upper half of the optimum range, most of the carbohydrates which the plant is making will be used and very few will be stored. On the other hand, at temperatures within the lower half, lesser quantities of carbohydrates will be used and greater quantities will be stored. The influence of night temperature within the optimum range is briefly summarized as follows:

OPTIMUM NIGHT TEMPERATURE RANGE

Lower half

Upper half

Moderately rapid rates of cell division
Moderately vigorous vegetative growth
Moderately rapid usage of carbohydrates
with moderate quantities available for
storage

Rapid rates of cell division
Vigorous vegetative growth
Rapid usage of carbohydrates
with low quantities available
for storage

The marked effect of temperature on the growth and development of horticultural crops is manifested by the care and attention given to the maintenance of night temperatures in greenhouses. The night temperature of greenhouses, particularly of commercial establishments, is always under practical control. In fact, many growers use thermostatically controlled heating systems. In this way heat is supplied to the plants within certain limits. In general, when the temperature approaches the lower limit of the optimum night temperature range a thermostat opens valves which admit hot water or steam into heating pipes; and when the temperature approaches the upper limit of the optimum range, the thermostat closes these valves. Thus, with the proper manipulation of other practices, the grower controls to a marked degree the type of growth he wants his plants to make.

Although the grower of outdoor crops cannot control temperature in precisely the same way as the grower of greenhouse crops, he can utilize favorable temperatures by taking advantage of southeasterly or northeasterly slopes, by using various soil types and elevations, and more particularly by planting at the right time. Study the data in Table 5.2.

Table 5.2. EFFECT OF TIME OF PLANTING ON YIELD
OF THE PORTO RICO SWEETPOTATO*

Approximate planting date	Number days planting to harvest	Yield, bu/acre		
		No. 1 grade	No. 2 grade	Total all grades
April 15	190	147	81	319
April 30	170	126	72	287
May 15	150	104	53	240
June 10	130	99	46	206
June 30	110	50	32	128

* *The figures on yields are the average results of experiments at four locations in the southeastern United States for three years.*
Source: Adapted from Table 4, U.S. Dept. Agr. Circ. 725, 1945.

Note that plants of the Porto Rico sweetpotato set in the field at the earliest practical date, usually one month after the last killing frost in the spring, produced more marketable roots than plants set at later dates. In fact, the data show that for each day's delay in planting, the grower lost 2.4 bushels of marketable roots per acre. Examples for other crops could be cited

Temperature, in combination with other factors, markedly influences the localization of horticultural crop industries. In general, cool-season crops grow best in regions characterized by relatively cool weather, and warm-season crops thrive best in regions characterized by relatively warm weather. For example, the temperature range of the summer season in Holland, Denmark, and Great Britain is particularly suitable for the growing of asparagus, spinach, lettuce, cabbage, Brussels sprouts, cauliflower, garden pea, and other cool-season crops. In these countries warm-season crops, such as oranges, grapefruit, lemons, limes, peaches, apricots, and cantaloupes, are raised in glass houses because the heat of summer is insufficient to bring these crops to full maturity. In the continental United States the cool-season vegetables are grown during the summer in the northern regions of the country and during the fall, winter, and early spring in the southern regions. In general, the apple and labrusca grape are confined to the northern regions, whereas citrus fruits, dates, European grapes, and other warm-season crops are grown in the southern regions.

Temperature also influences the adaptability of varieties within a given kind or species. For example, the Winesap and York Imperial varieties of apple require a comparatively high optimum temperature range, whereas Baldwin and McIntosh require a low optimum temperature range. The Earliana and Bonny Best tomato varieties thrive best in the northern regions, and Marglobe thrives best in the southern regions. The Tom Watson variety of watermelon thrives well in the southern region but fails to produce profitable crops in the northern region.

UNFAVORABLE EFFECTS

The unfavorable effects of temperature are classified as follows: (1) growing-season temperatures above the optimum night temperature range, (2) growing-season temperatures below the optimum night temperature range, and (3) unfavorable effects of winter temperature.

Growing-season Temperatures above the Optimum Night Temperature Range. Plants subjected to night temperatures *above* their optimum range, particularly during the later stages of growth, generally produce low yields. How are these low yields produced? As discussed in Chapter 1, the yield for any given plant equals the amount of carbohydrates made per unit of time minus the amount used. Since the initial carbohydrates are made by photosynthesis and are used in respiration, the yield equals the rate of photosynthesis minus the rate of respiration. In general, when the plants of any given crop are grown at comparatively high day temperatures combined with high night temperatures, that is, with night temperatures above the optimum range, the rate of photosynthesis remains at a high level but the rate of respiration increases markedly. As a result, the amount of carbohydrates available for growth and yield of

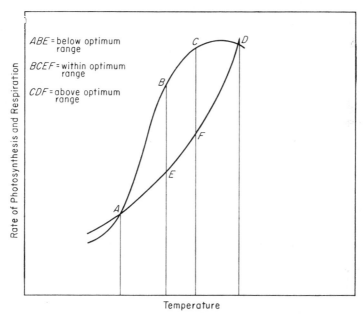

Fig. 5.1. Relation of photosynthesis and respiration to the available carbohydrate supply for growth and development of crop plants.

any given crop becomes increasingly less. Thus, the higher the night temperature above the optimum range, the lower is likely to be the yield.

The relation of temperature to the rate of photosynthesis and the rate of respiration to the yield is shown in Fig. 5.1. Note that at high temperatures the rate of photosynthesis remains at a high level, *but the rate of respiration increases quite markedly.* Also note that at point D the rate of respiration equals the rate of photosynthesis and that no carbohydrates are available for growth and development. Thus, in order for plants to grow and develop rapidly, the rate of photosynthesis must always be greater than the rate of respiration; and the greater the difference between the rates of these processes, the greater is likely to be the yield. This effect of temperature above the optimum range for growth explains why potatoes and other cool-season crops are grown in the southern United States during the spring and fall only; why carnations produce relatively large, fragrant flowers in cool weather and relatively small, nonfragrant flowers in warm weather; why garden peas fail to produce high yields during hot weather; why they produce abundant yields during cool weather; why the flowers of *Primula sinensis* var. *rubra* are red at comparatively low temperatures and are white at high temperatures; why the apple industry, for the most part, is located in the northern regions of the country and in the elevated regions in the upper South; and why the cool-season vegetable and flower crops are grown in the winter-garden areas in the South and during the summer in the

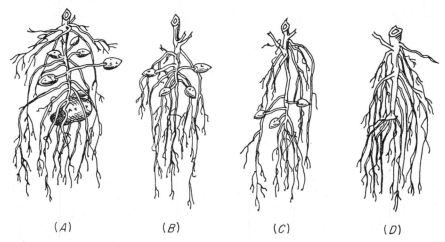

(*A*)   (*B*)   (*C*)   (*D*)

Fig. 5.2. Effect of temperature on the development of potato tubers. A: 68°F, 20.9 gm. B: 73°F, 5.0 gm. C: 79°F, 1.6 gm. D: 84°F, 0 gm. (Redrawn from Fig. 9, Minn. Agr. Exp. Sta. Tech. Bull. 34, 1925.)

North. Figure 5.2 shows the effect of temperature above the optimum range on the development of potato tubers. Note that as the soil temperature increases above the optimum range, the yield of the tubers decreases.

Growing-season Temperatures below the Optimum Night Temperature Range. Plants subjected to temperatures *below* their optimum night temperature range for growth also produce low yields. How are these low yields produced? Here again both photosynthesis and respiration are involved. The relation of temperature below the optimum range to the rate of each of these processes and the amount of carbohydrates available for growth is shown in Fig. 5.1. Note that at temperatures below the optimum range, the rate of photosynthesis and the rate of respiration decrease, *but the rate of photosynthesis decreases to a greater extent* *than the rate of respiration.* Also note that at point A, the rate of each of these processes is equal and no carbohydrates are available for growth and development. Further, at temperatures below the optimum night temperature range for any given plant, *the rate of protein formation in the making of new cells is low.* As a result, the rate of growth is slow and the yields, if any, are accordingly low. This effect of temperature below the optimum range for growth explains why warm-season vegetable crops thrive well only in favorable locations during the summer in the coastal regions of Alaska; why the northern limit of the commercial sweetpotato industry extends from New Jersey to southern Ohio, southern Indiana, and Iowa; why the tung industry in the United States is confined to a narrow belt extending from southern Louisiana to northern Florida; why the date industry in the United States is limited to the Coachella Valley of southern California; why an unusually cool growing season in apple and peach orchards is likely to make the plants susceptible to winter injury; and why peaches and apricots in northern Europe are grown on the south side of high walls.

Temperatures just below the optimum range also induce a condition called "bolting" in certain valuable vegetable crops, e.g., cabbage, collards, celery, onions, and beets. These kinds are biennials. Under favorable temperatures the plants develop the storage structure during the first

Fig. 5.3. Nonbolted and bolted cabbage plants. (Courtesy, E. L. Moore, Mississippi State University.)

year and flowering stalks, flowers, fruit, and seed during the second. If seedling plants of these crops are subjected to temperatures somewhat below the optimum range, that is, between 40 and 50°F for four to eight weeks depending on the kind and variety, they produce flowering stalks and seeds instead of producing the storage structure, e.g., the head in cabbage, the fleshy leaves in collards, the fleshy petioles in celery, the bulb in onion, and the fleshy root in beets. Why does bolting take place at temperatures just below the optimum range? In general, the rate of photosynthesis is fairly high and at the same time the rate of respiration and the rate of cell division are low. As a result, relatively low quantities of carbohydrates are used and large quantities of carbohydrates are stored. This more or less rapid accumulation of carbohydrates is associated with the formation of flower-forming hormones and the initiation of flower buds which, with the onset of warm weather, develop into flowering stalks which bear the fruit and seed. Thus, these biennials become annuals when the seedling plants are subjected to relatively low temperatures for a sufficient period of time. Note the two cabbage plants in Fig. 5.3.

QUESTIONS

1. What is meant by the optimum temperature range for plant growth and development?
2. Compare cool-season and warm-season crops from the standpoint of their optimum temperature ranges for photosynthesis and for cell division.
3. With other factors favorable, night temperatures within the upper half of the optimum range favor vigorous vegetative growth and the utilization of carbohydrates. Explain.
4. How does the greenhouse grower use night temperatures to regulate the vegetative and reproductive phases of plant growth?
5. With other factors favorable, temperatures within the lower half of the optimum range are more favorable for the development of large, highly colored flowers than temperatures within the upper half. Explain.
6. In general, the red varieties of tomatoes develop lycopin (the red pigment of tomatoes) more readily in the North in July, August, and September than in the South during the same months. Explain.
7. At what time of the growing season in the South would you expect tomato fruits to develop their highest color? Explain.
8. The Puget Sound district of the United States and the climate of England are particularly favorable for the growing of garden peas. Explain.
9. Cool-season vegetable crops are grown in the summer in the northern United States and in the fall, winter, and early spring in the southern United States. Explain.

10. How do night temperatures above the optimum range for growth produce low yields?
11. Investigations have shown that crops produce low yields when the rate of respiration approaches the rate of photosynthesis. Explain.
12. For the growing of greenhouse crops, the optimum cloudy day temperature range should be not much higher than the optimum night temperature range. Explain.
13. Carnations grown in greenhouses in the southern United States and harvested in February and March are likely to have larger flowers and thicker stems than those harvested from the same plants in April and May. Explain.
14. Garden peas planted three or four weeks before the average date of the last killing frost in the South generally produce greater yields than those planted two or three weeks later. Explain.
15. In your opinion can satisfactory crops of apples be produced in the South? If so, where? Explain.
16. How do temperatures below the optimum range for growth produce low yields?
17. In the British Isles cucumbers, cantaloupes, and tomatoes are grown more satisfactorily under glass than outdoors. Explain.
18. Sweetpotatoes are grown in regions which have a growing season of at least 150 to 170 days during which the temperature is relatively high. Explain.
19. How do temperatures just below the optimum range induce bolting in biennial vegetables?

WINTER TEMPERATURES

Harmful effects of winter temperatures are classified as follows: (1) injuries due to immaturity of the tissues, (2) injuries due to unseasonably high temperatures followed by low temperatures, (3) injuries associated with winter drought, and (4) injuries due to insufficient cold.

Injuries Due to Immaturity of the Tissues. The ability of woody plants to withstand low temperatures of the winter is dependent on the ability of the protoplasm to bind water. This in turn is related to the ability of the protoplasm to make compounds known as hydrophilic colloids. These hydrophilic colloids have a large surface in proportion to their size and absorb large quantities of water on these surfaces. The molecules of water are drawn to each other, and they act more like a solid than a liquid. This water is called bound water and cannot be frozen at the usual subfreezing temperatures. In general, the hydrophilic colloids are made from accumulated carbohydrates and mature tissues contain more carbohydrates than immature tissues. Thus, the rate of photosynthesis, the relative rate of carbohydrate usage and storage, particularly during the latter part of the growing season, and the ability of the plant to make hydrophilic colloids are all concerned. This explains (1) why a water deficit within woody plants during the latter part of the growing season is likely to predispose the tissues to winter injury; (2) why weakly vigorous trees are likely to be injured to a greater extent than moderately vigorous trees; (3) why excessively vigorous trees are susceptible to winter injury; (4) why unseasonably high temperatures combined with moist soil during the latter part of the growing season are likely to make woody plants susceptible to winter injury; and (5) why heavy applications of available nitrogen to moderately vigorous trees during the latter part of the season should be avoided. The high supply of available nitrogen combines with the sugars in the formation of proteins for the making of the protoplasm. This, of course, depletes the carbohydrate supply for the formation of the hydrophilic colloids. In cases (1) and (2) the rate of photosynthesis is low and very few carbohydrates are made; and in cases (3), (4), and (5) the rate of photosynthesis is high but most of the carbohydrates have been used. Very few are left for making the hydrophilic colloids.

In general, under favorable conditions horticultural plants vary in their ability to withstand low winter temperatures. Some are resistant, but others are not. As previously stated, resistant, or hardy, plants possess the ability to bind their water to a greater extent than nonresistant, or nonhardy, plants. Examples of relatively hardy and nonhardy horticultural crops are shown in Table 5.3.

Injury due to immaturity of the tissues may be severe or mild, depending not only on the degree of carbohydrate accumulation in trees and shrubs, but also on the time and severity of the low temperature. In general, a sudden drop in temperature of 30, 40, or 50°F is more

Table 5.3.   HARDY AND NONHARDY
            HORTICULTURAL PLANTS

Fruits	Vegetables	Ornamentals
Hardy		
Apple, plum, pear, peach, cherry, blueberry, cranberry, labrusca grape	The cool-season crops (potato excepted)	Flowering peach, quince, hawthorn, rose, spirea, barberry, lilac
Nonhardy		
Citrus, date, olive, fig, muscadine grape, raspberry, blackberry	The warm-season crops	Magnolia, nandina, cape jasmine, crepemyrtle, camellia

severe than a drop of 10, 15, or 20°F. For example, the late summer and fall of 1940 in the middle western United States were characterized by unseasonably high temperatures, abundant light, and relatively high rainfall. As a result, the trees and shrubs in this region were moderately to vigorously vegetative and, as would be expected, comparatively few carbohydrates were stored in the tissues. On November 11, the temperature in that area dropped from a high of 50 to 60°F to a low of 10°F within a very short period. The sudden drop in temperature severely injured the wood of many deciduous-tree fruits and ornamental shrubs. As a result, thousands of fruit trees were killed and the productive capacity of many of the trees which survived was considerably reduced. Thus, environmental conditions during the growing season and the time, duration, and intensity of cold determine, to some degree at least, the localization of fruit crop industries. Winter injury to old and young apple branches is shown in Fig. 5.4.

Injuries Due to High Temperatures Followed by Low Temperatures. Unseasonably high temperatures during late winter and early spring followed by low, usually freezing, temperatures are frequently injurious in peach, pecan, and tung orchards of the southern United States. The warm period may extend for two, three, or four weeks, and the daily temperature may fluctuate from 40 to 75°F. With internal conditions favorable for growth, the temperature range is sufficiently high to promote the absorption of water, cell division of the buds, and the opening of the flowers. What is more important is that the buds lose their hardi-

Fig. 5.4. Examples of winter injury. Left: bark on trunk of Golden Delicious apple tree. Center: freezing cracks on main branch. Right: freezing cracks on young branches. (Courtesy, A. B. Groves, Virginia Polytechnic Institute.)

ness, or resistance to low temperatures. As a result, the near-freezing or subfreezing temperatures which usually follow the warm period kill the protoplasm of the cells of the pistil(s) and stamens. Thus, for any particular kind of fruit, early blooming varieties are more susceptible to this type of injury than late blooming sorts and northern slopes would seem to be more desirable than southern slopes.

Injuries Associated with Winter Drought.   The tops of trees and shrubs lose water in the winter. In general, the rate of loss is more or less directly proportional to the evaporating power of the air. Thus, a dry atmosphere accompanied by winds of high velocity would induce a higher rate of transpiration than a moist atmosphere accompanied by winds of low velocity. The water lost by the tops must be replaced by the absorption of water by the roots. Consequently, the relative rates of water absorption and transpiration are involved. If the soil contains very little available water and if the rate of transpiration is very high, the protoplasm gradually becomes desiccated and the tissues finally die. This type of winter injury is more common in regions characterized by light summer rains, a dry atmosphere, and intense winter cold than in regions characterized by moderate rains, a humid atmosphere, and mild cold. How can this type of injury be reduced or avoided? Manifestly, practices which increase the water content of the soil and the water absorption of the tree and which reduce the rate of transpiration would be beneficial. Accordingly, the application of irrigation water and the judicious use of windbreaks are likely to be helpful.

Injuries Due to Insufficient Cold.   To appreciate the effect of insufficient cold on deciduous plants during the winter, the student should know the meaning of the rest period. As an example, let us study the behavior of three comparable lots of two-year-old moderately vigorous peach trees. Let us assume that these trees are grown in tubs (small, wooden containers), that they have shed all their leaves by the last week of October, and that on November 1 they are divided into three comparable lots—A, B, C—and placed under the following conditions: lot A is kept out of doors from November 1 to February 1 and then placed in a warm greenhouse; lot B is kept in a warm greenhouse from November 1 to May 1; and lot C is kept outdoors throughout this period. Let us also assume that the temperature outdoors varied between 20 and 65°F from November 1 to December 31 and between 15 and 60°F from January 1 to March 21 and that the temperature in the greenhouse varied from 55 to 85°F. Thus, the different temperature treatments are as follows: for lot A, a low temperature level for a period of three months followed by a high temperature level; for lot B, a high temperature level for the entire period; and for lot C, a low temperature level for the entire period. How would the buds of lot A and lot B appear on February 15? The buds of the plants of lot A would be open, and those of lot B would be inactive and show little, if any, signs of growth. What is the difference in temperature treatments between lots A and B? Note that lot A was subjected to a period of cold, but lot B was not. In other words, the trees of lot B failed to grow, even though environmental conditions were favorable for growth. Evidently, conditions within the trees were unfavorable for growth of the buds. *When internal conditions are unfavorable for growth of the leaf and flower buds, particularly for the processess of cell division and enlargement, we say that the trees and shrubs are in the rest period.*[3] Now let us compare lots A and C. Trees of lot C would show no signs of bud development, but since they received the same amount of cold as those of lot A, they are out of the rest period. In other words, the internal conditions were favorable for the growth of the buds, but an external factor, in this case, temperature, was unfavorable.

A certain amount of cold is necessary to break the rest period of both vegetative and flower buds of deciduous trees and shrubs in temperate climates. In general, these buds enter the rest period in late summer and fall, and the amount of cold required varies with the kind of plant and with varieties within a given kind. For example, the apple tree requires more cold than the peach, the peach requires more than the pecan, and the pecan requires more than the tung. Maygold and Mayflower, two commercial varieties of peaches, require 650 and 1,150 hours at or below 45°F, respectively; and Orient, one variety of pear, requires less cold than Waite, another variety of pear.

In certain districts—the southern half of Alabama, Georgia, Mississippi, and the northern half of Louisiana—the amount of cold required to break the rest of commercial varieties of peaches is not always assured. For example, the winters of 1948–1949 and 1949–1950 were extremely mild in these districts, and there was an insufficient amount of cold to break the rest. As a result, many trees in these districts failed to survive. Obviously, the amount of cold sets the southern geographical limits for commercial peach production.

In general, the amount of cold required to break the rest explains partially at least why commercial orchards of apples and peaches do not exist on the Gulf Coast or in Florida; why the chilling requirements of peaches for commercial production in the South should be considered; and why northern slopes may be more desirable than southern slopes. Figure 5.5 shows two Elberta peach trees in the spring of 1949. The tree on the left was part of an orchard near Albany, Georgia, and was photographed on April 19; the tree on the right was part of an orchard near Atlanta, Georgia, and was photographed on April 15. If the trees

[3] The term "dormancy" is frequently used as a synonym for "rest period."

Fig. 5.5. *Appearance of two peach trees in the spring of 1949 in the southeastern United States. The tree on the left is still in the rest period, while the tree on the right is growing vigorously. The trees were photographed within four days of each other.* (*Courtesy, J. H. Weinberger, U.S. Department of Agriculture.*)

in the Albany orchard had received the same amount of cold as the trees in the Atlanta orchard, they would have produced blossoms and leaves about 10 days or two weeks earlier than the trees in the Atlanta orchard, since Albany, Georgia, is about 150 miles south of Atlanta. At present, scientists are endeavoring to develop commercial types with short rest periods for southern peach-growing districts. In this way, the southern geographical limit of commercial peach production could be extended.

A certain amount of cold is also necessary for the growing of certain herbaceous crops. For example, rhubarb forcers allow the fleshy rhizomes to remain in the soil for a period of three to four weeks during the first part of the winter before removing them to the forcing structures. During this period the crowns receive sufficient cold to break the rest period. Thus, a period of chilling temperatures is necessary for the rapid production of the rhubarb petioles.

SPECIFIC TEMPERATURE EFFECTS

Temperature and Starch-Sugar Transformations of Harvest Products. The quality of many horticultural products is determined by the degree of sweetness. In crops where the principal reserve carbohydrate is starch the following reactions are involved:

(enzymes)
(1) sugar $\longrightarrow$ starch
(2) starch $\longrightarrow$ sugar
(3) sugar $\longrightarrow$ $CO_2 + H_2O$ + heat and other forms of energy

Low temperature decreases the rate of all three reactions, but the rate of decrease is not uniformly the same. Investigations have shown that reactions (1) and (3) are decreased more than (2). In this way sugars in the plant product accumulate and remain at a high level. High temperatures increase the rate of all three reactions, but (3) increases more than (1) or (2). Therefore, the sugars remain at a low level. In many cases they become depleted. The effect of high and low temperature on sugar content is illustrated in Table 5.4. Note that the low temperature actually conserves the sugars. This effect of temperature on starch-sugar transformation of certain harvested products explains why potato tubers become sweet when stored at temperatures of 32 to 40°F; why sweetpotato roots stored at 55°F are more sweet than those stored at 60°F; why sweet corn raised in Maine remains sweet for a relatively long time; why garden peas are the sweetest if cooked immediately after they are harvested; why apples contain more sugar when stored at 40°F rather than at 55°F; why sugar flows in the hard maple in the spring; and why sugarcane becomes sweet after the first frost.

Temperature and Diseases.   As with horticultural crops, many plant pathogens—fungi and bacteria which cause disease—have optimum temperatures for growth. In general, these organisms may be placed in either of two groups: (1) those which thrive best in cool weather and (2) those which thrive best in warm weather. Examples of cool-weather pathogens are the fungi which cause apple scab and peach leaf curl. Examples of warm-weather pathogens are fungi which cause bitter rot and black rot of apple, smut on corn, and fusarium wilt on tomato. These differences in temperature requirements explain why a certain disease is prevalent in one region of the country and nonexistent or of little consequence in another. For example, peach leaf curl is more prevalent in northern peach-growing districts. In fact, this disease does not exist in central Georgia, central South Carolina, and central Mississippi. On the other hand, black rot and bitter rot of apples are more prevalent in southern apple-growing

Table 5.4.   **STARCH-SUGAR TRANSFORMATION IN HARVESTED PRODUCTS**

Disposition of sugar in plant product	Temperature	
	High 55–65°F	**Low** 35–45°F
Units of sugar available	10.0	10.0
Units of sugar lost in reaction (1)	5.0	2.5
Units of sugar gained in reaction (2)	1.0	0.8
Units of sugar left	6.0	8.3
Units of sugar lost in reaction (3)	4.0	2.0
Units of sugar left	2.0	6.3

districts because of the higher temperature requirements of the organisms responsible for these diseases.

Insect pests are also influenced by temperatures. In general, there are more generations in the South than in the North simply because of the longer period of favorable temperature for reproduction. For example, the codling moth caterpillar, a serious insect pest of the apple, has only one generation in Maine, three or four in New Jersey, and seven or eight in western South Carolina; the cucumber beetle has two or three generations in Michigan and four or five in south Mississippi. In addition, the cold winter temperatures of the North destroy many insect pests. The mild winter temperatures of the South favor their hibernation.

QUESTIONS

1. Fruit trees and other woody plants low in carbohydrates at the end of the growing season are more susceptible to winter injury than trees high in carbohydrates. Explain.
2. Fruit trees and other woody plants with heavy crops are more likely to be injured by low temperatures during the winter than trees with moderate crops. Explain.
3. Partial defoliation, particularly during the latter stages of growth, makes woody plants susceptible to winter injury. Explain.
4. In general, the Great Plains region is unfavorable for the development of satisfactory crops of the deciduous fruits. Explain.
5. In the northern United States peach trees often have the past season's growth injured during the winter, and in the southern United States the flower buds are often the only part of the tree injured. Explain.
6. Many shrubs adapted to the northern United States do not thrive well in the southern United States. Explain.
7. Moderate cold following a period of rapid vegetative growth in the fall is likely to cause more winter injury than severe cold following a period of moderate vegetative growth. Explain.
8. What is meant by the "rest period"?
9. Under the usual conditions prevailing in a greenhouse, a peach tree, an apple tree, or a grape vine which has grown there for one season would not come out of its rest period in March or April (the usual time) but in late spring or early summer. Explain.
10. Explain why commercial apple and peach orchards do not exist along the Gulf Coast or in Florida.
11. A warm November and December and a cold January and February in the southern United States are usually followed by satisfactory crops of peaches. Opposite conditions often result in smaller crops. Explain.
12. In general, the chilling requirements of peach varieties for orchards in southern districts should be considered. Explain.
13. Explain why citrus orchards do not exist in the northern regions.

14. Garden peas become hard, yellow, and unpalatable if they are exposed to relatively high temperatures after being picked. Explain.
15. Peas and sweet corn stay comparatively sweet when kept cool after they are harvested. Explain.
16. Garden peas and spinach transported long distances in warm weather are shipped in refrigerator cars with crushed ice in the center of the basket. Explain.
17. Peas canned immediately after they are picked contain more sugar than those canned two hours after being picked. Explain.
18. Harvested sweet corn and English peas cease to remain sweet if subjected to high temperatures. Explain.
19. How would you expect high temperatures to affect quality and length of the harvest period of sweet corn?
20. Experiments have shown that sweet corn stored at 86°F loses its sweetness six times faster than sweet corn stored at 32°F. Explain.
21. One ton of husked green corn during the first 24 hours of storage at 86°F loses about 3 pounds of sugar. Explain. Can the loss of sugar be entirely prevented? Can it be retarded? If so, how?
22. When sweet corn is kept in storage, the loss of sugar is about two to four times as fast at 50°F as at 30°F. Explain.
23. How should garden peas, lima beans, and southern peas be handled immediately after the pods are picked in order to retain their sweetness and quality?
24. A home gardener wants information on the best way to harvest garden peas and sweet corn. Outline two methods for each.
25. Parsnips subjected to chilling temperatures become sweet. Explain.
26. Spinach canned in the fall is sweeter than spinach canned in the spring. Explain.
27. Certain diseases and insects are more prevalent in some regions than in others. Explain.

LIGHT AS THE
LIMITING FACTOR

Light is a form of radiant energy. It comes from the sun to the earth as discrete units or particles called quanta or photons. These discrete units travel at an average rate of 186,230 miles per second; they have weight and exert a pressure of 0.000,000,000,04 atmosphere.[1] Scientists have estimated that the weight of light emitted from the sun is about 240 million tons per minute and that about one ten-thousandth of an ounce falls every minute on each square mile of the earth's surface.

Primary Function. As shown on page 3, light is an integral part of the photosynthetic reaction in that it provides the energy for the combination of carbon dioxide and water in the formation of the first manufactured compounds. Since this energy, either directly or indirectly, comes from the sun, the greater the amount of light available, with other conditions favorable, the greater the rate of photosynthesis and the amount of carbohydrates available for plant growth and development. Thus, with other factors favorable, regions with an abundant light supply should produce a greater quantity of the products of photosynthesis from one season to the next than regions with a low light supply.

In addition to the necessity of light energy for photosynthesis, light has other effects on plant growth. To obtain a working knowledge of these effects, a study of light intensity, light quality, and relative length of the light and dark periods for any given 24-hour day is necessary.

[1] An atmosphere exerts a pressure of 15 pounds per square inch.

LIGHT INTENSITY

Light intensity refers to the number of quanta or photons impinging on a given area, or to the total amount of light which plants receive. In general, for any given location, the intensity varies with the day, with the seasons, and with the distance from the equator. It gradually increases from sunrise to the middle of the day and gradually decreases from the middle of the day to sunset; it is high in summer, moderately high in spring and fall, and low in winter; and it is highest at the equator and gradually decreases from the equator to the two poles. Other variations in light intensity are due to dust particles and water vapor in the atmosphere, to differences in slope of the land, and to differences in elevation.

How does light intensity influence plant growth and development? Its effect is discussed from three standpoints: (1) intensity within the optimum range, (2) intensity below the optimum range, and (3) intensity above the optimum range.

The Optimum Light Intensity Range.   The effect of the optimum range may be illustrated by the use of the line AB.

A   B
_____

The rate of photosynthesis is high.
The rate of respiration is normal.
Abundant carbohydrates are available for growth.

Note that within this range, with other factors favorable, the rate of photosynthesis is high, the rate of respiration is normal, and, as a result, the amount of carbohydrates available for growth and development is high. Thus, if the plants of any given crop are handled properly, particularly with respect to the vegetative and reproductive phases, the marketable yields are likely to be high.

The optimum, or favorable, light intensity range is not the same for all crops. For example, ferns, many foliage plants, and African violet require relatively low light intensity; carnation, chrysanthemum, and rose require relatively high light intensity; and dogwood, nandina, and arborvitae thrive well over a wide range of light intensity. In other words, the favorable light intensity range varies with the kind of plant. Some kinds have their highest rate of photosynthesis and make more foods per unit time at relatively low intensity, whereas other kinds have their highest rate of photosynthesis and make more foods per unit time at relatively high intensity. Although the optimum light intensity range for many crops is not definitely known, experience, particularly with ornamental plants, indicates that plants may be classified as follows: (1) plants which require low light intensity, the so-called shade plants;

(2) plants which require moderately high light intensity, the partial shade and sun plants; (3) plants which require high light intensity, the so-called sun plants; and (4) plants which thrive well over a wide range of light intensity, the shade or sun plants. Examples are presented in Table 6.1.

Intensity below the Optimum Range. The effect of light intensity below the optimum range is illustrated by the data in Table 6.2. This study was made at the Michigan Experiment Station with the Grand Rapids Forcing tomato, a variety adapted to greenhouse culture. The plants were grown in a greenhouse from February 15 to June 15, and at the beginning of the test, they were divided into three groups. The first group was grown in full sunlight, the second under one layer of cheesecloth, and the third under two layers. The one layer of cheesecloth admitted 50.4 per cent of the light, and the two layers admitted 25.0 per cent. Note that the plants in full sunlight had a greater chlorophyll content and produced a greater yield than those under one layer of cheesecloth, and the plants under one layer of cheesecloth had, in turn, a greater chlorophyll content and produced a greater yield than those under two

Table 6.1.   EXAMPLES OF PLANTS WITH VARIOUS LIGHT INTENSITY REQUIREMENTS

Shade 100–1,000 ft-c	Shade–Partial sun 1,000–5,000 ft-c	Sun 5,000–8,000 ft-c	Shade–Sun 1,000–8,000 ft-c
Foliage plants	Chinese azalea	Buddellia	Abelia (species)
Ferns	Euonymus (species)	Deutzia	Berberis (species)
African violet	Ilex (certain species)	Crepemyrtle	Buxus (species)
Azalea	Lonicera (certain species)	Flowering almond	Dogwood
Hydrangea (certain species)	Mahonia	Oleander	Forsythia
Vinca	Philadelphus	Pecan	Gardenia (species)
Shagbark	Pyracantha	Rose (species)	Ginkgo
Hickory	Weigela (certain species)		Ilex (certain species)
	Viburnum		Magnolia (certain species)
			Nandina

Source: C. O. Box, A Guide to the Use of Certain Plant Materials for Mississippi. Department of Horticulture, Mississippi State University.

Table 6.2.   **EFFECT OF LIGHT INTENSITY ON THE
GROWTH OF TOMATOES**

Treatment	Relative amount of light admitted	Average daily intensit, ft-c	Yield, lb of fruits	Relative chlorophyll content	Relative efficiency
Plants in full sunlight	100	1,140	65	High	High
Plants under one layer of cheesecloth	50	583	51	Moderately high	Moderately high
Plants under two layers of cheesecloth	25	261	32	Low	Low

layers. Thus, the plants grown in full sunlight had the highest rate of photosynthesis, and those grown under two layers of cheesecloth had the lowest.

Similar results were obtained in a study of the daily rate of photosynthesis of an eight-year-old McIntosh apple tree at Cornell University. For the entire tree the rate of photosynthesis increased with increases

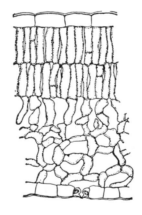

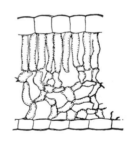

Fig. 6.1. Diagrams of sun and shade leaves of apple. Left: sun leaf. Right: shade leaf. (Courtesy, F. W. Emerson, "Basic Botany," New York, McGraw-Hill Book Company, Inc.)

in light intensity up to full sunlight. For example, on five cloudy days the average rate of carbon dioxide assimilation was 5.2 milligrams per hour per 100 square centimeters of leaf surface, and on five sunny days the average rate of photosynthesis was 20.6 milligrams. During the middle part of clear days there was more light than the leaves needed. In other words, some factor other than light intensity became limiting in photosynthesis. However, on the cloudy days there was insufficient light to carry on a high rate of photosynthesis. Figure 6.1 shows the relative thickness and number of rows of palisade cells of the leaves of unshaded and shaded apple trees. Note the greater thickness and larger number of palisade cells of the leaves grown in the sun.

Why are growth, development, and yield relatively low at deficient light intensities? As previously stated, light energy is needed for the combination of carbon dioxide and water in the photosynthetic reaction. With deficient light intensity the amount of energy available for the union of carbon dioxide and water is low and, as a result, the rate of production of the initial carbohydrates for the making of other compounds is comparatively low. Thus, growth and development are accordingly slow and, in general, yields are likely to be low. This effect of deficient light is shown diagrammatically by line XA.

X   A

    Decreasing rate of photosynthesis with
      normal rates of respiration
      Decreasing supplies of carbohydrates for growth and yields

Note that as light intensity decreases from A to X, the rate of photosynthesis decreases. At point X we can assume that the rate of photosynthesis equals the rate of respiration and the amount of carbohydrates available for growth is zero. This effect of light intensity below the optimum range explains, partially at least, why crop plants are planted at definite distances; why growth and development of crops in greenhouses during the winter are relatively low; why greenhouse roofs are washed in early fall; why the interior of greenhouses is painted white; why plants growing in dense shade have relatively shallow root systems; and why ornamental hedges should have a broad base and a relatively narrow top.

Intensity above the Optimum Range. The effect of light intensity above the optimum range is shown by the data in Table 6.3. This study was made at the Mississippi Experiment Station with the Stokesdale tomato, a variety adapted to certain parts of the southern United States. The three

Table 6.3. EFFECT OF EXCESS LIGHT INTENSITY ON YIELD OF TOMATOES

Treatment	Average daily intensity, ft-c	Relative amount of light admitted, %	Yield, lb/10 plants	
			Sept. 29– Oct. 19	Sept. 29– Nov. 3
Plants in full sun	7,725	100	2.2	16.5
Plants under nylon	3,440	45	5.4	24.1
Plants under muslin	2,132	28	4.9	19.4

Source: Adapted from Table 3, Proc. Am. Soc. Hort. Sci. 60:293, 1952.

levels of light intensity were obtained by growing the plants in full sun, under nylon, and under unbleached muslin. Note that the yield of the plants in full sun is relatively low.

The question arises: Why are yields low in excess light intensity? Three explanations are set forth. The first explanation concerns the chlorophyll content. With certain plants excess light intensity reduces the chlorophyll content and the leaves become yellowish-green. As a result, the rate of absorption of light is low and the rate of photosynthesis is correspondingly low. This effect is sometimes called solarization. The second explanation concerns the water supply. The excess light intensity markedly increases the temperature of the leaves. This in turn induces a high rate of transpiration, and the rate of absorption of water does not keep up with it. As a result, the guard cells lose turgor, the stomates partially or entirely close, and diffusion of carbon dioxide into the leaves is slowed down. Thus, the rate of photosynthesis is slowed down while respiration continues, and the supply of carbohydrates available for growth and development is low. The third explanation concerns enzyme activity. The excess light increases the temperature of the leaves. This in turn inactivates the enzyme system which changes sugars to starch. As a result, the sugars accumulate and, according to the law of mass action, the rate of photosynthesis slows down. This effect of light intensity above the optimum range explains, partially at least, why shading materials are placed on greenhouse roofs in late spring and summer; why cloth or plastics are suspended above plants in greenhouses during the summer; why certain ornamental plants are grown in lathhouses during the summer, particularly in the southern United States; and why companion cropping is practiced in many parts of the world. In companion cropping, two or more kinds are grown in the same area at the same time. One kind is tall and withstands high light intensities. The other kind is short and is injured by high light intensities. The tall, upright crop shades the low-growing crop. This reduces the light intensity for the low-growing crop, which in turn promotes high rates of photosynthesis and high yields.

LIGHT QUALITY

As previously stated, photons have weight and exert a pressure. They also exhibit the properties of waves, and quality of light refers to the length of the waves. These wave lengths are set forth as follows:

Invisible				Visible spectrum					Invisible
Ultraviolet	V	B	B-G	G	Y	O	R	F-R	Infrared
				Millimicrons					
15–390	390	460	490	530	585	610	650	735	760+

Note the parts: the visible, the invisible, and the composition, or color spectrum, of visible light. The question arises: How does light quality influence plant growth and development?

The Visible Spectrum. The composition of visible light affects the rate of growth, as measured in terms of dry weight, and the vegetative and reproductive phases. With reference to the rate of growth, investigations at the California Institute of Technology have shown that tomato plants grown in red or blue light produce a greater dry weight over the same period of time than comparable plants grown in green light, and that plants grown in red or blue light produce a greater dry weight than plants grown in "white" light. This indicates that green light actually inhibits plant growth and may explain why light bulbs which transmit large quantities of red and blue light are more satisfactory in greenhouse culture than those which transmit relatively small quantities.

With reference to the vegetative and reproductive phases, research at the Plant Industry Station, Beltsville, Maryland, has shown a remarkable interrelation between red light and far-red light. In general, the red light promotes the germination of seed and growth of seedlings of many plants and the initiation of flower-bud primordia in long day–short night plants, whereas the far-red light has opposite effects. It retards germination and growth of the seedlings and flower-bud initiation in long day–short night plants. This indicates that a photoreversible reaction exists in plants, which is undoubtedly related to the production of the auxinic hormones associated with the vegetative phase and the florigenic (or florigen-like) hormones associated with the reproductive phase.

The Invisible Spectrum. As shown on page 95, the invisible spectrum has two parts: ultraviolet and infrared. What is the influence of the ultraviolet? Despite the popular opinion that ultraviolet light is beneficial to the growth of plants, investigations have shown that ultraviolet light near the visible end of the spectrum has no advantage in increasing dry weight or in hastening the time of flowering. For example, at the United States Plant Industry Station, Beltsville, Maryland, tomato and pepper plants were started in hotbeds covered with ultraviolet-transmitting glass and hotbeds covered with greenhouse glass. There were no practical differences in behavior between the two lots of plants. The plants started under greenhouse glass grew as rapidly and produced the same yields as those started under glass admitting ultraviolet light.

What is the influence of the infrared? Although definite information on the influence of infrared light is meager, recent research shows that infrared light has very little, if any, beneficial effect on plant growth. Since excellent crops are produced in greenhouses and since greenhouse glass absorbs most of the ultraviolet and infrared light, the invisible part of the spectrum seems to be unnecessary for plant growth and development.

RELATIVE LENGTH OF THE LIGHT AND DARK PERIODS

The length of the light and dark periods refers to the period of light and period of dark for any given 24-hour "day" for any given location. To obtain a working knowledge of the variation in the length of the light and dark periods, the length of these periods on the following dates should be kept in mind. These dates are March 21, September 21, December 21, and June 21. On March 21 and September 21, the spring and fall equinox, respectively, the sun is directly over the equator and rises exactly in the east and sets exactly in the west. As a result, the length of the light and the length of the dark periods are the same at all places in both the northern and southern hemispheres. In other words, 12 hours of light and 12 hours of dark occur at all places on the surface of the earth on March 21 and September 21. On December 21, the sun is farthest south of the equator; the shortest light and the longest dark periods take place for all locations in the northern hemisphere, and the longest light and the shortest dark periods take place for all locations in the southern hemisphere. Conversely, on June 21, the sun is farthest north of the equator; the longest light and the shortest dark periods take place at all locations in the northern hemisphere, and the shortest light and longest dark periods take place at all places in the southern hemisphere. The length of the light and dark periods at representative locations in the northern hemisphere are set forth in Table 6.4.

Table 6.4. **RELATIVE LENGTH OF LIGHT AND DARK PERIODS IN HOURS AT FOUR LATITUDES NORTH OF THE EQUATOR**

Dates	Degrees latitude N							
	30*		40†		50‡		Arctic Circle	
	Light	Dark	Light	Dark	Light	Dark	Light	Dark
Mar. 21 and Sept. 21	12.0	12.0	12.0	12.0	12.0	12.0	12.0	12.0
Dec. 21	10.2	13.8	9.3	14.7	8.1	15.9	0.0	24.0
June 21	14.1	9.9	15.0	9.0	16.4	7.6	24.0	0.0

* *Shanghai, Chungking, New Orleans, Jacksonville, Alexandria.*
† *Darien, Kansas City, Philadelphia, Rome (Italy).*
‡ *Vancouver, Calais, Stalingrad.*

Note that the longest light period and the shortest dark period vary with distance from the equator. Thus, between northern and southern locations in the northern hemisphere, the length of the light period is longer in the northerly locations from March 21 to September 21, and the length of the light period is longer in the southerly locations from September 21 to March 21. Study the daylight curves for the three locations in Fig. 6.2.

How does the relative length of the light and dark periods influence growth and development? In general, these periods influence crop plants in three ways: (1) in relative amount of carbohydrates made of all crops,

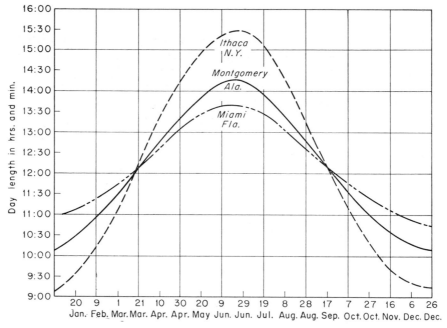

Fig. 6.2. *Day-length curves for Miami, Fla.; Montgomery, Ala.; and Ithaca, N.Y.* (*Courtesy, E. W. McElwee, University of Florida.*)

(2) in time of flower-bud formation of many crops, and (3) in development of storage structures of such crops as onions and potatoes.

Amount of Carbohydrates.   Naturally, the relative length of the light and dark periods influences photosynthesis and respiration. In general, the longer the light period, provided other factors are favorable, the greater will be the amount of foods made in photosynthesis; and the shorter the dark period, the lower will be the amount of foods used in respiration. Thus, a plant exposed to a favorable light period of 17 hours and to a favorable night period of 7 hours will have a greater quantity of carbohydrates for growth and development than a plant exposed to a favorable light period of 14 hours and a favorable night period of 10 hours. This explains, partially at least, why high marketable yields of many crops are secured in the more northerly latitudes during the summer months. During the long light period relatively large quantities of carbohydrates are made in photosynthesis, and during the short dark period small quantities are used in respiration. As a result, large quantities of carbohydrates are available for growth and yield.

Time of Flower-bud Formation.   The relative length of the light and dark periods also determines the time at which flower buds are formed in many crops. Many investigators have studied the effects of various lengths of light and dark periods. In general, they have found that some plants, e.g., spring radish and delphinium, require long light periods combined with short dark periods for the formation of their flower buds; other plants, e.g., poinsettia and kalanchoe, require short light periods combined with long dark periods for the formation of their flower buds; and still other plants, e.g., tomato and cotton, form flower buds during both long and short light periods. Plants which require long light and short dark periods for the formation of their flower buds are called long day–short night plants; those which require short light and long dark periods are called short day–long night plants; and those which form flower buds in both long light and dark periods and short light and long dark periods are called day-night neutral plants. In general, within any given 24-hour period, most long day–short night plants require 8 to 10 hours of continuous dark and most short day–long night plants require 10 to 14 hours of continuous dark for the formation of their flower buds.

When short day–long night plants are grown during long days and short nights, they manufacture abundant carbohydrates and make abundant proteins. These in turn are used for the development of the stems, leaves, and absorbing roots. Thus, short day–long night plants grown during long days and short nights are vegetative, nonflowering, and nonfruitful. On the other hand, when long day–short night plants are grown during short days and long nights, they manufacture very little carbohydrates and in turn make few proteins. Thus, long day–short night plants grown during short days and long nights, because of lack of light, are weakly vegetative and nonflowering.

Just how the length of the light and dark periods controls the flowering of long day–short night plants and short day–long night plants is not definitely known. One explanation is that the length of the light and dark periods controls the time when protein synthesis takes place. For example, certain species of salvia are short day–long night plants. These plants accumulate nitrates and carbohydrates in their tissues during short days and long nights. Apparently, the short days combined with long nights limit the synthesis of proteins, which in turn limits the making of protoplasm and the development of new cells. Because of the limited protein synthesis, the carbohydrates accumulate. This in turn results in the formation, or the laying down, of flower-bud primordia. Another and more widely accepted explanation is that the length of the light and dark periods determines the formation and translocation of flower-forming hormones, and that these hormones are made in the leaves. For example, if a young, physiologically active leaf of the cockleburr, a short day–long night plant, is exposed to 10 hours of dark, the plant does not form flower buds. Further, if a single leaf of a flowering plant is grafted on a nonflowering plant, the nonflowering plant forms flower buds and blooms even though it is growing under long day and short night periods. A brief list of each of the three groups of plants is presented in Table 6.5.

What practical use can be made of the differential response to the length of the light and dark periods? In general, fruit, vegetable, and flower growers select varieties which are adapted to the relative length of the light and dark periods in any given location, and florists, particularly the growers of commercial varieties of chrysanthemums, actually control the length of the light and dark periods. Under natural conditions the greenhouse chrysanthemum flowers in October. By giving the plants additional light during the winter and shortening the light period during the summer, growers are able to place greenhouse varieties of this crop on the market at all times of the year. Figure 6.3 shows how the light period is lengthened during the winter, and Fig. 6.4 shows how the light period is shortened during the summer.

Table 6.5. SOME SHORT DAY–LONG NIGHT, LONG DAY–SHORT NIGHT, AND DAY-NIGHT NEUTRAL PLANTS

Group	Short day–Long night	Long day–Short night	Day-Night neutral
Fruits	Strawberries (June bearing)		Strawberries (everbearing)
Vegetables	Potato (certain varieties), sweet-potato, multiflora, bean	Spinach, radish, lettuce	Tomato, pepper, okra
Ornamentals	Chrysanthemum (certain varieties), bouvardia, cosmos, stevia, kalanchoe, poinsettia, violet	Calendula, China aster, feverfew, gardenia, delphinium, stock	Carnation, cyclamen, dianthus, African violet

Fig. 6.3. An installation showing the use of electric lights to lengthen the period of light. (Courtesy, Alex Laurie, Whistling Pine Gardens, Eustis, Fla.)

Fig. 6.4. An installation showing the use of black cloth to shorten the period of light. (Courtesy, Alex Laurie, Whistling Pine Gardens, Eustis, Fla.)

Development of Storage Structures.   The length of the light and dark periods also influences the time of formation of certain storage structures, e.g., bulbs of the onion and tubers of the potato and Jerusalem artichoke. Investigations have shown that comparatively short light periods favor the development of tubers of certain varieties of the potato, that comparatively short light periods (10 to 11 hours) are required for the formation of bulbs of the Bermuda onion, and that long light periods (14 to 16 hours) are necessary for the formation of bulbs of American types. This explains, partially at least, why certain northern varieties of onions are unadapted to the length of the light and dark periods of the South and why the southern varieties are unadapted to the length of the light and dark periods of the North.

QUESTIONS

1. What is light? State the function of light in photosynthesis.
2. Within limits, increases in light intensity increase the rate of photosynthesis. Explain.
3. Light is generally the limiting factor in growing plants in greenhouses during the winter months. Explain.
4. Plants grown in dense shade have less extensive root systems as compared with plants grown in the sun. Explain from the standpoint of the light supply.
5. Holly trees growing in shade have a lesser rate of growth than those growing in sun. Explain.
6. The amount of light reaching the interior of thick-topped apple trees is from 1 to 10 per cent of that reaching the top of the trees. The fruiting wood in the interior of such trees is thin, weak, and unproductive. Explain.
7. Dead branches in the middle of flowering shrubs are likely to shorten the life of the plants. Explain from the standpoint of the light supply.
8. The covering of ornamental shrubs with opaque material in late fall is a bad practice. Explain.
9. The sugar content of many fruits (apples, peaches, grapes, cantaloupes) is positively associated with the amount of sunshine during the period of fruit growth. Explain.
10. Under what conditions is light intensity likely to be harmful? Explain.
11. For the raising of certain crops in greenhouses, lime or special shading material is placed on the roof during spring and summer and removed during fall and winter. Explain.
12. In general, the propagating houses of florists are more heavily shaded than other houses. Explain.
13. How do cloth houses promote the production of high-quality flowers during periods of excessive light intensity?

14 A bright sunny fall is more favorable for the winter conditioning of woody plants than a cloudy fall. Give two reasons.

15. When do the equinoxes occur? How long are the light and dark periods on these dates?

16. For any given location, on what date does the longest light period occur? The shortest?

17. What is a short day–long night plant? A long day–short night plant? A day-night neutral plant?

18. A home gardener writes: "I have been growing a certain variety of pole bean for a number of years. I find it never produces pods until October. I have tried to make it produce pods earlier by growing the plants in different soils and in different locations on the farm but with little success." Can you give any explanation?

19. In home gardens spinach is grown during late fall, winter, and early spring. Explain from the standpoint of the light supply.

20. How does the commercial florist lengthen the marketing season of large-headed varieties of chrysanthemums? Explain.

21. A variety of onion requires a minimum of 16 hours of light during the 24-hour period for the development of satisfactory bulbs. With other factors favorable, would this variety be adapted to your particular location? Explain.

7

THE ESSENTIAL
ELEMENTS AS
LIMITING FACTORS

*The green plant is
God's gift to all mankind.*

Essential Elements and Essential Raw Materials. The green plant
is a biochemical factory. Certain raw materials are used, either directly
or indirectly, in the making of the all-important foods, fibers, enzymes,
hormones, and vitamins. These raw materials meet at least two requirements: (1) They contain one or more essential elements for growth and
development; and (2) they exist in a form which plants can absorb and
use. For example, nitrogen is part of the molecule of all proteins and
part of the molecule of both chlorophyll a and chlorophyll b. Nitrogen
is therefore an essential element. Although nitrogen exists in many types
of compounds, crop plants absorb and use nitrogen from the soil mostly
in two relatively simple forms: the nitrate ion and the ammonium ion.
Because these ions are absorbed and used by plants in making the many
nitrogenous organic compounds, they are called essential raw materials.
Thus, *essential raw materials are chemical compounds or parts of chemical
compounds which contain one or more essential elements for plant
growth and are absorbed and utilized by plants.*

The essential elements necessary for plant growth and development
are carbon, oxygen, hydrogen, nitrogen, phosphorus, potassium, sulfur,
calcium, magnesium, manganese, iron, boron, zinc, copper, and molybdenum. Since any one of these elements may become a limiting factor
in growth and development, the student should learn what the role of
these elements is in plant life, how to recognize symptoms of essential-
element deficiency, and when and how best to replenish the supply.

104

CARBON AND OXYGEN

Role.   Carbon is a constituent of all organic compounds, and accounts for approximately 50 per cent of the dry weight of most crops. In fact, since carbon has the remarkable ability to combine with itself in the formation of the many kinds of straight-chain and cyclic compounds, it may be considered as the main structural element of all organic compounds.

Oxygen is a constituent of all carbohydrates, lipides, proteins, and related substances. Of these compounds the carbohydrates are relatively high in oxygen, the proteins are moderately high, and lipides are relatively low.

The Carrier.   The carrier of carbon and oxygen is carbon dioxide. In other words, of all of the many compounds which contain carbon and oxygen, plants obtain these two essential elements only as carbon dioxide. Thus, carbon dioxide is an essential raw material for plant growth and development.

As is well known, the supply of carbon dioxide for crop plants is the atmosphere—the huge canopy of air which surrounds the surface of the earth. In this canopy carbon dioxide exists as a gas in relatively low concentration, about 3 to 4 parts in 10,000 parts by volume (0.03 to 0.04 per cent) in open fields and in somewhat larger amounts in greenhouses and hotbeds. Although this concentration by volume is low, the actual amount of carbon dioxide in the atmosphere is tremendous. In fact, scientists have estimated that the total quantity of this gas in the troposphere—the lower part of the earth's canopy—is on the order of 600 billion tons and that about 70 billion tons are used each year by crop plants in photosynthesis.

Despite this enormous quantity used in photosynthesis, the total amount of carbon dioxide in the atmosphere remains relatively constant. How is the carbon-dioxide supply replenished? Carbon dioxide is released into the atmosphere for the most part by two similar processes: (1) the respiration of all living organisms and (2) the combustion of all organic compounds. The living organisms include both animals and plants on the land, in the soil, and in the waters of the earth. Of particular importance are the organisms which decompose organic wastes. In general, these organisms give off by far the greater quantities of carbon dioxide, and, in this way, they keep the amount of organic wastes at a minimum.

Carbon dioxide gets into the manufacturing tissues by the process of diffusion. As long as photosynthesis is taking place, the gas diffuses from the atmosphere through the stomates into the intercellular spaces of the chlorophyll-containing cells. On the surface of these cells carbon dioxide enters into solution with water, diffuses to the surface of the chloroplasts, and finally unites with water in the presence of light in the formation of the initial food substances and related compounds.

When is the concentration of carbon dioxide likely to be the limiting factor in photosynthesis and in plant growth and development? In general, when other factors influencing photosynthesis are in optimum supply, carbon dioxide is the limiting factor. This condition is likely to occur when the water supply within the plant is such that the guard cells are fully turgid and the stomates are open, when the temperature and light intensity are within their respective optimum ranges, when the periods of light and dark are favorable for the type of growth the plant should be making, and when all other essential raw materials are in optimum supply. With these optimum conditions, investigations have shown that an enrichment of air with carbon dioxide increases plant growth. The tests with this compound were conducted in greenhouses or in light-transmitting cabinets where the carbon dioxide supply could be more or less confined, and when other environmental factors were not limiting growth. In one experiment cucumbers supplied with air consisting of 31.3 parts of carbon dioxide in 10,000 parts by volume increased 60.0 per cent in dry weight over those supplied with 3.0 parts of this gas in 10,000 parts, the usual concentration. In other tests, alfalfa, potatoes, tomatoes, beets, and carrots showed significant increases in growth. In general, increases in the concentration of carbon dioxide from 0.03 per cent to 0.30 per cent by volume increased the rate of photosynthesis until some other factor became limiting in growth. At present, the use of carbon dioxide as a fertilizer is in the experimental stage and is of interest mainly to scientists and to growers of plants in greenhouses and similar structures.

HYDROGEN

Role.   Hydrogen, like carbon, is a constituent of almost all organic compounds made by plants. Hydrogen is therefore an essential element. In addition, the relative proportion of hydrogen to oxygen in the molecule of a given food determines the stored energy content of that food. For example, fats are relatively high in hydrogen in proportion to oxygen. They, therefore, contain relatively large quantities of chemical energy. For this reason, fats are excellent energy reserve materials.

The Carrier.   The carrier of hydrogen is water. Water is therefore an essential raw material. In photosynthesis water is decomposed into hydrogen and oxygen; the hydrogen is used in the formation of the manufactured compounds, and the oxygen is given off as the by-product.

However, the student should remember that of the total amount of water absorbed, the amount which combines with carbon dioxide in the photosynthetic reaction is very small, usually less than 1 per cent. Thus, most of the water absorbed is needed to maintain turgor of the living cells, particularly the guard cells, for the diffusion of carbon dioxide through the stomates. This important role of water is discussed more fully in Chapters 3 and 13.

NITROGEN

Role. Nitrogen enters into the formation of many compounds made by plants. It is part of the molecule of all proteins and enzymes, of chlorophyll a and chlorophyll b, of certain acids of the nucleus and certain hormones. For these reasons nitrogen is an essential element.

The Carriers. As previously stated, plants absorb most of their nitrogen in the form of nitrate-nitrogen or ammonium-nitrogen. For this reason these ions are called the carriers of nitrogen, or preferably the available forms of nitrogen. In acid soils plants absorb more nitrate ions, and in slightly alkaline soils they absorb more ammonium ions. For example, scientists at the New Jersey Experiment Station supplied apples and tomatoes with equal amounts of nitrate-nitrogen and ammonium-nitrogen growing on very acid (pH 4.0), moderately acid (pH 6.0), and neutral (pH 7.0) soils. On the acid soil (pH 4.0) the apple trees and tomato plants assimilated nitrate ions to a greater extent than ammonium ions; on the neutral soil (pH 7.0) they assimilated ammonium ions to a greater extent than nitrate ions; and on the moderately acid soil (pH 6.0) they assimilated both forms in practically equal amounts. Apparently, the relative amount of nitrate-nitrogen or ammonium-nitrogen which is assimilated depends to some extent on the soil reaction. Each form behaves differently in the soil. In general, *the nitrate ion leaches readily,* and the ammonium ion is fixed according to the exchange capacity of the soil. Which form is more readily lost by heavy rains or excessive irrigation?

Symptoms of Deficiency and Excess. Since relatively large or small quantities of available nitrogen may exist in the soil solution and since the relative amount of available nitrogen has marked effects on the vegetative and reproductive phases, the student should become familiar with the symptoms of nitrogen deficiency and the symptoms of nitrogen excess. Symptoms of nitrogen deficiency are as follows: *With monocots the middle portion of the leaf blade becomes yellowish-green, but the margins remain green; and with dicots the leaf blade becomes uniformly yellowish-green.* In both groups, the old leaves show symptoms first, and the chlorophyll content of the plant as a whole is relatively low. Thus, with the low content of chlorophyll, relatively low quantities of light

Fig. 7.1. Nitrogen-, phosphorus-, and potassium-deficient leaves of gardenia. Upper left: healthy. Upper right: nitrogen-deficient. Lower left: potassium-deficient. Lower right: phosphorus-deficient. (Courtesy, Alex Laurie, Whistling Pine Gardens, Eustis, Fla.)

are absorbed. As a result very few carbohydrates are made per unit time and growth and yields are likely to be low (see Fig. 7.1).

Symptoms of nitrogen excess with most plants are as follows: The vegetative phase proceeds rapidly; in other words, there is a rapid development of stems and large, dark green leaves. These large, dark green leaves contain large quantities of chlorophyll. As a result, relatively large quantities of light are absorbed per unit time, and large quantities of carbohydrates are made. Since under these conditions large quantities of available nitrogen are present, most of the sugars are used in making cells of the stems, leaves, and absorbing roots and very few carbohydrates are left for thickening the cell walls, developing the fibers, storing starch, and forming flowers, fruit, seed, and storage structures. Thus, the stems are soft and succulent, the cell walls are thin, the development of fibers is limited, flowering and fruiting are often delayed or entirely suppressed, and the yield of storage structures is likely to be low.

The Available Nitrogen Supply and the Vegetative-Reproductive Balance. As previously stated, sugars and available nitrogen combine in the formation of the initial proteins. These in turn combine with each other in the formation of the complex proteins, and these combine with certain carbohydrates and fatty substances in the formation of the living substance, the protoplasm. It follows, therefore, that with other factors favorable for growth, the available nitrogen supply determines the rate at which new protoplasm and new cells are made and the rate at which sugars are used. Thus, when a plant has a high rate of photosynthesis and a normal rate of respiration, and absorbs and *uses large quantities of available nitrogen,* and is subjected to temperatures within the upper half of the optimum range particularly during the night, the sugars will be used almost entirely for the production of stems, leaves, and absorbing roots. When, on the other hand, the plant has a high rate of photosynthesis, a normal rate of respiration, and absorbs and *uses moderately large quantities of available nitrogen,* the development of stems and leaves will be less rapid; and, as a result, there will be less rapid utilization of sugars for stem, leaf, and root growth. Some sugars will be left for the development of flower-forming hormones and flowers, fruit, seed, or storage structures. Thus, the amount of available nitrogen may regulate the type of growth to a marked degree, provided other factors are not limiting. In general, with abundant carbohydrates and abundant available nitrogen, vegetative processes are dominant over reproductive processes; and with abundant carbohydrates and moderately abundant available nitrogen, vegetative processes are less dominant and reproductive processes are more evident.

Sources of Available Nitrogen

Nitrogen in Organic Matter.   The nitrogen in organic matter is largely in the form of protein-nitrogen. As such, plants cannot use it; it must be changed into the ammonium or nitrate form. Certain fungi and bacteria effect this change. These organisms are minute plants, and since they lack chlorophyll, they obtain their energy from sources other than the sun. To obtain this energy they decompose organic matter. Vast numbers of these organisms exist in soils. Bacteriologists have estimated that as many as 46 billion bacteria exist in a gram of decomposing material, and that under average conditions, a fertile soil contains from $\frac{1}{2}$ to 1 ton per acre of these organisms, or about 100 to 250 billion per pound of soil. Obviously, these organisms have an important role in the growing of crop plants.

Two sets of organisms are necessary to complete the change of protein-nitrogen to nitrate-nitrogen. The first group comprise certain fungi and bacteria and are called the ammonifiers. They change the protein-nitrogen to ammonia. The second group are bacteria only and are called the nitrifiers. They change the ammonia to nitrites and finally to nitrates.

Nitrogen in the Atmosphere.   The nitrogen in the atmosphere is in the form of gaseous nitrogen. As with protein-nitrogen, higher plants cannot use it in its raw form. Before this gaseous nitrogen is used, it is changed into proteins. Certain algae, fungi, and bacteria effect this change. These organisms use the gaseous nitrogen in the formation of their body proteins, and the process is called nitrogen fixation.

Two distinct groups of nitrogen-fixing bacteria are the nonsymbiotic and the symbiotic.[1] The nonsymbiotic bacteria live independently of green plants and belong to two genera: *Azotobacter* and *Clostridium*. Certain symbiotic bacteria live in conjunction with a certain group of higher plants which, because of their characteristic fruit, are called legumes. These bacteria have been placed in the genus *Rhizobium*. They change the gaseous nitrogen into amino acids, which in turn are used by the leguminous plant. In return for this nitrogen the higher plants supply the bacteria with the necessary carbohydrates. This is a fine example of mutual cooperation, or symbiosis.

Different classes of legumes require different kinds or strains of *Rhizobium* bacteria. The kind that is adapted to alfalfa will not grow on peas or beans and vice versa. Thus, legumes should be inoculated with proper cultures. Agricultural experiment stations have developed quick and economical methods of mixing seeds of crops of the legume family with these bacteria—a practice known as inoculation. In general, growers have found that inoculation pays.

The student will note that three rather distinct groups of soil organisms change the nitrogen in organic matter and the nitrogen in the atmosphere into the available forms. In general, these organisms are extremely beneficial. The ammonifiers and the nitrifiers get rid of the large quantities of organic wastes as they accumulate from day to day, and the nitrogen fixers make available for crop plants the large quantities of gaseous nitrogen in the atmosphere.

The changes which protein-nitrogen and gaseous nitrogen undergo in the formation of the available forms of nitrogen are illustrated as follows:

$$\text{Protein N} \xrightarrow{\text{ammonifiers}} \text{amino acids} \longrightarrow NH_3 + O_2 \xrightarrow{\text{nitrifiers}}$$
$$NO_2 + O_2 \longrightarrow NO_3$$

$$\text{Gaseous N} + \text{sugars} \xrightarrow{\text{nitrogen fixers}} \text{protein N}$$

Activity of Ammonifiers, Nitrifiers, and Nitrogen Fixers.   If the fungi and bacteria which make ammonium-nitrogen and nitrate-nitrogen were nonexistent, the farmer's bill for nitrogen fertilizers would be enormously

[1] The word "symbiosis" means living with other kinds of organisms to mutual advantage.

increased. In other words, these fungi and bacteria make large quantities of available nitrogen, a quantity which certain scientists have estimated as varying from 50 to 300 pounds per acre per year. Their activity is markedly affected by the soil environment. Principal factors are (1) temperature, (2) water supply, (3) oxygen supply, and (4) acidity.

TEMPERATURE. Temperature affects the activity of the ammonifiers, nitrifiers, and nitrogen fixers in much the same way as it affects higher plants. When the soil is cold or extremely hot, their activity is retarded. In general, temperatures for their greatest activity are moderately high (60 to 85°F). Consequently, the curve of nitrate-nitrogen formation, other factors being equal, varies with the temperature of the season, the locality, and the soil. Thus, for any given location and soil, the rate of nitrate-nitrogen formation is more rapid in warm soils than in extremely hot or cold soils.

WATER SUPPLY. Moist soils are more favorable than dry soils. The effect of water in the soil is twofold: (1) It aids in the decomposition of organic matter; and (2) it brings essential raw materials into solution. Since bacteria and fungi make protoplasm and new cells, they require essential elements for growth in much the same way as do higher plants. In other words, the carriers of the essential elements must be in solution before their absorption into the cells can take place.

OXYGEN. In general, abundant supplies of oxygen are necessary for the respiration of the ammonifiers, nitrifiers, and nitrogen fixers. For this reason soils should be well drained. In fact, nonaerated, poorly drained soils contain certain bacteria called *Bacillus denitrificans*. These organisms live in the absence of free oxygen. Fortunately, these organisms do not thrive in well-drained soils. The decomposition of nitrate-nitrogen to gaseous nitrogen is illustrated as follows:

$$2HNO_3 \longrightarrow 2N + H_2O + 2\tfrac{1}{2}O_2$$

Note that this reaction depletes the soil of nitrogen.

ACIDITY OF THE SOIL. Investigations have shown that the nitrifying and nitrogen-fixing organisms do not thrive well in very acid soils. For these organisms, the optimum range seems to be from pH 6.0 to 7.0. Thus, satisfactory nitrate formation does not take place in very acid or alkaline soils.

To summarize the effect of the soil environment on the activity of the ammonifiers, nitrifiers, and nitrogen fixers, these organisms thrive best in warm, moist, well-aerated, well-drained, and slightly acid soils. Any deviation from these desirable conditions may correspondingly reduce the available nitrogen supply.

Table 7.1.   ACID AND BASIC NITROGEN CARRIERS

Acid-forming carriers	N, %	Basic-forming carriers	N, %
Ammonium nitrate	33	Anhydrous ammonia	82
Ammonium phosphate	11	Calcium nitrate	16
Ammonium sulfate	21	Cyanamide	22
Urea	46	Sodium nitrate	16

Nitrogen in Commercial Fertilizers. Despite the relatively large amounts of available nitrogen made by soil organisms, only in exceptional cases are the quantities sufficient for the satisfactory growth of crop plants. Thus, applications of nitrogen-carrying fertilizers are necessary. From the standpoint of their effect on the soil and plants, nitrogen fertilizers are classified as follows: (1) physiologically acid and (2) physiologically alkaline. Regarding physiologically acid carriers plants absorb the cation to a greater extent than the anion. Regarding physiologically alkaline carriers plants absorb the anion to a greater extent than the cation. The continued use of the former makes soils more acid, and the continued use of the latter makes soils more alkaline. Consequently, the choice of either type of fertilizer depends to some extent on the soil reaction. Several acid- and basic-forming nitrogen carriers are shown in Table 7.1.

PHOSPHORUS

Role. Phosphorus is esssential for photosynthesis and respiration, for cell division, and for sugar-starch transformations in plants. In photosynthesis and respiration, compounds containing energy-rich phosphate bonds are needed for the energy transformations in these reactions; in cell division, compounds containing phosphorus, the nucleoproteins, are required for the formation of the nucleus; and in sugar-starch transformations, the enzyme called invertase contains phosphorus.

Symptoms of Deficiency. Symptoms of phosphorus deficiency are not so frequent as those of nitrogen deficiency. A lack of phosphorus is indicated by a slowing down of growth and by late maturity. *In monocots the leaves of plants in the vegetative stage usually show reddish or purplish areas instead of the desirable dark green. In dicots the main veins of old leaves frequently become reddish or purple while the young leaves are dark green or grayish-green.* In fruit trees the blossoms drop off, the fruit is small, unattractive in color, matures slowly, and few flower buds are formed for the next year's crop. Note the phosphorus-deficient leaf blades in Fig. 7.1.

Available Form and Carriers. Plants absorb phosphorus only as phosphate ions. These ions are dihydrogen phosphate (H_2PO_4), monohydrogen phosphate (HPO_4), and phosphate (PO_4). Of these ions the H_2PO_4 form is absorbed the most because of its greater solubility. However, the availability of the dihydrogen ion depends on the degree of acidity of the soil solution. In general, the range of maximum availability seems to be between pH 5.5 and 6.8. In very acid soils, especially where abundant iron or aluminum silicates exist, the monocalcium phosphate changes to insoluble iron and aluminum phosphate; and in alkaline soils, especially where abundant calcium exists, the monocalcium phosphate changes to the relatively insoluble tricalcium phosphate. *Unlike nitrate ions, the phosphate ion is readily "fixed" by soils.* Consequently, very little movement, or leaching, of phosphorus takes place and excessive amounts in the soil solution do not exist. Therefore, phosphates may be applied when convenient, preferably close to the plant's roots. For most crops it is usually applied at the time of soil preparation and as side dressings during the early states of growth.

The principal carrier is superphosphate. This material is made by treating raw rock phosphate with sulfuric acid or phosphoric acid. Note the equations.

$$Ca_3(PO_4)_2 + 2H_2SO_4 \longrightarrow Ca(H_2PO_4)_2 + 2CaSO_4$$

$$Ca_3(PO_4)_2 + 4H_3PO_4 \longrightarrow 3Ca(H_2PO_4)_2$$

In the first case a mixture consisting of monocalcium phosphate and gypsum is formed. The product is called superphosphate and varies from 16 to 20 per cent P_2O_5, depending on the relative amount of phosphate and gypsum in the mixture. In the second case monocalcium phosphate is formed only. The product is called double or treble superphosphate and varies from 40 to 50 per cent P_2O_5.

QUESTIONS

1. The green plant is essentially a chemical factory. Explain.
2. What is right and what is wrong with the following statement? Plants make foods and plants absorb foods from the soil.
3. State the role of carbon dioxide in plant growth.
4. How is the supply of carbon dioxide maintained?
5. In general, the average concentration of carbon dioxide for any given 24-hour period is 0.03 per cent. At what part of the 24-hour day would you expect the concentration to be greater than 0.03 per cent, and at what part of the day would you expect the concentration to be less? Explain.

6. Calculate the amount of carbon dioxide above 1 acre of the earth's surface.
7. Under what conditions is carbon dioxide likely to be the limiting factor in plant growth?
8. In general, soils high in organic matter give off more carbon dioxide than soils low in organic matter. Explain.
9. Water is an essential raw material for plant growth. Explain.
10. State the role of nitrogen in plant growth.
11. Available nitrogen is needed for the development of meristematic tissues. Explain.
12. Distinguish between nitrogen-deficiency symptoms in the leaf blade of monocots and in the leaf blade of dicots.
13. In general, plants growing in soil containing low quantities of available nitrogen store carbohydrates. Explain.
14. For the same period of time a plant growing in a small pot produces a smaller top than a plant growing in a large pot. Explain from the standpoint of the nitrogen supply.
15. Tomatoes and cucumbers growing in old barnyards are frequently vigorously vegetative and begin to produce fruit late in the season. Explain.
16. In general, cotton in the Mississippi Delta produces a larger top and a greater yield than cotton in the hills. Explain.
17. Investigations have shown that certain varieties of tomatoes fertilized with mixtures high in nitrogen are more vegetative and less productive than those fertilized with mixtures comparatively low in nitrogen. Explain.
18. Outline the changes taking place in organic matter from protein-nitrogen to nitrate-nitrogen and from gaseous nitrogen to nitrate-nitrogen.
19. What is ammonification? Nitrification? Nitrogen fixation?
20. Name the soil factors influencing the activity of the ammonifiers, nitrifiers, and nitrogen fixers.
21. The natural nitrate supply is low in winter and comparatively high in summer. Explain.
22. Experiments at the Louisiana Station have shown that a complete fertilizer is necessary for the fertilization of spring crops of snap beans and that a fertilizer without nitrogen is necessary for fall crops. Explain.
23. Side dressings of readily available nitrogen to crops in the seedling stage in the southern United States are frequently necessary during cold, wet weather. Give two reasons.
24. Decomposition of organic matter in winter in the greenhouse is more rapid than outdoors. Explain.
25. Show how the continual use of a physiologically acid fertilizer makes the soil more acid and how the continual use of a physiologically alkaline fertilizer makes the soil less acid and more alkaline.
26. In what form do plants absorb phosphorus?
27. State three roles of phosphorus in plant growth.
28. Distinguish between phosphorus deficiency in monocots and dicots.

29. Name the chief sources of phosphorus.
30. Phosphorus becomes unavailable in soils with greater than pH 8.5. Explain.
31. Phosphorus becomes unavailable in soils with less than pH 5.0. Explain.

POTASSIUM

Role. Potassium differs from carbon, hydrogen, oxygen, and other essential elements in that it is not a constituent of the manufactured compounds or a part of any living tissue. Nevertheless, plants do not grow in the absence of potassium. In general, this element appears to be necessary for the synthesis of amino acids, since plants growing in cultures high in ammonium ions and low in potassium ions accumulate large quantities of ammonium in the tissues.

Symptoms of Deficiency. The symptoms of potassium deficiency vary somewhat with different crops. With fruit crops, e.g., apple, pear, plum, gooseberry, and black and red currant, *potassium deficiency is first evidenced by a faint yellowing of the leaf margins.* Later the yellowing proceeds along the veins and the margins turn dark brown. This condition is known as scorch. It is very serious in Great Britain, Quebec, and Nova Scotia and occurs to some extent in the northern and western United States. With cucumbers the margins of the old leaves become yellow, but the midrib and veins remain green. With potatoes and sweet-potatoes the leaves become rough and puckered and the margins curl downward, turn yellow, and finally turn brown. With many dicotyledonous flower crops the margins of the leaves turn yellow and finally dark brown, but the remainder of the leaves remains green. With sweet corn and other monocots yellowing begins at the tips and goes down the edges, leaving the center green. With both the dicots and monocots *the old leaves usually show the symptoms first.* Note the appearance of the margins of the leaves in Fig. 7.1.

Available Form and Carriers. Plants absorb potassium as potassium ions, and the principal source seems to be the ions attached to the surface of colloidal particles. These ions are exchanged for hydrogen ions, hence, the term exchangeable potassium. Important carriers are potassium chloride (KCl) and potassium sulfate (K_2SO_4), both 48 to 50 per cent K_2O; and potassium nitrate (KNO_3), 44 per cent K_2O. In general, these compounds are quite soluble in water, and they dissociate into potassium ions and chloride, sulfate, and nitrate ions, as the case may be. Most soils fix potassium ions to a lesser degree than they fix phosphate ions. Consequently, if comparatively large quantities are applied, leaching may take place and excessive amounts in the soil solution may exist.

SULFUR

Role. Sulfur is part of the molecule of glycine, an essential amino acid, and of vitamin B_1, the coenzyme for respiration. Thus, sulfur is necessary for the making of new protoplasm and new cells and for the maintenance and repair of the tissues. In addition, sulfur is necessary for chlorophyll formation, since crop plants growing in deficient supplies lack adequate quantities of this pigment.

Symptoms of Deficiency. Investigations have shown that, with many flower crops, *the veins of the leaves are lighter green than the tissue between the veins.* Note this condition is exactly opposite to that for magnesium, manganese, and iron deficiency. In general, the leaves on the upper part of the plant show sulfur-deficiency symptoms first. This indicates that sulfur is not readily transferred from one part of the plant to another.

Available Form and Sources. Plants absorb sulfur only in the form of sulfate ions (SO_4), a highly oxidized form of sulfur. Important sources are sulfur in organic matter, sulfur in the atmosphere, and sulfur in commercial fertilizers.

The sulfur in organic matter is in the form of protein-sulfur. Since plants cannot use it as it is, it must be changed into the sulfate form. As in the formation of nitrates from organic matter, this change is effected by certain soil organisms. In general, the protein-sulfur is changed into hydrogen sulfide. This in turn is oxidized into sulfuric acid, which combines with minerals in the soil solution and forms a salt. This change from protein-sulfur to sulfate-sulfur is illustrated as follows:

$$\text{Organic matter containing sulfur} \xrightarrow{\text{(soil organisms)}} H_2S$$

$$+ 2O_2 \xrightarrow{\text{(sulfur bacteria)}} H_2SO_4$$

$$H_2SO_4 + MOH^* \longrightarrow MSO_4{}^* + H_2O$$

The sulfur in the atmosphere is washed into the soil by rain. In the soil the sulfur is oxidized. This oxidized sulfur combines with water in the formation of sulfuric acid which, in the presence of a mineral, forms a salt. In regions near certain industrial establishments the atmosphere contains relatively large quantities of sulfur. The change of elemental sulfur into sulfate-sulfur is illustrated as follows:

$$S + O_2 \longrightarrow SO_2 + O \longrightarrow SO_3 + H_2O \underset{\text{(rain)}}{\longrightarrow} H_2SO_4 + M \longrightarrow MSO_4{}^*$$

* M stands for minerals in soil solution.

Commercial fertilizers containing sulfur are ammonium sulfate, super-phosphate, and gypsum. In general, ammonium sulfate and superphosphate are used primarily to supply available nitrogen and available phosphorus, respectively. However, ammonium sulfate dissociates in the soil solution into ammonium ions and sulfate ions, and superphosphate contains certain quantities of calcium sulfate. In certain sections of the country, gypsum applied alone or with commercial fertilizers has increased the growth and yield of certain crops, e.g., alfalfa and other closely related legumes in Oregon, Washington, and British Columbia, and white clover in Mississippi.

CALCIUM

Role. Calcium is necessary for the formation of calcium-pectate which together with magnesium-pectate binds the cellulose chains together in cell wall formation. Hence, in healthy, rapidly growing plants, large quantities of calcium are necessary for the meristem of the roots, the stems, and the cambia. Calcium also appears to be necessary for the absorption of nitrate-nitrogen, since investigations have shown that calcium-deficient plants accumulate sugars and starches in the tissues and are unable to absorb nitrate-nitrogen. Immediately after calcium-starved plants are supplied with this element, nitrates, if available, are found within the tissues in a relatively short time.

Symptoms of Deficiency. Unlike nitrogen, phosphorus, and potassium, but like sulfur, calcium is relatively immobile in plants. Thus, *young leaves show symptoms of deficiency before old leaves.* Investigations at the New Jersey Experiment Station have shown that calcium-deficient plants of the Marglobe tomato become stunted, stiff, and woody. The upper leaves become yellowish-green, and the lower leaves remain normal green. The margins are usually less dark green than the central portion. Roots become short, bulbous, and brownish at the tips. Fruits are few. Calcium-deficiency symptoms of the apple are somewhat similar. The young leaves are yellowish-green, and mature leaves are dark green. On young trees the leaves may be abnormally small. On large trees the leaves may be normal in size except those near the tips of the twigs. In severe cases the margins of the leaves turn brown, and the growth of the roots is seriously retarded. These roots may form, but they live for a short time only. Investigations at the Ohio Experiment Station have shown that plants of many herbaceous flowering crops become stunted, the terminal buds fail to develop, and the roots die back at the tips in a relatively short time.

Available Form and Carriers. Plants absorb calcium as calcium ions. The principal carriers are the three forms of lime: calcium oxide, calcium hydroxide, and calcium carbonate. In soils, calcium oxide and calcium hydroxide gradually change to calcium carbonate, according to the following equations:

(1) $CaO + HOH = Ca(OH)_2$

(2) $Ca(OH)_2 + CO_2 = CaCO_3 + H_2O$

Growers usually use the hydrated and carbonate forms.

Relation of Soil Acidity to Growth and Development

In addition to supplying calcium for the specific roles of this element, the various forms of lime are used to make soils less acid. The degree of acidity of the soil solution has marked effects on the growth and yield of many economic crops. If the soil solution is either very acid or very alkaline, growth and development of many crops are markedly reduced. In addition, crops vary in acidity requirements. Some thrive well in markedly acid soils; others thrive best in moderately acid or slightly acid soils; and others thrive best in slightly acid or neutral soils. Since soils vary in degree of acidity and since plants vary in acidity requirements, the student should have a working knowledge of the factors which cause acidity, how the acidity of the soil influences growth and yields, and how the acidity may be modified to produce high marketable yields.

Nature and Measurement of Acidity and Alkalinity. The soil solution, like any aqueous solution, always contains a certain concentration of hydrogen ions and hydroxyl ions. The acidity of the solution is due to hydrogen ions, and its alkalinity is due to hydroxyl ions. Water ionizes, forming hydrogen and hydroxyl ions according to the following equation:

$$H_2O \rightleftharpoons \overset{+}{H} + \overset{-}{OH}$$

Thus, the soil solution contains water molecules, hydrogen ions, and hydroxyl ions. Scientists have developed a scale called the pH scale, which measures the degree of acidity of solutions. This scale has the following characteristics: (1) It is divided into 14 main divisions from 0 to 14, and the value of 7.0, the midpoint, is the reference point. (2) At this value, the solution is neutral; at values lower than 7, the solution is acid; and at values greater than 7, the solution is alkaline. (3) The values on the scale are negative logarithms to the base of 10. Thus, for every decrease in unit pH, there is a tenfold increase in H-ion concentration and a corresponding tenfold decrease in the OH-ion concentration.

For example, a solution of pH 6.0 is ten times more acid than a solution of pH 7.0, and a solution of pH 4.0 is one hundred times more acid than a solution of pH 6.0.

Soil Reaction and Essential-element Availability. A definite relation exists between the degree of acidity of soils, essential-element availability, and plant growth. In very acid soils, usually less than pH 5.0, nitrate-nitrogen formation is low, since both the nitrifying and nitrogen-fixing bacteria do not thrive well in very acid soils; monocalcium phosphate changes to iron and aluminum phosphate, which are relatively insoluble; and compounds which supply available calcium and magnesium are usually present in insufficient quantities for rapid plant growth. On the other hand, in alkaline soils, usually greater than pH 8.5, nitrate-nitrogen formation is also low, since the nitrifying bacteria do not thrive well in alkaline soils; monocalcium phosphate changes to tricalcium phosphate, which is relatively insoluble; and compounds which supply potassium, manganese, iron, and boron are likely to become unavailable. Thus, high acidity and high alkalinity should be avoided. In fact, most crops thrive best in moderately acid or slightly acid soils. The optimum pH range of certain horticultural crops based on growers' experience and the latest experimental evidence is presented in Table 7.2.

Table 7.2. SOIL-ACIDITY REQUIREMENTS OF SOME HORTICULTURAL CROPS

Optimum pH range	Crop
Very acid (pH 4.0–5.0)	Azalea, philodendron, mountain laurel, blueberry, huckleberry, and cranberry (Many of these plants have mycorrhizal fungi in their roots. These fungi supply the plants with nitrogen and possibly other essential elements.)
Moderately acid (pH 5.0–6.0)	Snap bean, potato, sweetpotato, watermelon, aster, lily of the valley, orchid, holly, juniper, lily, phlox, and hydrangea
Slightly acid (pH 6.0–6.8)	Asparagus, spinach, lima bean, beet, celery, cantaloupe, lettuce, onion, sweet cherry, rose, chrysanthemum, sweet pea, and snapdragon
Slightly and moderately acid (pH 5.0–6.8)	Apple, pear, peach, plum, pecan, grape, grapefruit, raspberry, blackberry, strawberry, cabbage, radish, squash, tomato, pepper, sweet corn, carrot, carnation, and gerbera

Source: Data for this table have been obtained from several sources.

DETERMINING SOIL REACTION. Experiment stations have developed comparatively simple tests to determine the degree of acidity of the soil solution. In general, these tests involve the use of an indicator —a compound allowed to percolate slowly through a small mass of soil. The change in color of the indicator denotes a certain degree of acidity. These tests are fairly accurate, reliable, and inexpensive and permit making many determinations in a comparatively short time.

REDUCING ACIDITY. Many soils in many districts in humid sections are very acid, usually less than pH 5.5. To reduce the acidity of these soils for the growing of crops which thrive best in moderately acid or slightly acid soils, lime is added. The amount required depends largely on (1) soil type and (2) acidity requirements of the crop. In general, sands and sandy loams are sensitive to changes in acidity because of low buffer capacity. Hence, comparatively light applications are needed. Crops which thrive best on slightly acid soils require more lime than those which thrive best on moderately acid soils. In districts where the soils are naturally deficient in magnesia-bearing rock, as for example the Atlantic Coastal Plain, dolomitic limestone, a form of limestone containing large quantities of magnesium carbonate, is used to a greater extent than ordinary limestone.

INCREASING ACIDITY. Certain soils in humid sections are moderately or slightly acid. To increase the acidity of these soils for crops which thrive best in very acid soils, ammonium sulfate or flowers of sulfur is added. The amount required depends on the exchange capacity of the soil and the change in pH that should be made. In general, applications vary from 50 to 500 pounds per acre.

MAGNESIUM

Role. Magnesium has at least two important roles. This element is the center of the molecule of both chlorophyll a and chlorophyll b, and it is part of the molecule of magnesium-pectate which together with calcium-pectate binds the cellulose chains in the formation of the cell walls. Thus, magnesium is necessary for photosynthesis and for cell division.

Symptoms of Deficiency. The outstanding symptom for practically all crops is the loss of chlorophyll of the tissues between the veins of the leaves. In other words, *the intervascular areas change from dark green to light green and from light green to yellow, but the veins remain green.* This change from green to yellow starts at the tips and gradually proceeds to the center of the blades. As with a deficiency of nitrogen, phosphorus, and potassium, *the old leaves show the symptoms first.* Thus, when magnesium is deficient, it is transferred from the old to the young

Fig. 7.2. Healthy and magnesium-deficient leaves of chrysanthemum. Leaf to left is from a plant grown with a normal supply of magnesium; leaves to right are from a magnesium-deficient culture. (Courtesy, Alex Laurie, Whistling Pine Gardens, Eustis, Fla.)

tissues. Because of the low chlorophyll content, there is a low rate of light absorption and a corresponding low rate of photosynthesis; and as a rule the tissues are low in sugars and starch, the cells are thin-walled, the strengthening tissue is poorly developed, and the roots are small and few in number. Figure 7.2 shows healthy and deficient leaves of chrysanthemum. Note the chlorotic condition of the interveinal areas.

Soils vary greatly in natural magnesium, the amount being determined by the amount of magnesia in the drainage water. Figure 7.3 shows the magnesium content of the drainage water of soils in various parts of the continental United States. Note the relatively low concentration, 1 to 3 ppm, in the drainage water of soils of the Atlantic Coastal Plain and of the extreme Northwest and the high concentration, over 20 ppm, in the drainage water of the soils in the Middle West and West. The question arises: Why do soils vary in magnesium? Two important factors are (1) the amount of magnesia in the parent rocks and (2) the acidity of the soil. In regions where the magnesium content of the soil is low, the rock material from which the soil is formed is naturally low in magnesium, and the acidity of the soil is generally higher than in regions where the magnesium content of the soil is high. Within the regions of low magnesium content magnesium-deficiency symptoms first appeared in intensively cropped areas, e.g., the truck-crop districts in the vicinity of Norfolk, Virginia, and Charleston, South Carolina, and the potato district in Aroostock County, Maine. In these districts growers use fertilizers containing available magnesium.

Available Form and Carriers. As with potassium and calcium, plants absorb magnesium as magnesium ions. Principal carriers are dolomitic limestone (a mixture of calcium and magnesium carbonate), magnesium sulfate, and sulfate of potash magnesia (a mixture of potassium sulfate

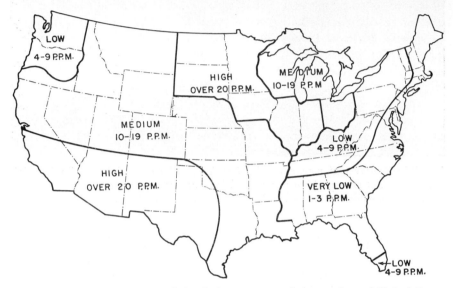

Fig. 7.3. Magnesium content of the drainage waters of the continental United States. (Redrawn from Virginia Truck Exp. Sta. Bull. 89, 1935, and published with permission of S. B. Detwiler, Soil Conservation Service, U.S. Department of Agriculture.)

and magnesium sulfate). Pound for pound, dolomitic limestone is less soluble but longer lasting than either of the other two compounds.

MANGANESE AND IRON

Manganese and iron are discussed together because their role in plant growth, symptoms of deficiency, and behavior in the soil are quite similar.

Role. Although the role of manganese and iron is not definitely known, it is known that with deficient supplies of either element chlorophyll fails to develop. Many plant scientists believe these elements are part of enzyme systems for the making of chlorophyll. However, the student should remember that neither one can take the place of the other in the formation of this important compound. Both are needed.

Symptoms of Deficiency. In general, *the interveinal areas of young leaves become light green and yellow, but the veins remain green.* Since both these essential elements are relatively immobile in the plant, *the young leaves show symptoms first.* As the deficiency becomes severe, necrotic, or dead, areas appear in the interveinal areas. According to deficiency-symptom experiments conducted at the Ohio Experiment Station, manganese deficiency induces relatively small dead areas along the middle of the leaf only, whereas iron deficiency induces relatively large dead areas in all of the interveinal tissues.

Available Forms and Behavior in Soil. As with other essential cations, plants absorb manganese and iron as manganese and iron ions. The degree of acidity of the soil solution has marked effects on the availability of these ions. In general, excessive supplies are usually present in very acid soils, moderate and adequate quantities are present in slightly acid soils, and deficient supplies exist in very slightly acid, neutral, and alkaline soils. In fact, certain tests have shown that manganese is almost insoluble in soils which have pH values from 6.2 to 8.0. In other words, the optimum pH range for manganese and iron availability seems to be from 5.5 to 6.2. Thus, the degree of acidity of the soil should be determined to confirm any suspected deficiency or excess of these two elements.

Carrier of Manganese. The common carrier is manganese sulfate. When artificial applications are necessary, this material may be applied either as a foliage spray or directly to the soil. At present applications are required in certain citrus orchards in California and Florida, in many apricot, peach, and cherry orchards in Utah, in the truck-crop areas near Charleston, South Carolina, and Norfolk, Virginia, and in certain ornamental nurseries and plantings in Florida. In some cases, particularly where the soils are slightly acid or neutral, spraying the foliage may be more economical than applying the material to the soil. For example, experiments in Florida have shown that spraying manganese sulfate at the rate of 10 pounds per acre on manganese-deficient snap beans was as effective in correcting the deficiency as a soil application of 20 to 25 pounds per acre. In general, the rate of application varies from 5 to 100 pounds per acre depending on soil type, degree of acidity, and manganese requirements of the crop.

Carriers of Iron. Common carriers of iron are ferrous sulfate, an inorganic compound, and chelates (pronounced keylates) containing iron, a group of organic compounds, e.g., ethylenediaminetetraacetic acid, called EDTA, and diethylenetriaminepentaacetic acid, called DTPA. These compounds hold iron in an available form and facilitate the entrance of iron into the plant and the distribution of iron within the plant. In addition they are not broken down in soils. The chelates may be applied either in solution with water or in the dry form. They have corrected chlorosis in many areas: in citrus and vegetable areas of central Florida, in orna-

Fig. 7.4. Manganese-deficient and healthy leaves of tung. (Courtesy, R. D. Dickey, University of Florida.)

Fig. 7.5. Healthy and iron-deficient leaves of rose. Left: minus iron. Right: with iron. (Courtesy, Alex Laurie, Whistling Pine Gardens, Eustis, Fla.)

mental plant–growing districts in Pennsylvania and Massachusetts, and in certain high-lime soil areas in California. Compare the healthy and deficient leaves in Figs. 7.4 and 7.5.

BORON

Role.   Although the exact physiological role of boron is unknown, this element appears to be necessary for cell division, for the development of the phloem, and for the transport of certain hormones. In the absence of adequate supplies the middle lamella of new cells develops poorly and the phloem tubes break down. Thus, calcium and boron have related roles in plant growth. In fact, investigations have shown that if the calcium content of the growing tissues is high, the boron content should be high also.

Symptoms of Deficiency.   Since rapid cell division does not take place in the absence of boron, the meristems are profoundly affected. As would be expected, *vegetative and flower buds fail to develop, leaves are small, lopsided, and misshaped, and the flesh of storage structures breaks down.* Since boron, like calcium, is immobile, *the younger parts of the plants show symptoms of deficiency first.* Note the boron-deficient cabbage head in Fig. 7.6.

Available Form and Carriers.   Plants absorb boron as the negatively charged borate ion, and they require this element in relatively low concentration, usually from 0.1 to 1.0 ppm in the soil solution. If the concentration becomes greater than 1.0 ppm, toxic effects are likely to occur.

Factors influencing the amount of available borate are (1) soil type and (2) soil reaction. Soils most deficient are old soils, sandy soils, mucks and peats, those derived from igneous rocks, and alkaline and neutral soils. At present applications are made in many commercial crop industries, e.g., cauliflower districts in the Catskill Mountains, New York; turnip and rutabaga fields in the northeastern United States and maritime provinces of Canada; celery districts in southern Michigan, central Florida, Oregon, and certain areas in California; cabbage fields in central Mississippi; and apple and pear orchards in the New England states. In fact, in 1939 a deficiency of boron was reported in one or more crops in 24 of the United States.

The principal carrier is fertilizer borate ($Na_2B_4O_7 \cdot 4H_2O$). In general, when applications are necessary, fruit trees are given from 2 to 16 ounces of borax per tree, and herbaceous crops from 5 to 30 pounds of borax per acre. This form is highly soluble and subject to rapid leaching. A

Fig. 7.6. A boron-deficient head of cabbage. Note the dark area in the basal portion of the stem. (Courtesy, J. A. Campbell, Mississippi Agricultural Experiment Station.)

less soluble form, colemanite ($Ca_2B_6O_{11} \cdot 5H_2O$), has been tested with satisfactory results at the South Carolina Experiment Station. Thus, with the use of the calcium form losses due to leaching may be avoided.

ZINC

Role. Recent work indicates that zinc is necessary for the formation of tryptophan, the precursor of indoleacetic acid—a plant hormone which gives the cell walls the ability to stretch. Thus, zinc appears to be necessary for cell elongation.

Symptoms of Deficiency. Zinc-deficiency symptoms vary somewhat with the crop. With apples, peaches, and pecans *deficient branches have small, narrow, mottled leaves,* and they usually die back each year; with citrus *the leaves are small and extremely mottled;* and with herbaceous plants *the leaves have yellow interveinal areas and green veins.* Note that in all cases inadequate quantities of chlorophyll develop. As a result, the rate of photosynthesis of zinc-deficient crops is low and the yields and quality are low. Note the small, narrow leaves of the zinc-deficient peach tree in Fig. 7.7.

In the continental United States zinc deficiency has been found in many crops, mostly in regions of high light intensity. For example, deficient trees have been found in citrus, peach, pecan, and tung orchards in the southern region; in avocado, citrus, and cherry orchards and in bean, sweet corn, and tomato plantings on the Pacific Coast; and in apple, cherry, and peach orchards in the intermountain region.

Available Form and Carrier. Plants absorb zinc in the ionic form, and the usual carrier is zinc sulfate ($ZnSO_4 \cdot 7H_2O$). This compound is

Fig. 7.7. A zinc-deficient peach tree. (Courtesy, R. D. Dickey, University of Florida.)

quite soluble in water and is applied as a foilage spray or directly to the soil. Of these methods, spraying is more widely used, since zinc is readily fixed by soil colloids and becomes unavailable in neutral and alkaline soils. In fact, these soils usually contain large quantities of zinc which are unavailable to crops. Thus, the fixing power of the soil for zinc and the degree of acidity are important. In general, the available concentration varies from 1 to 10 ppm with the midpoint of this range as the optimum concentration. The use of zinc chelates, organic carriers of zinc, is in the experimental stage.

COPPER

Role. Copper is an essential constituent of certain oxidizing enzymes, e.g., tyrosinase, the enzyme which in the presence of oxygen darkens the flesh of the potato tuber; and ascorbic acid oxidase, the enzyme which oxidizes ascorbic acid. Since with deficient supplies *the interveinal areas of leaves become yellow,* copper is necessary for the formation of chlorophyll.

The need of certain soils in the continental United States for copper was discovered in the Florida Everglades in 1927. Crops sprayed with Bordeaux mixture, a suspension consisting of copper sulfate and calcium hydroxide, or dusted with copper sulfate produced satisfactory yields, whereas crops not sprayed or dusted with the copper-containing compound made scant growth. Subsequent tests showed that applications of 50 pounds of copper sulfate per acre changed the soil, a saw grass peat, from a low to a remarkably high state of fertility. Since that time tests conducted in various regions have shown that copper has a beneficial effect on the growth of many plants. Applications of available copper have cured the "frenching," or spotting, of leaves in citrus and almond trees in California, corrected copper chlorosis of corn and citrus in Florida and of deciduous fruits in South Africa, increased the thickness of the scales and improved the color of onions grown on the muck soils in New York and Michigan, and increased the yields of potatoes, sweetpotatoes, onions, and snap beans in Delaware.

Available Form and Carrier. Here again, plants absorb copper in the ionic form. The usual carrier is copper sulfate. It may be applied either as a foliage spray or directly to the soil. As with certain other compounds, the amount applied depends largely on the amount of available copper in soils. In general, acid soils, or those usually less than pH 5.5, the low-lime mucks, and sands require more copper than the moderately acid or slightly acid soils. Applications vary from 10 to 250 pounds per acre, and usually one application supplies sufficient copper for a period of several years.

MOLYBDENUM

Role. Molybdenum is essential for the reduction of nitrates in the leaves and presumably in the growing points also. This indicates that molybdenum is part of an enzyme system which changes nitrates to ammonium compounds in amino-acid formation. Thus, in the absence of molybdenum, with other factors favorable, nitrates are likely to accumulate in the tissues. Undoubtedly, molybdenum has other functions, since plants deficient in this element contain low quantities of glucose, fructose, starch, glutamic acid, and ascorbic acid and large quantities of inorganic phosphorus.

Symptoms of Deficiency. Recent research has shown that at least 30 economic crops require molybdenum. These crops include the members of the citrus family, the members of the cabbage family, tomatoes, cucumbers, and snap beans. With oranges and grapefruit, *the leaves have clearly defined yellow areas.* With cauliflower, *the leaves are long and narrow with cupped or wavy margins;* and with tomatoes, cucumbers, and snap beans, *the leaves turn brown or yellow at the margins, which turn upward.* In all cases growth is slow, the plants become stunted, and yields and quality are low.

Molybdenum deficiency has been found in many parts of the world, e.g., in the Coastal Plain area of eastern United States, in the Serpentine soils of central California, in the Palouse district of Washington, and in Great Britain, Ireland, the Netherlands, France, India, Japan, Australia, and New Zealand. Molybdenum deficiency usually occurs in very acid soils. In fact, scientists have found a close positive correlation between the degree of acidity of the soil solution and the presence of available molybdenum. In general, very acid soils have less available molybdenum than slightly acid or neutral soils.

Available Form and Carrier. Plants absorb molybdenum as the negatively charged molybdate ion, and the usual carrier is sodium molybdate. This material may be applied in solution with water or dry, either alone or with other fertilizers or even with pest-control materials. In general, adequate applications vary from 1 ounce to 1 pound per acre.

CHLORINE

Recent investigations have shown that chlorine is essential for the growth of 11 species of plants. According to research workers at the University of California, about 100 ppm of the dry weight of the species is the minimum requirement.

The natural source of supply is rain. In general, the amount varies with the distance from oceans. In other words, the rainfall along the coasts contains a greater amount of chlorine than that some distance away.

The behavior of the chlorine ion in soils is similar to that of the nitrate and borate ions. In other words, it is not fixed by soils and it is susceptible to leaching.

OTHER ELEMENTS

Investigations have shown that aluminum, iodine, and silicon are essential for the growth of certain plants. However, at present, these elements are not deficient in soils given over to the production of horticultural crops in the continental United States. Thus, applications of compounds supplying these elements are unnecessary.

QUESTIONS

1. State the role of potassium in plant growth.
2. What part of the leaf is first affected by potassium deficiency?
3. How would you distinguish potassium deficiency from nitrogen deficiency in the leaf blade of monocots?
4. Name two commercial sources of potassium.
5. State the roles of sulfur in plant growth.
6. In what form do plants absorb sulfur?
7. Outline the changes taking place from protein-sulfur to sulfate-sulfur and from sulfur to sulfate-sulfur.
8. Name two commercial fertilizers containing sulfur.
9. State the roles of calcium in plant growth.
10. Calcium-deficient plants store carbohydrates. Explain.
11. Young leaves show calcium-deficiency symptoms before the old leaves do. Explain.
12. State the three principle carriers of calcium.
13. What are acidity and alkalinity due to?
14. Soil with a pH 3 is acid; with a pH 8, alkaline; with a pH 7, neutral. Explain.
15. Yields of most crops are low when the plants are grown in very acid soils, usually less than pH 5.0. Give three reasons.
16. State the roles of magnesium in plant growth.
17. Describe the outstanding symptoms of magnesium deficiency.
18. In what section of the country is magnesium naturally deficient in soils? Give two reasons.
19. How does dolomitic limestone differ from ordinary limestone?
20. Dolomitic limestone is used to a greater extent in the Southeast than ordinary limestone. Explain.

21. How would you distinguish magnesium deficiency from manganese and iron deficiency?
22. Chlorotic plants are lower in sugars and carbohydrates and grow more slowly than healthy plants. Explain.
23. Chelates containing iron are more effective in controlling iron chlorosis than are inorganic compounds containing iron. Explain.
24. State the outstanding symptoms of boron deficiency.
25. How is boron deficiency corrected? State the substances which are used and how they are applied.
26. How is zinc deficiency corrected?
27. Although large quantities of zinc may be present in the soil, it is not always available. Explain.
28. In your opinion, how do applications of copper sulfate benefit onions growing on muck soils in New York, Michigan, and Florida?
29. State the role of molybdenum in plant growth.

PRINCIPAL HORTICULTURAL PRACTICES 2

PROPAGATION

8

Propagation of crop plants involves the formation and development of new individuals. These new individuals are used in the establishment of new plantings. In general, two methods are employed: (1) the using of seed and (2) the using of vegetative parts of plants, called vegetative, or asexual, propagation. Table 8.1 presents examples of crops which are propagated by seed, by using vegetative parts, and by both of these methods.

PROPAGATION BY SEED

> *Behold a sower went forth to sow.*
> Matthew 13:3

What Is a Seed? Essentially, a seed consists of an embryo with nourishing and protecting tissue. The embryo is a minute plant. Principal parts are plumule, radicle, hypocotyl, epicotyl, and cotyledons. The plumule is the first growing point of the stem; the radicle is the first growing point of the root; and the hypocotyl and epicotyl together constitute the first, or original, stem of the plant. The nourishing tissues are endosperm, or cotyledons. In well-developed mature seed, these tissues are packed with stored food—starch, hemicellulose, reserve proteins, or fats—depending on the kind of plant. For example, sweet corn stores starch and dextrin; asparagus, onion, and date store hemicellulose; pea and bean

135

Table 8.1.   EXAMPLES OF CROPS PROPAGATED BY SEED, BY VEGETATIVE PARTS, AND BY BOTH SEED AND VEGETATIVE PARTS

Type of propagation	Fruit crops	Vegetable crops	Flowers and ornamentals
By seed	Cocoanut, tung	Asparagus, cabbage, celery, onion, spinach, tomato, vine crops	Aster, calendula, centauria, delphinium, forget-me-not, marigold, pansy, salvia, sweet pea
By vegetative parts	Banana, pineapple, raspberry, strawberry	Potato, sweetpotato, rhubarb, globe artichoke	Carnation, chrysanthemum, geranium, poinsettia, iris, peony, phlox
By both seed for rootstocks and vegetative parts for cion	Apple, peach, pecan, citrus, tung		Dogwood, flowering peach, flowering cherry, crabapple, juniper

store reserve proteins and carbohydrates; and pecan, walnut, lettuce, okra, the cucurbits,[1] and ornamental sunflowers store comparatively large quantities of fat. These stored, or reserve, materials change to soluble forms for the respiration of the embryo in storage and for the respiration and growth of the embryo in germination. The protecting tissue is the seed coat.[2] In general, the coat retards the rate of transpiration; in some kinds of plants, it retards the rate of respiration while the seeds are in storage and protects the delicate embryo from mechanical injury to some extent. Thus, *a seed may be defined as a minute plant with nourishing and protecting tissues.*

THE GARDEN SEED BUSINESS

Vegetable and flower crop seed, like seed of other agricultural crops, should do two things: (1) produce profits to the grower, or the person who buys the seed, and (2) produce profits to the seedsman, or the person who develops and sells the seed.

How does seed of the many varieties and strains of a given kind produce

---

[1] The cucurbits include cucumber, cantaloupe, pumpkin, squash, and watermelon.
[2] In some plants, e.g., carrots, strawberries, and sweet corn, part of the fruit becomes attached to the seed coat and the entire structure is commonly called "seed."

profits to the grower? In general, varieties and strains of a given kind are developed in the locality or region where they are to be grown for home garden or commercial production. This practice is based on a fundamental principle which may be stated as follows: *The various factors of the environment have marked effects on the expression of the hereditary factors, or genes.* This is particularly true of the temperature level, the light intensity, and the relative length of the light and dark periods. For example, varieties of onions adapted to the northern United States should have the ability to produce bulbs at the relatively low light intensity and the long light and short dark periods during the late summers of this region; and varieties adapted to the southern United States should have the ability to produce marketable bulbs at the high light intensity and the relatively short light and long dark periods during the springs of this region. In other words, varieties of onions adapted to the southern region, if grown in the northern United States, would develop bulbs before they had made sufficient vegetative growth or leaf area for large bulb production; and varieties adapted to the northern region, if grown in the southern United States, would remain vegetative and not form satisfactory bulbs. This marked influence of the environment on the expression of the genes explains why seeds are bred in the region or locality where they are to be grown for home garden or commercial production, why private seed-breeding companies maintain and establish seed-breeding stations throughout the various regions of the country, and why many agricultural

Fig. 8.1. A modern seed-breeding station given over to the maintenance of standard varieties and to the development of new and improved types. (Courtesy, Associated Seed Growers, Inc., New Haven, Conn.)

Table 8.2.   **PRINCIPAL SEED-PRODUCING DISTRICTS OF CERTAIN CROPS**

Crop	Seed-producing districts
Garden pea	High areas of Washington, Montana, Idaho, and Wyoming
Cabbage, spinach, beet	Puget Sound and Vancouver Island
Lettuce	Santa Clara Valley and Delta of California
Cucumber, cantaloupe	Colorado River Valley
Snap bean	Idaho, Montana, California
Many flowering plants	California

experiment stations have plant-breeding projects for the benefit of the growers in their respective locations. Note the seed-breeding station in Fig. 8.1.

How is seed grown so that the seedsman may receive a profitable return for his investment? In general, seed for sale is grown in the environment most favorable to the production of high yields of high-quality seed and to low production costs. For example, after a seed breeder has developed a new strain or variety, he may have only a handful of seed of that strain or variety. Obviously, this small quantity of seed should be multiplied rapidly in order to supply the demand of the growers. To supply this demand, the seedsman selects the environment in the United States and elsewhere which is favorable to the production of high yields of this new lot of seed. This effect of environment on quantity and quality explains why seed of certain kinds, e.g., onion, lettuce, celery, and snap beans, are grown in the irrigated districts of the western United States. The low rainfall and the long periods of sunshine, combined with the application of irrigation water in this region, promote a rapid rate of photosynthesis, large yields, proper ripening and curing. It explains why other kinds, e.g., cabbage, spinach, and beet seed, are grown in relatively moist, temperate climates. The relatively moist climate, combined with a moderately low and uniform temperature, promotes high rates of photosynthesis and high yields. It also explains why seed of many flower crops is grown in the coastal areas of the West. The moist air from the ocean, combined with the night and morning fogs, tends to prevent the pods from dehiscing during the harvest. Note the seed-producing districts of the crops listed in Table 8.2.

HOME SAVING OF SEED

Under what conditions is the home saving of seed likely to produce satisfactory results? To answer this question three important facts should be kept in mind: (1) Varieties and strains of a given kind of crop cross-pollinate, and the amount of cross-pollination may vary from less than 1 per cent to 50 per cent or more. Even the so-called self-pollinated crops, e.g., garden peas and tomatoes, cross from 0.1 to 5.0 per cent. (2) In general, this uncontrolled or random cross-pollination does not promote uniformity in plant performance. (3) For effective isolation from unwanted pollen, varieties of the same kind in flower at the same time should be separated by a distance of at least 1 mile. This explains why the saving of seed from home gardens in a city or village or from varieties of the same kind in flower at the same time in the same home garden is likely to lead to disappointing results; and why the saving of seed from isolated gardens, especially when only one variety of a given kind is grown, is likely to result in the development of superior sorts. An example of a new variety developed under isolated conditions is the Alabama No. 1 pole bean. The original lot of seed was obtained from a farm family which had been saving seed from superior plants for numbers of generations. Tests at the Alabama station showed that this variety was resistant to the root-knot nematode—a serious pest in many home and commercial gardens in the South. Another example is one of the parents of Clemson Spineless okra. This parent has spineless, light green pods, and the original lot of seed was obtained from a farm family which had been saving seed from spineless podded plants for numbers of generations. This plant was crossed with a spiney, dark green podded sort, and selections were made for dark green pods for six generations. The new variety was released as Clemson Spineless okra.

VARIETY TRIALS AND SELECTING ADAPTABLE VARIETIES

As previously explained, varieties and strains differ in productivity and adaptability. For any given region some varieties of the same kind and some strains of the same variety are adaptable and thus profitable, and other varieties and strains are nonadaptable and thus relatively unprofitable. For example, in 1935, tests at the truck-crop station at Charleston, South Carolina, showed that four different strains of Drumhead Savoy cabbage differed markedly in plant performance. One strain produced a high percentage of offtype, unmarketable heads, and another strain produced a high percentage of "seeders"—plants which produce seedstalks instead of heads. Several years ago a similar test at Cornell University showed that two strains of the Copenhagen Market cabbage differed markedly in earliness of maturity of the heads. Earliness of maturity is particularly important in growing this type of cabbage in New York and adjacent states; the earlier strain was more profitable than the later.

In other words, there are marked differences in the behavior of varieties and of strains within varieties. Thus, a certain variety or strain may be adaptable to one region of the country and unadaptable to another. To determine the differences in behavior of seed-propagated vegetable and flower crops, experiment station and extension workers and seed-breeding companies conduct variety trials; and agricultural experiment stations and extension services throughout the United States and other countries maintain up-to-date lists of strains and varieties adaptable to the local environment.

STORING SEED

The principal process concerned is respiration. The stored food combines with water in the formation of soluble food which, in turn, combines with oxygen in the formation of carbon dioxide and water with the liberation of heat and other forms of kinetic energy. Note the equation:

$$\text{Stored food} + \text{water} \xrightarrow{\text{(hydrolyzing and oxidizing enzymes)}} \text{soluble food} + O_2 \longrightarrow CO_2 + H_2O + \text{heat and other forms of energy}$$

While seeds are stored the rate of respiration should proceed very slowly. Principal environmental factors in the storage of seed of most crops are (1) the amount of water in the air and (2) the temperature of the air. How does the moisture content of the air and the temperature level influence the rate of respiration and the longevity of seed in storage? *In general, seeds have the ability to absorb water from the air.* As shown in the equation, water is necessary to change the stored food which is relatively insoluble into soluble forms. Thus, if the moisture content of the air is high and the temperature level is also high, large quantities of water will be absorbed, the rate of change of the insoluble compounds to soluble forms will be high, and the rate of respiration will be high. As a result, storage life will be relatively short. Many investigations have shown that the relative water content of the air or relative humidity is a prime factor in seed storage. For example, studies of the deterioration of 10 kinds of vegetable seed were made at the Plant Industry Station, Beltsville, Maryland, in 1940. The results showed that the moisture content of the seed was positively associated with the relative humidity of the air and that seed with a high moisture content deteriorated very rapidly. Thus, in warm-humid regions, such as the Gulf Coast of the United States, the percentage of germination and vitality of seed may decrease seriously during the period between shipment of the fresh seed to the local dealer by the producer and the time of sowing by the grower. On the other hand, if the seed is protected from the high moisture content of the air, the rate of change of the insoluble compounds to soluble forms will be low and the rate of respiration will be accordingly low, even in the presence of high temperatures. To retard deterioration in warm-humid climates, many kinds of seed are stored in sealed cans and in other kinds of waterproof containers. Just before the seed is placed in the cans it is dried, without injury to the embryo, to a low moisture content, usually from 5 to 7 per cent. The cans serve at least three purposes: They protect the seed from high moisture in the air; from rodents, insects, and disease organisms; and from mechanical injury during handling, storing, and shipping operations. These effects of moisture in the air and temperature level explain why many kinds of vegetable and flower crop seed are stored and shipped in sealed containers and why certain kinds of seed retain their vitality if they are protected from the high moisture content of the air.

LONGEVITY OF SEED

Some plants develop seed which retains its vitality longer than the seed of others. In fact, vegetable and flower crop seed may be placed in three groups: (1) kinds dependable for a short period (one or two growing seasons), (2) kinds dependable for a moderately long period (two or three growing seasons), and (3) kinds dependable for a long period (three to five growing seasons). Examples are shown in Table 8.3.

TESTING SEED

The prime object of testing seed is to determine the rate of planting. As is well known, thinning due to excess rates of planting or poor stands due to nonviable seed always increases the cost of production. In general, the rate of planting is determined more accurately by the vitality of the seed than by its percentage of germination. Vitality refers to the rate of growth of the seedling plant. Two lots of seed may have the same percentage of germination, but the sprouts of one lot may make a greater

Table 8.3. LONGEVITY OF VEGETABLE AND FLOWER SEED

Dependable for:		
1 or 2 seasons	**2 or 3 seasons**	**3 or 4 seasons**
Onion, sweet corn, celery, parsnip, primrose, lantana, viola, verbena	Asparagus, pea, bean, cabbage, lettuce, spinach, okra, petunia, salvia	Cucurbits, dahlia, dianthus, lupine, carnation, amaranthus

amount of growth during the same period of time. The lot with the more vigorous sprouts is said to have the greater vitality.

At least two methods are available for testing seed: (1) the planting of seed in soil or sand and (2) the germination of seed between folds of blotting paper, cotton flannel, or burlap. Each method has advantages and disadvantages. Modern seed houses conduct their own germination tests, and they record the results for any given lot of seed on the package. In addition, the U.S. Department of Agriculture and many states have laboratories for the testing of seed of horticultural and agronomic crops.

TREATING SEED

The prime object of treating seed is to protect seedling plants from certain parasites. A parasite is an organism which cannot make its own foods and feeds on living tissues. Parasites attacking seed are divided into two groups: (1) those which attack seeds of most crops and (2) those which are specific and attack seed of certain crops only.

Parasites which attack seed of most crops are present in many garden soils. They usually attack the plants in the seedling stage, particularly when they are growing in greenhouses, hotbeds, and cold frames. Because of the high humidity frequently maintained in these structures, these parasites, usually a group of fungi, produce a condition which is characterized by growers as "damping off." Usually the stem of the young seedling is attacked just before or after it appears above the surface of the soil. Many chemicals called protectants, e.g., Captan, Diclone (Phygon), thiram (Arasan), zinc oxide, and Chloronil, have been tested to control this disease. In general, these chemicals are applied in the dust or slurry form; directions for their application are usually printed on the container and should be carefully followed.

Parasites which attack seed of specific crops are fungi and bacteria. As in the case of damping off, scientists have developed methods of controlling these pests. The chemical most frequently used is mercuric chloride, popularly known as corrosive sublimate. The usual concentration is one part of the chemical to 1,000 parts of water (by weight), and the period of soaking varies from 5 to 20 minutes depending on the kind of seed used. The U.S. Department of Agriculture and experiment stations throughout the country and elsewhere have developed tables and charts on the use of chemicals for treating the seed of major local crops.

GERMINATION OF SEED

Germination is essentially a quickening of the growth of the embryo or seedling plant. Before germination begins the young plant is relatively small and dormant. As germination proceeds the growing points of the radicle and plumule divide rather rapidly. Usually, the radicle emerges from the seed coat first, proceeds downward, and develops into the root system; the plumule proceeds upward and develops into the shoot system. The fundamental process concerned is respiration. The stored insoluble foods are changed to soluble foods, and auxinic hormones are made in the endosperm or cotyledons. These soluble foods and hormones are translocated to the rapidly dividing meristems where they are utilized for the making of new cells and for the liberation of kinetic energy. *Germination, therefore, is entirely a food utilization process.*

Processes going on in seed during germination are (1) absorption of water, (2) secretion of enzymes and hormones, (3) hydrolysis of stored foods into soluble forms, and (4) translocation of soluble foods and hormones to the growing points. These processes are either wholly or in part influenced by the following factors: (1) food reserves, (2) hormone supply, (3) water supply, (4) oxygen supply, and (5) temperature level.

Food Reserves. The main function of the reserve food is to nourish the young seedling until it can make its own foods, enzymes, and hormones. Thus, if the reserve food supply is low, the young seedling is likely to become weak and stunted. In extreme cases it may not have sufficient food to provide the energy to push its radicle very far into the soil or its plumule above the surface of the soil. In general, relatively small, shriveled, immature seed is usually low in food reserves. This seed is separated from plump, nonshriveled seed during seed processing.

The Hormone Supply. The main function of the hormones is to give the cell walls the ability to stretch. The stretching of the cells takes place in the region of elongation. The seat of production of the cell-stretching hormones is the endosperm and the cotyledons. Thus, if the endosperm or cotyledons are not developed fully or have been injured during harvesting, processing, or storing, the supply of hormones necessary for cell elongation is likely to be low and growth of the seedling is accordingly retarded.

The Water Supply. Functions of water in germination are (1) to soften the seed coat, (2) to combine with stored foods in the formation of soluble foods, (3) to serve as the transportation medium of soluble foods and hormones to the meristems, and (4) to serve with the hormones in enlarging the new cells. Seeds germinate slowly in comparatively dry soil. In fact, tests have shown that soils should be maintained at or near field capacity for the rapid germination of seed of many crops. Quite often the use of special devices is necessary to facilitate the germination of small seed which, of necessity, must be planted shallowly. For example, celery and lettuce seed are firmed into the surface of finely pulverized, carefully leveled soil, and burlap is spread on the surface to prevent washing of the seed. Recently, glass-wool wick was tested for its ability to supply water for the germination of certain flower crop seed in flats. The plant wick is in sections 5 to 6 inches long, and one end is placed through a hole in the center of the bottom of a flat and flared out like the spokes of a wheel. The flat is filled with a sterilized mixture, one-third consisting of sand, and two-thirds of soil. Seed is planted in rows and watered thoroughly. The flat is then placed on a shallow pan containing water and covered with a pane of glass for one or two days. With this method only one watering is necessary. Excellent results have been secured with delphinium, snapdragon, stock, cineraria, begonia, petunia, and calceolaria.

The Oxygen Supply. Functions of oxygen in germination are (1) to oxidize fats and other reserve compounds in the formation of sugars and other soluble compounds and (2) to oxidize the sugars in the process of respiration. This need of most kinds of seed for oxygen explains why soil should be moist but not wet; why the germination media should be loose and friable; why, in most cases, greater percentages of germination are obtained in sand or sandy loams than in clays; and why certain seeds are planted shallowly.

Temperature Level. In general, temperature markedly influences the rate of many germination processes: absorption of water, translocation of soluble forms and hormones, respiration, and cell division and elongation. Since germination should proceed rapidly in the establishment of new plantings, high temperature levels, usually within the upper half of the optimum range for the growth of any given plant, should be utilized or maintained.

Light. Investigations have shown that light stimulates the germination of seeds of some horticultural crops and reduces the germination of others. For example, the germination of freshly harvested seed of lettuce, celery, and primrose is markedly stimulated by exposure to weak light. On the other hand, the germination of onion, garlic, and chive seed is retarded by light. However, the germination of most kinds of vegetable and flower crop seed is not influenced by light; they germinate equally well in the light or in the dark.

Rest Period of Seed. Although the seed of most vegetable and flower crops germinates immediately after it is harvested, the seed of many fruit and ornamental crops requires a rest or afterripening period before it germinates. In other words, certain physiologic and biochemical changes must take place within the seed before the young plant will grow. These changes may be related to the secretion of enzymes, the production of hormones, the absorption of water, the diffusion of oxygen into the seed, the diffusion of carbon dioxide away from the seed, or some other process. In general, the rest period is broken by storing the seed in moist media at temperatures from 40 to 45°F for a period of one to three months, depending on the kind of seed. The student will note that this temperature range is quite similar to that required for breaking the rest of buds of the deciduous-tree fruits. Plants which have seeds with a rest period are apple, pear, peach, plum, pecan, some of the alpines, and many woody ornamental shrubs.

PLANTING SEED

Seed is planted by hand or by machine. Seed planted in containers (pots, pans, flats) and in greenhouse beds or benches is usually planted by hand. Seed planted in gardens, fields, and orchards is usually planted by machine. Machines which plant seed are called drills. Seed drills may be operated by hand or by tractor. In general, they plant seed at the required depth, at a uniform rate, and firm the soil around the seed. Some drills are equipped to place commercial fertilizer at varying rates on the side of the seed. Note the six-row seed drill in Fig. 8.2.

The depth of planting depends on (1) type of germination and (2)

ig. 8.2. *A tractor-drawn, six-row seed drill in operation. Note the well-prepared ₂edbed and row marker on each side of the machine. (Courtesy, International ₁arvester Co., Chicago, Ill.)*

moisture and oxygen content of the soil. In general, seedlings with coty-ledons which emerge from the soil usually require more shallow planting than seedlings with cotyledons which stay in the soil. For example, the cotyledons of snap bean and lima bean emerge from the soil, and al-though the seed is large, it should be planted shallowly. Note the differences in behavior of the hypocotyl and epicotyl of certain plants in Fig. 8.3.

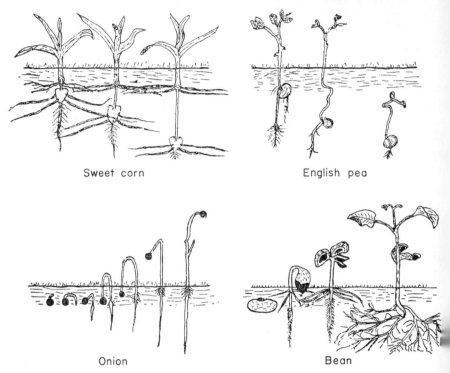

Sweet corn

English pea

Onion

Bean

Fig. 8.3. Relation of type of germination to depth of planting. Top: cotyledons remain in the soil. Bottom: cotyledons "lifted" above the soil.

As previously stated, the water and oxygen supply exists in the pore spaces of the soil. Thus, if the pore spaces on the upper level of soil are nearly saturated, the oxygen supply is likely to be the limiting factor and relatively shallow planting is required. On the other hand, if the pore spaces of the upper level contain low quantities of available water, the water supply is likely to be the limiting factor and relatively deep planting is required. This explains why seeds are usually planted at a greater depth in the summer than in the fall, winter, and early spring.

Time of planting seed in the garden and field depends largely on the temperature requirements of the crop and the temperature of the locality. Since warm-season crops cannot withstand comparatively low temperatures, their seeds are not planted until the soil is sufficiently warm for at least moderately rapid germination. Consequently, the time of planting the seed of these crops is determined largely by the average date of the last killing frost in the spring and the first killing frost in the fall. On the other hand, since many cool-season crops withstand temperatures as low as 20°F, seed of these crops may be planted before the last killing frost in the spring and after the first killing frost in the fall. This is true especially in regions characterized by mild winter temperatures.

PELLETING SEED

Pelleting consists of coating an individual seed with a finely divided clay called montmorillonite. Each pellet is round and uniform in size regardless of the size and shape of the individual seed. On a theoretical basis, pelleting permits uniform planting, eliminates thinning, and presents the possibility of incorporating chemicals (fertilizers, growth regulators, and fungicides) with the clay. However, more research is necessary to eliminate the placing of two or three seeds in a single pellet and to facilitate a more uniform rate of germination. Seeds which have been tested are sugar beet, garden beet, lettuce, cabbage, cauliflower, broccoli, carrot, tomato, and petunia.

QUESTIONS

1. Name the two methods by which new plantings are established.
2. What is a seed?
3. In general, new varieties and strains are developed in the regions where they are to be grown. Explain.
4. In general, most vegetable and flower crop seed are produced in regions favorable for high yields of high-quality seed. Explain.
5. Under what conditions would you recommend the saving of seed from crops grown in the flower or vegetable garden?
6. What are variety trials? What is their purpose?
7. How would you obtain reliable information on adapted strains and varieties of horticultural crops for your location?
8. State the fundamental process concerned in the storage of seed.
9. Seeds while stored gradually decrease in dry weight. Explain.
10. In general, seed stored in the arid West retains its vitality longer than seed stored in the humid East. Explain.
11. Seed stored in a warm room and protected from high moisture of the air is likely to have a longer storage life than seed not so protected. Explain.
12. In the absence of refrigeration how would you store small lots of garden seed in a warm, humid climate? Give reasons.

13. Outline a practical and effective method of storing a small quantity of okra or watermelon seed.
14. What is the primary purpose of testing seed?
15. Growers should always try to obtain a full stand at the first planting. Give two reasons.
16. Why are many kinds of seed treated with certain chemicals called protectants?
17. Germinating seeds quickly decrease in dry weight. Explain.
18. The germination of seed is primarily a food utilization process. Explain.
19. Name four important processes going on in seeds during germination. State the principal environmental factors conditioning these processes.
20. Open, porous, well-drained soils facilitate germination to a greater extent than closed, nonporous, poorly drained soils. Give two reasons.
21. Saturated soils may retard or entirely prevent the germination of most vegetable and flower crop seed. Explain.
22. Seed of cool-season flower and vegetable crops may be planted earlier in the spring than seed of warm-season crops. Explain.
23. In general, firming of the soil immediately after planting the seed facilitates germination. Explain.
24. For any given kind of vegetable and flower crop seed, depth of planting varies with type of germination and with the moisture and oxygen supply of the soil. Explain.
25. Flats or seed pans containing germinating seed should always be set level. Explain.
26. How does the use of glass-wool wick provide water for germination?
27. On a theoretical basis, how does pelleting provide for precision in machine planting?

VEGETATIVE PROPAGATION

A good tree bringeth forth good fruit,
but an evil tree
bringeth forth corrupt fruit.
Matthew 7:17

As stated before, vegetative propagation consists in using vegetative structures—stems, leaves, or roots. These structures contain or develop buds which grow and develop into new individuals. This method of propagation is essential for the raising of many economic crops, e.g., the deciduous fruit crops, evergreen fruit crops, nut fruits, many flowering and ornamental crops, and certain vegetable crops.

Reasons for Vegetative Propagation. The prime reason for vegetative propagation is that *many crops, if propagated by seed, would not resemble the parents which produced the seed.* For example, if seed from a Winesap, Delicious, or Baldwin apple is planted, the trees which would develop from this seed would bear apples quite unlike those of the parent. They would vary greatly in size, shape, color, quality, season of maturity, keeping ability, chemical composition, and other characteristics. On the other hand, if a vegetative bud from a Winesap, Delicious, or Baldwin tree is grafted on the stem of a young apple tree, the tree that would grow from this bud would eventually bear apples exactly like those of the tree from which the bud was taken. The same situation exists with many other fruit crops, with many flowering and ornamental plants, and with certain vegetable crops. Obviously, *a primary advantage of vegetative propagation is that valuable varieties or individuals are perpetuated, which in turn makes possible the production of a standardized high-quality product.*

Other reasons for vegetative propagation are as follows: (1) Certain valuable plants produce little or no seed, e.g., flowering cherry, flowering almond, flowering peach, and gardenia. (2) Other plants produce seed which germinate with difficulty, e.g., holly, some of the viburnums, and rose. (3) Some plants are more resistant to diseases, others are more resistant to nematodes, and others are more vigorous when they are grown on roots of related kinds. For example, certain species of the European grape are resistant to the root louse, certain species of peach are resistant to nematodes, and certain species of the labrusca grape impart vigor to the tops. (4) Some plants are propagated more economically by vegetative means, e.g., strawberry, blueberry, and potato. A discussion of four principal methods of vegetative propagation follows.

CUTTAGE

Cuttage consists in producing new individuals *after* the piece of stem, whole leaf, piece of leaf, or piece of root has been severed from the parent plant. Detached stems with or without leaves are called stem cuttings, and detached roots are called root cuttings. Of these types, stem cuttings are the more widely used. They are classified as follows: (1) cuttings which require leaves and (2) cuttings which do not require leaves at the time they are severed from the parent plant. Since these two types differ in maturity and carbohydrate content of the tissues, they are discussed separately.

CUTTINGS WHICH REQUIRE LEAVES

Cuttings which require leaves are taken from herbaceous plants or from woody plants when the wood is immature. With these cuttings rapid healing of the wounded surface and rapid production of roots are indispensable to the welfare of the cutting. If the cut surface heals slowly or not at all, most of the all-important water within the cutting escapes, and rot-producing organisms are likely to invade the tissues. How does the cutting heal the wounded surface? In general, immediately after the cut is made the intercellular spaces and the cells just beneath the cut become filled with sap. The sugars in the sap change to unsaturated fatty acids, and these in turn combine with oxygen of the air in the formation of a skinlike, varnish-like layer of material called suberin. Suberin possesses the remarkable property of keeping the water within the cutting and resisting the attacks of rot-producing organisms. However, this layer is effective for a short time only, since it is very shallow and nonelastic and cannot adjust itself to changes in water pressure within the cutting due to the intake and outgo of water. For these reasons a more permanent layer is formed. How does the cutting develop this layer? In general, in very young dicotyledonous herbaceous stems the permanent layer develops from the pericycle or cortex. These tissues have the ability to change into meristem and thus produce new cells. On the other hand, in relatively old dicotyledonous herbaceous stems and in immature woody stems, the permanent layer develops from the cambium. In both cases the walls of the new cells are impregnated with suberin, tannin, and other materials and they are corky in nature. Since this layer is being renewed constantly, it is durable; since it is several cells thick, it is deep-seated; and since it is elastic, it withstands the stress and strain due to changes in water absorption and transpiration. How does the cutting develop the root system? In general, the pericycle in young stems and the cambium in the somewhat older stems develop growing points, and these growing points develop into individual roots.

The Factors.   Is there anything that can be done to facilitate the development of the temporary and permanent protective layers and the production of roots with rapidity? Important factors are discussed herewith.

TEMPERATURE.   Since with cuttings which require leaves the problem consists in producing roots from shoots, growth of the tops is retarded and growth of the roots is accelerated. The problem, therefore, is to keep the tops cool and the basal end of the cuttings relatively warm. In general, this is done by maintaining a relatively low air temperature and by applying artificial heat to the medium in which the cuttings are placed. The low air temperature, combined with high humidity of the air, maintains a low rate of transpiration. This low rate of transpiration keeps the guard cells turgid and the stomates open. As a result, carbon dioxide diffuses into the leaves and carbohydrate and hormone manufacture take place. The relatively high temperature at the base of the cuttings promotes rapid oxidation of the fatty acids in the formation of suberin and speeds up the rate of cell division in the formation of the corky layer and the development of the root system.

The application of heat to the basal portion of cuttings is known as "bottom heat." Bottom heat is supplied in various ways: by lead-covered electric resistance wire, by steam in pipes, and by hot water in pipes. Many experiments have shown that high rooting-media temperatures, combined with relatively low air temperatures, facilitate rapid root production. For example, tests at the Ohio Experiment Station have shown that chrysanthemum cuttings kept in sand at 60°F produced a satisfactory root system in 10 days, whereas a comparable lot kept in sand at 50°F required 20 days.

RELATIVE HUMIDITY AND LIGHT INTENSITY. These factors affect both transpiration and photosynthesis. The student will recall that relative humidity and light intensity have opposite effects on the rate of transpiration. In general, high relative humidity promotes low rates of transpiration and high light intensity promotes high rates. Since low rates of transpiration are needed and since light is needed for the making of the carbohydrates and the hormones, the higher the relative humidity, the greater will be the amount of light the leaves can absorb without wilting. For this reason a high relative humidity is maintained.

To provide low rates of transpiration, combined with high rates of photosynthesis, the intermittent-mist system has been developed and is now widely used. In general, the equipment maintains a film of water on the leaves and a high relative humidity of the air. In this way the rate of transpiration is reduced to a minimum. Thus, the guard cells remain turgid, and, with other factors favorable, the manufacture of carbohydrates and hormones proceeds unabated, even in the presence of relatively high light intensity. Although several types of equipment are available for applying the mist, a practical and inexpensive type consists of a time clock and a solenoid valve which controls the intervals of mist flow and pipelines with suitable nozzles that break the water into a very fine mist. In general, the intermittent mist is operated during the daylight period only.

OXYGEN AND MOISTURE SUPPLY. The formation of suberin requires abundant oxygen, and the rapidly dividing meristem requires both abundant oxygen and water. Hence, in the rooting of cuttings media are used which will enable the growing points to obtain abundant oxygen and, at the same time, sufficient moisture for rapid root production. In general, washed, sharp, silica sand, mixtures of sand and peat moss, vermiculite, and mixtures of sand and perlite are satisfactory propagating media for herbaceous and softwood cuttings. These materials are porous, easily drained, and hold sufficient moisture for rapid root development.

Recently, scientists at the New Jersey Experiment Station have developed a method by which cuttings can be rooted without sand, peat, or other solid media. The cuttings were placed in specially constructed cabinets in which the stems were exposed to a very moist atmosphere, close to 100 per cent relative humidity. A water trough in the upper part of a box from which strips of absorbent cloth were suspended supplied the moisture necessary to maintain the high humidity. Herbaceous cuttings of begonia, chrysanthemum, coleus, geranium, perennial phlox, ivy, and philodendron produced roots in less than three weeks; and hardwood cuttings of hydrangea, deutzia, and philadelphus rooted satisfactorily in six, seven, and eight weeks.

THE LEAF AREA.   The healing of the cut surface and the production of roots require a supply of carbohydrates and auxinic hormones. These substances are made in nonwilted leaves. To prevent continuous wilting, the number of leaves, particularly on stem cuttings, is frequently reduced. However, if reduction of the leaf area of any given lot of

Fig. 8.4. Examples of herbaceous cuttings. Left to right: geranium, carnation, coleus, and impatiens. (Redrawn from Maryland Agr. Exp. Sta. Bull. 335, 1932.)

cuttings is necessary, it is reduced only enough to prevent continuous wilting, and a high relative humidity is maintained to keep the leaves turgid.

ACTIVITY OF THE ROOT-PRODUCING TISSUE.   The tissues of both herbaceous and woody plants vary in ability to form growing points. For example, certain herbaceous plants have an active, well-developed pericycle in their stems, and certain woody plants have active cambia. These active tissues form growing points very readily. This may explain, in part at least, why cuttings of some kinds root relatively easily and why cuttings of other kinds root slowly or with difficulty.

Types of Cuttings.   In general, cuttings which require leaves may be divided into three groups: (1) the herbaceous stem cutting, (2) the leaf and leaf-bud cutting, and (3) the softwood cutting.

THE HERBACEOUS STEM CUTTING.   The herbaceous stem cutting usually consists of the terminal portion of stems of herbaceou plants. In general, terminal portions of stems of moderately vigorous plants are preferred. With most kinds considerable reduction of the leaves is necessary, and the cuttings are prepared just before they are to be placed in the rooting medium. Many valuable herbaceous plants are propagated by stem cuttings. Examples are set forth in Table 8.4 and illustrated in Fig. 8.4.

THE LEAF AND LEAF-BUD CUTTING. Leaf and leaf-bud cuttings consist of whole leaves with or without the petiole or of whole leaves with a piece of stem supporting the petiole. In general, they are usually taken from plants which develop thick, fleshy leaves and are prepared and rooted in much the same way as the herbaceous stem cutting. In fact, herbaceous stem cuttings and leaf and leaf-bud cuttings are frequently placed side by side in the propagation house. Examples of plants propagated by leaf or leaf-bud cuttings are shown in Table 8.4.

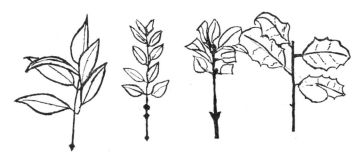

Fig. 8.5. Examples of evergreen cuttings. Left to right: privet, boxwood, euonymus, and holly. (Redrawn from Maryland Agr. Exp. Sta. Bull. 335, 1932.)

THE SOFTWOOD CUTTING. Softwood cuttings are taken from both deciduous and evergreen woody plants. Invariably, the terminal portion of stems is used, and the cuttings are severed from the parent plant when the wood is immature. Since the wood is immature, low quantities of carbohydrates have been stored in the tissues and, as would be expected, leaves are necessary not only for making additional carbohydrates, but also for making auxinic hormones. Thus, as with the herbaceous cutting, the leaves are maintained in the turgid condition.

The time of taking softwood cuttings varies somewhat with the kind of plant. In general, cuttings from deciduous plants are taken before or immediately after the new shoots have ceased to elongate; cuttings from broad-leaved evergreens are usually taken in the late summer; and cuttings from coniferous evergreens are taken in the fall or early winter. Examples of plants propagated by softwood cuttings are presented in Table 8.4 and illustrated in Fig. 8.5.

CUTTINGS WHICH DO NOT REQUIRE LEAVES

Cuttings which do not require leaves are taken from woody plants when the current season's wood is mature. At this time the tissues are well supplied with carbohydrates. In general, there are two types: (1) the deciduous hardwood cutting and (2) the root cutting.

The Hardwood Cutting. Principal factors concerned are (1) activity of the buds and (2) activity of the vascular and wound cambium in the healing of the cut surface and the formation of roots. Buds produce root-forming hormones. These hormones are translocated from the buds to the base of the cutting, where they are needed for cell division and cell elongation. Both the vascular cambium and the wound cambium possess the ability to form new roots. In general, roots which develop at the base of the cut arise from the wound cambium and those which develop from the nodes arise from the vascular cambium. Since both types of cambia are more active at the nodes than at the internodes, the basal cut is made just below the bud. Operations in the handling of this type of cutting are (1) securing the cuttings during the nongrowing season (usually, medium-sized wood from 6 to 10 inches long is used), (2) healing over the cut surface during the winter, (3) planting in the field in the spring, and (4) allowing the cuttings to grow for a season or two before they are transplanted. Figure 8.6 shows hardwood cuttings of four kinds: grape, mock orange, forsythia, and currant.

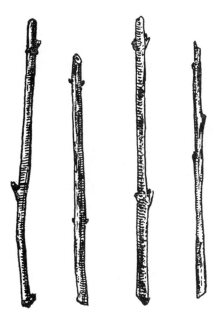

Fig. 8.6. Examples of hardwood cuttings. Left to right: grape, mock orange, forsythia, and currant. (Redrawn from Maryland Agr. Exp. Sta. Bull. 335, 1932.)

The Root Cutting. Root cuttings are pieces of roots. New shoots develop from adventitious buds, and the new roots develop from the old root or from the base of the new individual. In general, root cuttings are made 2 to 6 inches long from roots about the size of an ordinary lead pencil. There are two methods by which the cuttings are handled. The first consists in taking the cuttings in early winter, storing them in sand, and planting them the following spring. The second consists in starting the cuttings in hotbeds or greenhouses in winter and transplanting

Table 8.4.   **KINDS OF CUTTING USED IN PROPAGATING CROPS**

Kind of cutting	Horticultural crops
Herbaceous stem	Coleus, carnation, chrysanthemum, geranium, lantana, tomato
Leaf and leaf bud	Begonia, bryophyllum, gloxinia, Saintpaulia
Softwood	Dogwood, Japanese barberry, lilac, spirea, weigela, azalea, boxwood, holly, privet, arborvitae, Japanese yew, juniper
Hardwood	Currant, fig, grape, gooseberry, philadelphus
Root	Blackberry, bouvardia, wisteria

the young plants to the field the following spring. The cuttings may be planted either horizontally or vertically. If they are planted vertically the end next to the crown of the plant is placed uppermost. Plants which develop "suckers" readily are propagated easily by root cuttings. Table 8.4 lists examples of plants propagated by hardwood and root cuttings.

Chemical Treatments and Rooting of Stem Cuttings

Many investigations have shown that the application of certain chemicals promotes the development of roots of stem cuttings. Of the numerous chemicals which have been tested indoleacetic acid (IAA), indolebutyric acid (IBA), and naphthaleneacetic acid (NAA) have produced the most striking results. These chemicals not only speed up the healing of the wound and the production of roots, but they also induce the development of a large number of roots and are now used widely in the propagation of many plants. These chemicals act like the auxinic hormones. They are effective in very dilute concentration and are usually made up for application as a dust. In this way, these hormone-type chemicals or growth regulators are quickly and easily applied. Generally, the cuttings are placed in groups or small bundles, the basal end of the cuttings is dipped in water and then in the dust, and the cuttings are then ready for placing in the propagation bed.

LAYERAGE

Layerage consists in producing new individuals, usually on stems, *before* they are severed from the parent plant. Two advantages are: (1) The parent plant supplies the new individual with water and food, particularly carbohydrates and proteins, and with hormones, particularly the auxins, until it makes its own food and hormones; and (2) the expensive equipment necessary for cuttage is unnecessary. Two disadvantages are: (1) This form of propagation is usually limited to plants which form growing points readily; and (2) this method does not facilitate the production of a large number of individuals in a relatively short time. In other words, the number of individuals which can be produced from any given parent plant by layerage is relatively few compared with the number which can be produced by cuttage.

Principal factors influencing the production of roots and shoots on layered stems are (1) temperature, (2) moisture and oxygen supply, (3) lack of light, and (4) age of wood. In general, as previously explained, temperature, moisture, and oxygen directly influence the rate of cell division and enlargement, lack of light stimulates the production of

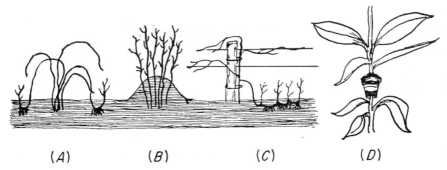

(A)   (B)   (C)   (D)

Fig. 8.7. Types of layerage. A: tip layering. B: mound layering. C: trench layering. D: pot layering. (Adapted from Missouri Agr. Exp. Sta. Circ. 191, 1936.)

roots, and growing points form and develop more readily in young wood. When the new plant has developed an adequate stem and root system, it may be severed from the parent plant.

The main kinds of layerage are (1) tip, (2) simple, (3) trench, (4) mound, and (5) pot, or air. In the discussion of each of these methods, note how adequate moisture and oxygen are provided, how light is excluded, and that young wood is used (see Fig. 8.7).

Tip layering consists in covering the tips of stems with moist soil. During the latter part of the growing season the stems bend and the tips come in contact with, and grow downward in, the soil for a short distance and then bend upward. In due time the meristem at the tips develops roots and shoots, and the following spring the young plants may be severed from the parent stem and planted in a new location. In general, this method is limited to plants which have flexible stems, e.g., black and purple raspberries, trailing blackberries, loganberries, and dewberries.

Simple layering consists in covering a stem just back of the tip with moist soil or other appropriate media. The layered portion of the stem usually is slit or notched, and the top of the stem with its leaves is allowed to remain above the surface of the soil. Slitting or notching of the stem promotes the development of growing points of the root system, and the leaves manufacture food and hormones for the development of the root system. Forsythia, yellow jasmine, and climbing roses may be propagated by this method.

Trench layering consists in placing the basal and middle portions of young stems in a shallow trench and covering these sections 2 to 4 inches deep with moist soil. The terminal portion is left exposed to manufacture foods and hormones for the developing plants. A modification of this method is discontinuous, or serpentine, layering. With this method only the nodes of the basal and middle portions are covered with soil. Muscadine grapes are propagated by these methods. The canes are placed in trenches during the late fall or winter, and shoots develop from the nodes during the following spring or summer. In late fall or early spring the new plants may be removed from the parent stem. With some plants wounding is necessary to induce root formation. For example, rhododendron stems are notched, ringed, or slit. Other plants propagated by this method are rose, spirea, and other deciduous shrubs.

Mound layering consists in cutting back the stems of the plant during the nongrowing season and covering the young stems with a mound of soil. These stems produce roots in the soil and are removed the following fall or spring and set out as separate plants. Currants, gooseberries, quinces, certain ornamental shrubs, and certain root stocks of the apple are propagated by this method.

Air layering consists in surrounding stems of the previous season's growth with peat moss held in place by a split pot, a wooden box, or sheets of plastic film, as for example polyethylene. In general, these films have high permeability to carbon dioxide and oxygen and low permeability to water vapor and they withstand weathering for long periods. Usually, the stem is girdled to facilitate the production of roots just above the girdle. When the roots are well developed, the stem is severed from the parent plant. Air layering is practiced usually with such plants as codiaeum, ficus, litchi, and Persian lime.

QUESTIONS

1. State the prime reason for vegetative propagation. State three other reasons.
2. State the four general methods of vegetative propagation.

3. Name the two different kinds of stem cuttings.
4. State the essential steps in healing of the cut of the herbaceous cutting.
5. Show how relatively high temperatures at the basal end of the cutting, in the presence of high relative humidity, promotes rapid healing of the cut surface of herbaceous and softwood cuttings.
6. Show how relatively high humidity, in the presence of high rooting temperature, promotes rapid healing of the cut surface of herbaceous and softwood cuttings.
7. What is mist propagation? How does mist propagation promote the production of roots of cuttings with leaves?
8. In general, immediately after herbaceous and softwood cuttings are prepared, they should be placed in a humid atmosphere. Explain.
9. Herbaceous and softwood cuttings, while being prepared, should not be placed in the hot sun or in wind. Explain.
10. Investigations have shown that herbaceous cuttings of many flower crops root faster at 70°F than at 60°F. Explain.
11. Given two lots of cuttings. Lot A is placed in dry air (40 per cent humidity). Lot B is placed in moist air (95 per cent humidity). Other factors being equal, which lot is likely to have the greater percentage of survival? Give two reasons.
12. Florists and nurserymen use washed silica sand, peat, and mixtures of sand and peat instead of soil for propagating herbaceous and softwood cuttings. Explain.
13. Leaves are necessary for the production of roots in herbaceous and softwood cuttings. Give two reasons.
14. The leaf area of herbaceous and softwood cuttings should not be reduced if wilting can otherwise be avoided. Explain.
15. Given two lots of softwood cuttings. Lot A has two leaves; lot B has three leaves. With environmental factors favorable, which lot is likely to produce more roots in a given time? Give your reasons.
16. Sweetpotato vine cuttings have a very active pericycle. Under favorable conditions they root easily. Explain.
17. In your opinion, how do the so-called growth regulators promote the rooting of cuttings?
18. In the hardwood cutting, why is the cut made just below a bud? Explain.
19. Crops which produce suckers readily can be propagated by root cuttings. Explain.
20. How does layerage differ from cuttage?
21. Name two advantages and one disadvantage of layerage.
22. Name the four types of layerage.
23. How does girdling a layered stem facilitate root formation?

GRAFTAGE

Graftage involves the union of two separate, usually woody, structures—the union of a root and a stem or, more frequently, the union of two separate stems. In general, the upper part of the union is called the *cion* (scion) and the lower part is called the *stock*.

Reasons for Graftage. Graftage makes possible (1) the changing of the tops of trees, usually from an undesirable variety to a desirable variety; (2) the growing of several kinds of flowers or fruit on one tree or plant; and (3) the utilization of stocks which influence the growth of the cion, which thrive well in poorly drained or heavy soils, or which are resistant to certain pests. For example, certain apple stocks impart a dwarfing effect on the growth of the cion but not on the size of the fruit; certain species of citrus tolerate unfavorable soil conditions; and certain species of peach are resistant to nematodes.

Limitations of Graftage. In general, the principal tissues concerned in graftage are the cambia, particularly the vascular cambium. As previously stated, cambia have the ability to make new cells, and the formation of cells is necessary for the unification, or the growing together, of the cion and stock. Thus, graftage is limited to plants which develop the secondary plant body: the conifers and the dicots. Monocots cannot be grafted very readily. Another limitation is that even within the conifers and the dicots, only structures which are closely related botanically will grow together. In general, the wood of two horticultural varieties within the same botanical species forms successful unions, and in some instances the wood of each of two species within the same genus grows together satisfactorily, e.g., apple and crabapple, pecan and hickory, garden rose and wild rose.

Formation of the Graft Union. How do the cion and the stock grow together? In general, the two structures are prepared in such a way that the vascular cambium of each structure is placed close to or in contact with each other and held together until the two structures grow together. Principal steps in the formation of the union are as follows: (1) The exposed cells of the cambium of each of the two structures produce a mass of parenchyma cells; (2) these parenchyma cells intermingle and interlock with each other; (3) certain cells of this parenchyma tissue become meristematic and form a cambium which connects with that of the cion and that of the stock; and (4) this cambium divides and forms secondary phloem and secondary xylem which in turn connect with the secondary phloem and secondary xylem of the cion and the stock. These tissues which form the union are called callus. Thus, the callus forms a bridge of living tissue between the cion and the stock. In this way, water and essential raw materials pass from the stock to the cion and the manufactured foods and hormones pass from the cion to the stock.

Types of Grafting. Two types are recognized: (1) budding and (2) grafting. Budding consists in uniting a vegetative bud to a seedling tree or to a mature tree. Two important kinds are T-budding and patch budding.

T-budding consists in making an incision in the bark of the stock in the form of a T and inserting the bud under the bark. Raffia, rubber bands, or adhesive tape are used to hold the bud tightly to the stock. T-budding is commonly used in the propagation of apples, peaches, nectarines, apricots, almonds, and plums. In the southeastern United States, the budding of peaches is done in June or early July, and the trees, called "June buds," are ready for sale at the end of the growing

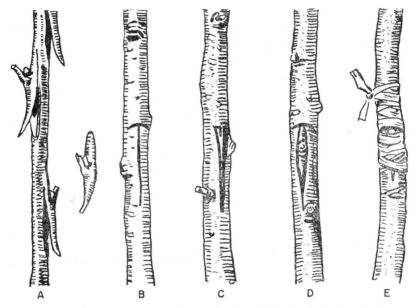

A   B   C   D   E

Fig. 8.8. T-budding. A: bud stick. B: T-cut through bark. C: bark raised to admit bud. D: bud in place. E: bud wrapped with raffia. (Redrawn from U.S. Dept. Agr. Farmers' Bull. 1567, 1932.)

season. In the northern United States the budding is usually done in August or early September. At this time the buds are in the rest period and are inactive. The following spring they develop rapidly, and the trees are ready for sale in the fall. In both cases, the stock consists of young trees raised from seed of the wild peach, the cion consists of a single bud of a current season's growth of the desired variety, and the budding is done in the nursery row. In the preparation of the buds, the leaves are removed by cutting the petiole just below the leaf blade. In this way, the piece of the petiole which remains serves as a handle to facilitate the insertion of the bud beneath the bark of the stock. Note the operations set forth in Fig. 8.8.

Patch budding consists in removing a square or rectangular piece of bark from the stock and replacing it by a similar patch of bark which includes the desirable bud. The wrapping material usually used is waxed cloth or budding tape. Patch budding is commonly used in the propagation of thick-barked trees, such as pecan and walnut. In the budding of the pecan, nuts from seedling trees or standard varieties are planted in rows, the cion buds are inserted in August of the second summer, and the trees are headed back 6 inches above the bud. When the shoot no longer requires the support of the stub, it is removed. Note the steps presented in Fig. 8.9.

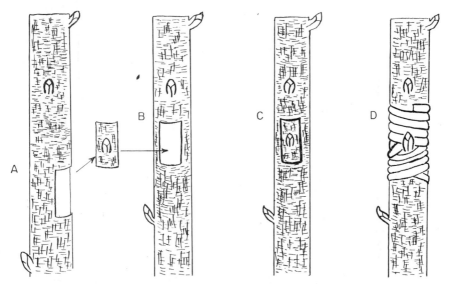

Fig. 8.9. Patch budding. A: cion removed from bud stick. B: patch of bark removed from stock. C: cion from A inserted in B. D: cion wrapped with waxed cloth. (Redrawn from Mississippi Agr. Exp. Sta. Bull. 375, 1943.)

Grafting consists in uniting a piece of twig with two or more vegetative buds to a seedling tree or to a mature tree. The many kinds of grafting are classified according to the relative diameter of stock and cion. On this basis two kinds are recognized: (1) those of which the diameters of the stock and the cion are similar; and (2) those of which the diameter of the stock is greater than that of the cion.

DIAMETERS OF STOCK AND CION SIMILAR. Naturally, the stock consists of relatively young wood and is practically the same age as that of the cion. Principal kinds are (1) tongue, root, or whip grafting; and (2) approach grafting. The tongue, whip, or root graft is used extensively in the propagation of apples and pears. In general, one-year-old seedling trees are dug in the fall and the grafting is done in the winter. Sloping cuts about 1½ inches long are made at the base of the cion and at the top of the stock, and a reverse cut is made on each piece about ⅓ inch from the tip and ½ inch in depth. The two pieces are then fitted together and wrapped. Note the steps set forth in Fig. 8.10.

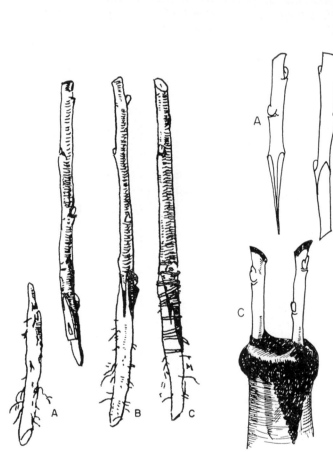

Fig. 8.10. Root, tongue, or whip grafting. A: cion and stock prepared. B: cion and stock fitted together. C: cion and stock wrapped with raffia. (Redrawn from U.S. Dept. Agr. Farmers' Bull. 1567, 1932.)

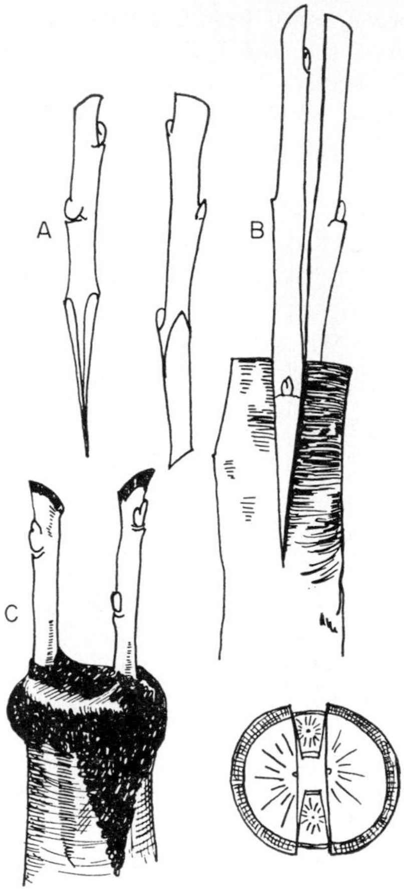

Fig. 8.11. Cleft grafting. A: cions prepared. B: cions inserted in stock. C: cut surface waxed. (Redrawn from U.S. Dept. Agr. Farmers' Bull. 1567, 1932.)

Approach grafting consists in joining the stems of plants growing on their own roots. This method is used in the propagation of coniferous evergreens. The plants used as stocks are potted and placed close to the plants which are to be used as cions. The bark on one side of the stock is sliced away for a distance of 1 or 2 inches. A similar cut is made on the side of the cion. The two wounded surfaces are then pressed together and bound with waxed cloth, waxed strips, or tape to prevent the cut surface from drying out and to hold the cambia close to each other. The stock and cion are allowed to remain undisturbed throughout the growing season, during which time the two plants grow together.

DIAMETER OF STOCK GREATER THAN THAT OF CION. Naturally, the stock is older and has a diameter larger than that of the cion. Common kinds of grafts are (1) cleft, (2) bark, (3) notch, and (4) wedge. Cleft grafting consists in (1) splitting the stock branch down the center, (2) holding the wedge open while the cions are inserted, (3) placing the cion in the cleft in such a way as to ensure contact of the cambia, and (4) waxing over the cut surface. The main advantage of cleft grafting is that it can be done during the dormant season. Its main disadvantage is that wood-decaying organisms may get into the graft. Note the operations illustrated in Fig. 8.11. Bark grafting consists in (1) splitting the bark of the stock, (2) nailing the cion in place, and (3) waxing over the cut surface. Bark grafting can be done only in the spring when the bark begins to slip, and the cion wood must be gathered when dormant and stored until needed. Notch grafting consists in (1) notching the bark of the stock, (2) cutting the cion to fit the notch, (3) nailing the cion in place, and (4) waxing over the cut surface. Notch grafting combines the advantages of cleft and bark grafting, since it can be done over a considerable period of time and the stock is not split. However, notch grafting, when properly done, requires consider-able time. Wedge grafting consists in (1) removing a V-shaped wedge of tissue down the middle of the stock, (2) making a tapering wedge at the base of the cion, and (3) inserting the cion in the wedge of the stock so that the cambia of the stock and cion are in contact with or close to each other. Camellias are frequently propagated by this method.

Bridge Grafting. Bridge grafting is not a method of asexual prop-agation. It is done to save valuable trees. Each year the base of the trunk of many valuable fruit trees is girdled either partly or completely by rodents or by mechanical means. The question arises: How does girdling the trunk of a tree kill the tree? The tissues of the stems of coniferous and dicotyledonous trees may be divided into two parts: the bark and the wood. The bark contains the layer of cork, cork cambium, secondary phloem, and vascular cambium; and the wood contains secondary xylem only. When such a tree is girdled, the second-ary phloem is severed. As a result, the foods, hormones, and vitamins made in the tops are no longer translocated to the roots. Thus, when the carbohydrates and other compounds of the root system, which were present before girdling, are exhausted, the root system dies and the top dies. This explains why a girdled tree may live for one or two or more seasons before death finally takes place. In general, bridge grafting consists in inserting one-year-old cions above and below injured areas of trunks or limbs. The cions usually are collected during the dormant season and are inserted in the tree when the bark begins to slip. Note the operations illustrated in Fig. 8.12. If young suckers are present at the base of the tree, they may be used to bridge over the injured area. This method is sometimes called inarching.

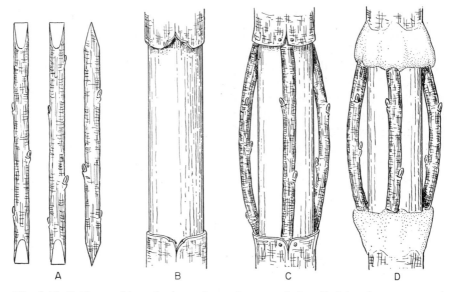

Fig. 8.12. Bridge grafting. A: three views of prepared cion. B: injured area prepared to receive cions. C: cions inserted. D: cions and bark waxed. (Adapted from Calif. Agr. Ext. Circ. 96, 1936, and Mississippi Agr. Exp. Sta. Bull. 375, 1943.)

Closely related to girdling is the effect taking place within a tree which develops a heavy crop of fruit and seed and then dies. For some reason, the growth of the root system has been retarded or entirely prevented. As a result, large quantities of carbohydrates are stored in the stems and an excessively large number of flower buds are layed down. During the following year, these buds develop into flowers and the ovaries of the flowers grow and become ripe and contain mature seed. With the development of the flowers and the growth of the fruit, large quantities of carbohydrates are used, and with the ripening of the fruit and maturation of the seed, large quantities of carbohydrates are stored. As a result, insufficient carbohydrates are available for making the water-retaining colloids in the fall, for respiration and maintainance of the living tissues during the winter, and for growth and development of the stems and leaves and absorbing system the following spring.

Grafting Waxes and Tools. The primary function of waxes is to protect the wounded surfaces from wood-decaying fungi, to retard transpiration from the tissues, and to permit the normal exchange of oxygen and carbon dioxide in respiration. For these reasons, suitable waxes must not crack or melt at ordinary temperatures and must be free from substances toxic to the tissues.

Various kinds of waxes are hot, or hard, wax; hand, or soft, wax; and emulsified asphalt. The ingredients, preparation, and application and the advantages and disadvantages of each type may be obtained from any standard text on plant propagation or from the horticultural department of your local land-grant college or university.

USING STORAGE STRUCTURES

The use of storage structures is limited to plants which develop specialized storage structures or organs. In general these storage structures are bulbs, corms, tubers, rhizomes, and fleshy roots.

Bulbs are produced by monocots and, specifically, by certain members of the lily family. In general, an individual bulb consists of the basal portion of leaves, called scales, which are attached to a small disk-shaped platelike stem. There are two types: (1) tunicate and (2) scaly. Tunicate bulbs have concentrically arranged, thin, membranous outer scales and concentrically arranged, thick, fleshy inner scales, e.g., the bulbs of onion and tulip. On the other hand, nontunicate, or scaly, bulbs are not surrounded by thin membranous scales and the fleshy scales are not concentric but separated from each other. An example is the scalelike bulbs of lily. Easter lilies, tulips, and narcissus are propagated by using young bulbs. In general, small bulbs form around, above, or at the base of the mother bulb. When mature plants are removed from the soil, the young bulbs are separated from the mother plant; and when planted separately, they develop into new individuals (see Fig. 8.13).

Corms are produced by certain monocots also. In general, an individual corm consists of the enlarged base of a stem which is surrounded by dry, scalelike leaves. Like bulbs, roots develop from the lower portion of a corm, but only one stem develops from the upper part. In general, small corms called cormels develop just above the mother corm. These, in turn, are separated from the parent plant and, when planted in a new location, develop into new individuals. Gladiolus and crocus produce corms and are propagated by the planting of cormels.

Tubers are produced by certain dicots. In general, an individual tuber is a short, thick, fleshy underground stem with scalelike leaves subtending nodes, commonly called "eyes," e.g., the tubers of the potato, the Jerusalem artichoke, and caladium. Shoots arise from the nodes and develop into independent plants. In the vegetative propagation of the potato and Jerusalem artichoke large tubers are cut into several pieces. Each piece has one or more nodes and stored food, chiefly starch, for the nourishment of the seedling plant.

Rhizomes are produced by certain monocots and dicots. In general, an individual rhizome is a stem with well-developed nodes and internodes and which grows in a horizontal direction along the surface of the soil or in the soil. Rhizomes may be divided into two groups: (1) short, thick, and fleshy and (2) relatively long, slender, and nonfleshy. Thick, fleshy rhizomes are packed with stored food, particularly at the end of

Fig. 8.13. *Young and old bulbs of lily and tulip. (Redrawn from Calif. Agr. Ext. Circ. 132, 1947, and U.S. Dept. Agr. Circ. 372, 1936.)*

the growing season, and are cut or divided into pieces for the production of new individuals. In general, cutting into pieces, called division, is done usually in the spring or late fall and seldom in the summer. Many herbaceous perennials are propagated by using pieces of rhizomes—lily of the valley, aster, hollyhock, violet, rudbeckia, gaillardia, coreopsis, chrysanthemum, Shasta daisy, campanula, phlox, delphinium, and rhubarb. Slender, nonfleshy rhizomes produce new individuals at the nodes, particularly when the new individual is connected with the parent plant. Certain grasses, e.g., bent grass and Bermuda grass, are propagated through the use of slender rhizomes.

Fleshy roots are produced by certain dicots. In general, an individual fleshy root is short and thick, has the anatomy typical of roots, and, unlike stems, does not have nodes and internodes, e.g., the fleshy roots of sweetpotato and dahlia. With the sweetpotato, adventitious buds arise from the root itself and the buds develop into seedling plants. With the dahlia, a piece of stem containing at least one bud is allowed to remain attached to the fleshy root.

QUESTIONS

1. The cambia are the chief tissues concerned in graftage. Explain.
2. Grafting is limited to coniferous and dicotyledenous plants. Explain.
3. Describe briefly the essential steps in the formation of the callus.
4. In general, the callus serves as a living bridge between the cion and the stock. Explain.
5. State two distinct reasons for graftage.
6. Differentiate between budding and grafting.
7. In general, buds in the middle portion of one-year-old wood make the best unions in budding and grafting. Explain.
8. In the budding of fruit crops the buds are wrapped tightly until they form a union with the stock. Explain.
9. In the South, peach budding is done usually in June; in the North, usually in August. Explain.
10. Why are tongue-grafted trees usually not planted immediately after the graft is made?
11. The cut surface of a cleft graft in tops of trees is usually covered with grafting wax. Give two reasons.
12. How does girdling the base of the trunk of a tree kill the tree?
13. How does bridge grafting save girdled trees?
14. A tree develops an excessively large amount of fruit and then dies. Explain from the standpoint of the carbohydrates.
15. Name two requirements of a satisfactory grafting wax.
16. Give the similarities and differences between a bulb and a corm.
17. What is the main difference between a tuber and a fleshy root?
18. In cutting potatoes for seed each piece should contain at least one eye. Explain.
19. In propagating dahlias each piece of stem with the root should contain at least one bud. Explain.

9

CLIMATES, SITES, AND SOILS

The United States is the land of abundance,
and the land of blessings.

CLIMATES

The continental United States is a big country. The 48 contiguous states are about 3,000 miles wide, from 1,500 to 2,000 miles long, and comprise an area of 3,026,789 square miles. Within this large area there is a wide variation in the environmental factors which influence plant growth and development. In particular, there are marked variations in temperature, intensity and duration of sunshine, direction and intensity of the wind, relative humidity of the atmosphere, and kind, amount, and distribution of rainfall. In fact, the variation in these climatic factors is so wide that different climates exist in the United States. These climates are classified as follows: (1) the cool-humid climate of the Northeast and Great Lakes, (2) the warm-humid climate of the Southeast and Gulf Coast, (3) the subhumid climate of the Great Plains, (4) the arid climate of the intermountain region of Idaho, Utah, Colorado, New Mexico, Arizona, and California, and (5) the summer-dry climate of the Pacific Coast. The student should keep in mind that the climates of adjacent regions gradually merge into each other. Note the boundary of each region in Fig. 9.1.

Climate of the Northeast and Great Lakes Region. This climate is characterized by comparatively cool summers, long, cold winters, moderate rainfall, and moderate light intensity. The frost-free growing season varies from 80 days in the central part of the Upper Peninsula of Michigan to

150 days in Long Island, New York. The annual rainfall varies from 30 to 40 inches, and the photoperiod of the summer is very long and that of the winter is very short. Although summer temperatures sometimes reach a maximum of 90 to 95°F, in general, they are sufficiently cool to permit the successful production of practically all hardy deciduous-tree fruits and practically all cool-season vegetable and flower crops. At the same time, the temperatures are sufficiently high to permit the successful production of certain warm-season vegetable and flower crops. For example,

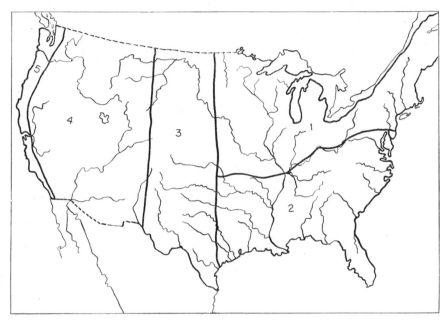

Fig. 9.1. *Climates of the continental United States. 1: cool-humid of Northeast and Great Lakes. 2: warm-humid of Southeast and Gulf Coast. 3: subhumid of Great Plains. 4: arid of intermountain region. 5: summer-dry of the Pacific Coast.*

the summer temperatures provide sufficient heat for the growing of certain varieties of tomatoes and beans; yet at the same time they fail to provide sufficient heat for the growing of sweetpotatoes and late maturing varieties of watermelons. The winter temperatures are relatively low, frequently reaching a minimum of −10°F. These temperatures often damage trees of the deciduous-fruit industries and limit the growing of vegetables and flowers to greenhouses during the winter months.

Climate of the Southeast and Gulf Coast Region. The climate of this region is characterized by long, warm summers; short, mild winters; moderate to heavy rainfall; and high light intensity. The frost-free growing period varies from 180 days in the mountains of North Carolina to 320 days in southern Florida. The annual rainfall varies from 45 to 80 inches, and the photoperiod of the summer is moderately long and that of the winter is moderately short. In this region temperatures are quite variable. In the elevated section of the northern part, summer temperatures are sufficiently cool to permit the successful production of hardy deciduous-tree fruits and cool-season vegetable and flower crops; and in the southern part, they are sufficiently high to permit the successful production of warm-season plants, such as orange, lemon, grapefruit, lime, persimmon, avocado, fig, pecan, sweetpotato, watermelon, okra, camellia, azalea, and gardenia. Winter temperatures vary from a mean minimum of 10°F in the elevated sections to 50°F in southern Florida and the regions bordering the Gulf Coast. In fact, the temperatures of the coastal areas are sufficiently mild to permit the successful production of most cool-season vegetable crops during the fall, winter, and early spring. Most of the winter-garden areas of the United States are located on the South Atlantic and Gulf Coasts.

Climate of the Great Plains Region.   This climate is characterized by wide fluctuation in temperature, low rainfall, and a high light intensity. The frost-free growing season varies from 109 days in central North Dakota to 314 days in south Texas. Although summer temperatures in the northern section are frequently as hot as those in the southern section, winter temperatures in the northern section are particularly severe, frequently reaching a minimum of −30°F, whereas in the Gulf Coast region of Texas they are particularly mild. In general, the average rainfall varies from 15 to 20 inches. Thus, since rainfall does not exceed evaporation, applications of irrigation water to most horticultural crops are necessary. The short frost-free growing period and the severe winter temperature in the northern section decidedly limit the production of warm-season vegetables and flowers and the production of tree fruits, since only the most hardy kinds will survive in this area. On the other hand, the long frost-free growing season and the mild winter temperature of the southern section permit the production of a great variety of horticultural products —strawberries in Oklahoma; tomatoes, sweetpotatoes, and rose stocks in east Texas; onions, spinach, and carrots in the winter-garden region of south Texas; and grapefruit, cabbage, and tomatoes in the Rio Grande Valley.

Climate of the Intermountain Region.   Here the climate is characterized by variable temperatures, low rainfall, and high light intensity. The temperatures of the southern section are relatively high, and the frost-free growing period varies from 250 to 280 days. In the remainder of the region temperatures are relatively low and the frost-free growing period varies from 80 to 180 days. This wide variation in frost-free growing period is due largely to differences in latitude and to the wide variations in elevation throughout the region. The annual rainfall varies from 10 to 20 inches. Because of the low precipitation, all horticultural crops grown in this region, with the exception of dryland beans and peas, are irrigated. Moist winds from the Pacific Ocean are forced up the mountains and usually spill their load on the western slopes. This occurs at each successive range eastward. This precipitation is held as snow and is released later to supply the needs of the various crops. The low relative humidity is unfavorable for the development of foliage diseases; thus, many crops for seed are grown in this region.

Climate of the Pacific Coast Region. The climate of the Pacific Coast is characterized by comparatively cool summer temperatures along the coast between the shore line and the coastal range, by high summer temperatures in the intermountain valleys, and by comparatively mild winter temperatures throughout the region. The average summer rainfall (June, July, and August) varies from 8 inches for the Puget Sound area to practically no rain for southern California, and the average winter rainfall (December, January, and February) varies from 50 inches for the Puget Sound area to 10 inches for southern California. Because of the mild winters, the relatively long frost-free growing period (from 200 days for the Puget Sound area to 320 days for southern California), and the abundant sunshine, a large number of horticultural industries are located in this region. Large quantities of citrus fruits and large quantities of a wide variety of vegetables are raised in southern California; large quantities of vinifera grapes and peaches are raised in central California; and large quantities of apples are raised in Washington, Oregon, and northern California. The practically rainless summers are favorable for a high rate of photosynthesis and for the natural drying of a large number of horticultural products—prunes, grapes (raisins), peaches, apricots, apples, pears, figs, dates, and seed of many vegetable and flowering plants.

Within these climatic regions there are marked differences in the temperature of the growing season. The differences are due primarily to (1) elevation and (2) proximity to large bodies of water.

Influence of Elevation. The altitude of the surface of the land above sea level has marked effects on the temperature. In general, for each 300 feet in elevation there is an average decrease of 1°F. Thus, with an elevation of 4,000 feet a decrease of about 13°F is obtained. These differences in elevation within any particular region are chiefly responsible for differences in the length of the frost-free growing period and the maximum temperatures that occur. For example, at Clemson, South Carolina, the elevation is 774 feet; at Highlands, North Carolina, 50 miles west of Clemson, the elevation is 4,500 feet. These differences in elevation make for marked differences in temperature between the two places. At Clemson the length of the frost-free growing period is 215 days and the summer temperature is sufficiently high to permit the successful production of long-season, warm-temperature crops, such as sweetpotato, but it is disastrous for the growing of cool-season crops, such as cabbage, potato, or garden pea. On the other hand, at Highlands the mean length of the frost-free growing period is 178 days and the summer temperature is favorable for the production of the cool-season crops, such as cabbage and potato, but it is too low for the growing of warm-season crops, such as sweet-potato.

Influence of Large Bodies of Water. Large bodies of water modify the temperatures of any one season. In the summer the water absorbs heat, thus decreasing the air temperature; and in the winter the water gives off heat, thus increasing the air temperature. As a result, the climate of maritime lands is more moderate than the climate of inland sections.

Large bodies of water within and surrounding the continental United States make possible the growing of certain horticultural crops which would not exist otherwise. The modifying influence of the Atlantic Ocean is partially responsible for the existence of the winter-garden areas of the South; the modifying influence of the Great Lakes makes possible the growing of peaches and grapes in southern Michigan and western New York; and the modifying influence of the Pacific Ocean makes possible the growing of garden peas in the Puget Sound district of Washington and the growing of lima beans, lettuce, and other crops in the coastal regions of California.

SITES

Sites include two factors: (1) topography and (2) soil. In horticulture, topography refers to the contour of the land, its elevation or depth, and similar features of the terrain. As previously stated, the soil is the home of the plant's roots and the reservoir for the plant's essential elements and water.

Kinds of Sites. In general, sites are (1) level or slightly sloped and (2) sloped. Factors concerned in the selection of the site are (1) kind of crop enterprise, (2) kind and degree of soil erosion, (3) air drainage, and (4) exposure.

Kind of Crop Enterprise. In general, vegetable crops and herbaceous flowering plants are grown on level and slightly sloped sites. Most vegetable and flower crops require cultivation and pest control, and harvesting operations can be performed more efficiently on level land than on sloped land. On the other hand, deciduous- and evergreen-tree fruits are grown on sloped land. With these crops air drainage requires more consideration than it does for herbaceous crops. Note the contour lines of the young peach orchard in Fig. 9.2 and the straight rows and the level land of the field in Fig. 9.3.

Soil Erosion. In the United States, soil erosion is a serious problem. In fact, many scientists believe that soil erosion is more respon-

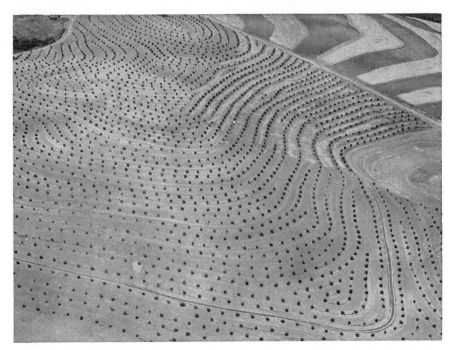

Fig. 9.2. A peach orchard in the Spartanburg-Inman district of South Carolina planted on the contour. (Courtesy, John T. Bregger, Soil Conservation Service, U.S. Department of Agriculture.)

Fig. 9.3. Part of a 640-acre field of celery in 1949, near Belle Glade, Fla. The narrow rows are 24 inches apart, and the wide rows are 48 inches. The wide rows are necessary to accommodate the wheels of the spray rig. In this field the height of the water table is controlled to maintain adequate supplies of water. (Courtesy, J. C. Hoffman, Vegetable Breeding Laboratory, U.S. Department of Agriculture.)

sible for the losses in soil fertility than any other single factor. Clearly, soil erosion should be reduced to a minimum. Two types are considered: (1) erosion by wind and (2) erosion by water.

EROSION BY WIND.   This is severe on all soils in the Great Plains region and moderately severe on mucks and sandy soils in the middle west and northeast regions. Since the carrying power of the wind is a function of its velocity, decreases in velocity will correspondingly decrease the erosive action. In general, this is done by growing cover crops and by using wind breaks. Types of wind breaks are (1) trees; (2) shrubs; (3) fences of boards, slats, or cloth; and (4) strips of grain or forage crops.

EROSION BY WATER.   This is severe in the humid regions, particularly in areas of high rainfall. As with the action of the wind, the carrying capacity of water is a function of its velocity. Thus, a decrease in the rate of water flow will correspondingly decrease the erosive action. In general, this is done by (1) terracing the land, (2) contour planting, (3) strip cropping, and (4) growing cover crops.

Terracing the land consists in following the contours of the land and dividing the area into separate drainage systems. The function of each terrace is to reduce the rate of water flow and to hold the water within each drainage area. This allows the water which has fallen within any given area to gradually soak into the soil. Broad, relatively flat terraces are most commonly used.

Contour planting consists in planting crops with the contour. In this way, the cultivation of a particular row is done on level land rather than up and down or at right angles to the slope. Contour tillage retards erosion by holding water in the small terrace made by the cultivator.

Strip cropping consists in planting cultivated and noncultivated crops alternately in narrow or broad strips with the contour of the land. The noncultivated crops absorbs the water falling on the noncultivated area and the runoff from the adjacent cultivated area. Thus, soil erosion is reduced. The width of each cultivated or noncultivated strip is determined by the steepness of the slope, the rate of percolation of water through the soil, the water-holding capacity of the soil, and the amount and character of the rainfall. Obviously, the steeper the slope, the lesser the rate of percolation and water-holding capacity, and the greater the rainfall, the narrower are the cultivated and noncultivated strips.

Cover crops reduce soil erosion by holding the soil particles and by increasing the rate of percolation and the water-holding capacity of the soil.

Air Drainage.   Air drainage involves the flow of air from areas of high elevation to areas of low elevation. Cold air flows from the high lands— the hills and mountains—into the low lands—the valleys. How does this flow of air take place? During the night radiation takes place, and the earth's surface cools. This in turn cools the layer of air next to the soil, and since cold air is heavier than warm air, the cold air flows downward and the warm air flows upward. This phenomenon is called *temperature inversion,* and when it occurs, the high lands are warmer than the low lands.

For the successful production of the many tree fruits, adequate air drainage is particularly necessary. The cold air must be carried away from the immediate vicinity of the orchard, particularly during the blossoming season. Frequently during the period of flowering, the temperature of the cold air is from 1 to 5°F below the killing temperature of the flowers and buds. At the same time the temperature of the warm air is from 1 to 5°F higher. In many orchards, observations have shown differences of from 15 to 20°F between the top and bottom of moderate slopes, and that variations in temperature much less than these often mean the difference between live and dead trees. In general, the higher the land in relation to adjacent areas and the greater the area of low land which receives the cold air, the greater the freedom of air flow and the freedom from injury. Thus, before orchards are planted, the frost hazard of proposed sites is carefully evaluated.

Exposure. Exposure refers to the direction of the slope. In general, a southern or eastern slope (1) promotes early blooming and early maturity of the crop, (2) offers some protection against north or west winds, and (3) permits early planting of herbaceous crops. On the other hand, a northern slope (1) delays blooming of orchard trees and (2) offers some protection against sunscald in regions of high light intensity.

SOILS

Two important components of soils are (1) decomposed mineral matter and (2) decomposed organic matter. Soils which are derived from and contain large quantities of mineral matter are called mineral soils. Soils which are derived from and contain large quantities of organic matter are called muck or peat soils. Of these, mineral soils have the wider adaptation and distribution.

MINERAL SOILS[1]

Mineral soils consist of mixtures of sand, silt, and clay. Sand particles are relatively large (from 0.15 to 1.0 millimeter in diameter); silt particles are small (from 0.002 to 0.05 millimeter); and clay particles are very small (from 0.0001 to 0.002 millimeter). In fact, mineral soils can be classified according to the proportion of sand, silt, and clay which they

---

[1] This discussion is limited to soils in the humid regions. Since the amount of organic matter in mineral soils varies greatly, some soils naturally fall outside the ranges of organic matter which are presented.

contain. Principal classes are (1) sands, (2) sandy loams, (3) loams, (4) silt loams, and (5) clay loams. In horticultural crop production, each class has advantages and disadvantages.

Sands. In general, sands are coarse-textured, well drained, relatively infertile, and very acid. They contain 80 to 95 per cent sand and 5 to 20 per cent silt and clay, with 0.1 to 1.0 per cent organic matter. The large proportion of sand facilitates rapid drainage, aeration, and rapid decomposition of organic matter. On the other hand, the low proportion of silt and clay and the low content of organic matter provide for relatively small quantities of available water and small quantities of potential nitrate-nitrogen. In addition many sands are deficient in certain essential elements, particularly calcium and magnesium. Thus, the crop-producing capacity of sands is increased largely by reducing acidity, adding deficient elements, and increasing the organic matter. Despite the relatively low fertility of sands, with good management they produce satisfactorily such crops as peach, raspberry, asparagus, sweetpotato, and watermelon.

Sandy Loams. In general, sandy loams are moderately coarse-textured, well drained, moderately fertile, and moderately to slightly acid. They contain 50 to 80 per cent sand and 20 to 50 per cent silt and clay, with 0.1 to 3.0 per cent organic matter. This proportion of sand is sufficient to permit rapid drainage, abundant aeration, and a moderately rapid oxidation of organic matter. At the same time, the proportion of silt and clay and the higher content of organic matter provide for a moderately high water-holding capacity and fairly high quantities of potential nitrate-nitrogen. Despite the somewhat high fertility of sandy loams as compared with sands, the crop-producing capacity is increased in much the same way as that of the sands, by reducing acidity, applying sufficient fertilizers, and maintaining adequate supplies of organic matter. Sandy loams have a much wider adaptation than sands. Most ornamental plants, small fruits, peaches, plums, nuts, market-garden crops near large centers of population, and truck crops grown in the winter-garden areas of the South thrive well on these soils.

Loams. In general, loams are moderately fine-textured, moderately well drained, moderately fertile, and moderately to slightly acid. They contain 30 to 50 per cent sand and 50 to 70 per cent silt and clay, with 1.0 to 4.0 per cent organic matter. As compared with sandy loams their lesser proportion of sand and greater proportion of silt and clay, combined with their greater organic matter content, permit moderately rapid drainage, fairly abundant aeration, a moderately rapid oxidation of organic matter, and a moderately high water-holding capacity and nitrate-nitrogen supply. In general, loams have practically the same crop adaptation as sandy loams.

Silt Loams. In general, silt loams are fine-textured, fairly well drained, fertile, and slightly acid. They contain 20 to 30 per cent sand and 70 to

80 per cent silt and clay, with 1.0 to 4.0 per cent organic matter. This greater proportion of silt and clay permits moderately slow drainage, fair aeration, and a moderately slow oxidation of organic matter. The greater amount of organic matter provides for a high amount of available water and an abundant supply of potential nitrate-nitrogen. In these soils the maintenance of good tilth is more difficult than in loams and sandy loams. In marked contrast to the sands and sandy loams, the crop-producing power of silt loams is increased by improving the drainage and aeration.

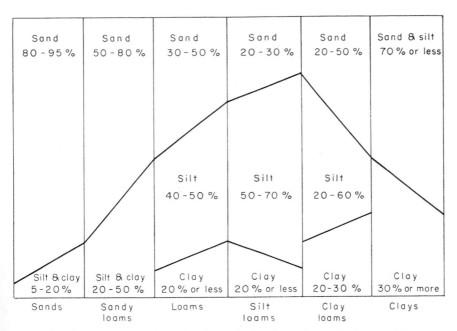

Sand 80-95 %	Sand 50-80 %	Sand 30-50 %	Sand 20-30 %	Sand 20-50 %	Sand & silt 70 % or less
			Silt 40-50 %	Silt 50-70 %	Silt 20-60 %
Silt & clay 5-20%	Silt & clay 20-50 %	Clay 20% or less	Clay 20% or less	Clay 20-30 %	Clay 30% or more
Sands	Sandy loams	Loams	Silt loams	Clay loams	Clays

Fig. 9.4. The proportion of sand, silt, and clay in various soil classes. (Courtesy, Jackson B. Hester, Elkton, Md.)

Clay Loams. In general, clay loams are very fine-textured, poorly drained, fertile, slightly acid, and slightly alkaline. They contain 20 to 50 per cent sand, 20 to 60 per cent silt, and 20 to 30 per cent clay, with 1.0 to 6.0 per cent organic matter. This large proportion of silt and clay markedly decreases aeration and drainage, and the large amount of organic matter provides for a large amount of available water and potential nitrate-nitrogen. As with silt loams, the maintenance of good tilth is difficult, and the crop-producing capacity is increased by drainage and aeration. Figure 9.4 shows the proportion of sand, silt, and clay in each of six soil classes.

Like the other types of soils, silt and clay loams have their place in crop production. In general, they are adapted to crops when large yields are more important than early yields. For example, most tomatoes and sweet corn for the cannery are grown on silt and clay loams. On the other hand, silt and clay loams are not well adapted to crops grown for their fleshy roots or to tree fruits, unless the subsoil is well drained and permits deep and extensive penetration of the root system.

Soil Layers.   A downward section of mineral soils shows distinct layers, or horizons. These layers are called the topsoil, the subsoil, and the substratum. Of these the topsoil is more fertile, more subject to weathering and tillage operations, and, usually, more porous and better aerated. Soil organisms are therefore more abundant in this layer. The lower layers usually have a finer texture and a more compact structure. In some sections the subsoil becomes very compact, forming an impermeable layer called "hardpan" which retards drainage and resists root penetration.

The texture and acidity of the subsoil have an important bearing on the depth and penetration of the root system and the ability of plants to withstand drought. As previously stated, plants with deep root systems can obtain water and essential ions in the lower levels of the soil. In this way, the plants possess the capacity to withstand drought during hot weather, particularly when the transpiration rate is high. Tight, impervious subsoils resist root penetration, and highly acid subsoils are unfavorable for root growth. In many areas subsoils are limed in order to make them more favorable for the growth and deep penetration of the roots.

MUCK OR PEAT SOILS

Muck or peat soils are composed of partially or highly decomposed plant remains which have accumulated through the ages in low, wet places and contain from 20 to 70 per cent organic matter. If the soil has a fine texture and the plant remains are in an advanced state of decomposition, it is called muck. On the other hand, if the vegetable remains are still coarse and fibrous so that they mat together, the soil is called peat. Of these, mucks are more valuable for horticultural crop production. They are classified according to their acidity or lime content. There are three kinds: (1) strongly acid, or low-lime, (2) moderately to slightly acid, or high-lime, and (3) alkaline.

Low-lime Mucks.   In general, low-lime mucks are strongly acid (pH 3.0 to 5.5). Because of this high acidity, comparatively few horticultural crops are adapted to them, e.g., cranberry and blueberry. Cranberries are grown extensively on the muck soils of New Jersey and Wisconsin.

High-lime Mucks.   High-lime mucks are moderately to slightly acid (pH 5.5 to 6.8). In sharp contrast to the low-lime mucks, the acidity of these mucks is within the optimum reaction range for the growth of many horticultural crops, e.g., celery, onion, cabbage, lettuce, and carrot. In fact, most of the commercial crops of onions and celery grown in New York and Michigan are produced on these so-called high-lime mucks.

For any particular crop the management of mucks differs greatly from that of mineral soils. In general, mucks require packing when prepared for planting, maintenance of the water table close to the surface, application of large quantities of potash, and protection from wind erosion. Packing of the soil is necessary to close air spaces in the muck and to facilitate capillary action. The high water table, usually kept within 2 to 4 feet from the surface, is necessary to supply the plants with adequate water, to help prevent injury from summer frost in northern climates, and to reduce wind erosion. Applications of large quantities of potash are necessary, since muck soils are notably deficient in potassium. Mixtures frequently used are 0-8-24, 0-10-20, 2-8-16, 3-9-18, and 3-12-12.

Alkaline Mucks. As the name suggests, alkaline mucks are alkaline in reaction (pH 7.1 to 8.2). Because of this alkalinity, these mucks are generally unadaptable for the growing of horticultural crops. In some instances, slightly alkaline mucks have been made productive by applications of flowers of sulfur.

In general, peat is used for mulching ornamental trees and shrubs, for growing crops in greenhouses, and for shipping herbaceous and ornamental plants.

QUESTIONS

1. From the horticultural standpoint, state briefly the advantages and limitations of each of the climatic regions.
2. Given 1 acre of land in the Northeast and Southeast respectively, with soil of moderate fertility in each region and supplied with optimum water and essential ions. In your opinion, which acre with efficient management should produce the greater quantity of photosynthetic products for any given year? Give reasons.
3. Florida, California, Michigan, and New York are important horticultural states. Explain.
4. How do large bodies of water influence the climate of the immediate vicinity?
5. Many horticultural industries are centralized within definite areas or belts. Explain.
6. A sloped topography is most desirable for tree fruits. Explain.
7. How do sloped sites protect the blossoms of fruit trees (apples, peaches, and tung) from killing temperatures?
8. Open sites for fruit trees are generally more satisfactory than closed sites. Explain.

9. For fruit trees a northern slope may be more desirable in one section of the country and a southern slope more desirable in another. Explain.
10. Level sites are generally used for vegetable and flower crops. Explain.
11. What is the main difference between sand and silt?
12. Soils made up of fine particles, such as silt, hold more available water than soils made up of coarse particles, such as sand. Explain.
13. On which type of soil, a sandy loam or a clay loam, would a plant, either tomato or pepper, come into the reproductive type of growth earlier? Explain.
14. What type of soil is best adapted to vegetables grown for early market? Give reasons.
15. The texture of the subsoil is of particular importance to the grower of tree fruits. Explain.
16. A hardpan near the surface of the soil is likely to limit seriously the development of the root system of fruit trees. Explain.
17. State the composition of muck soils.
18. What properties do muck soils and the heavy loams have in common?
19. What properties do muck soils and the light loams have in common?
20. Onions, lettuce, celery, cabbage, and carrots thrive exceptionally well on slightly acid muck soils. What reasons can you offer to explain the response of these crops?

10

SOIL ORGANIC MATTER

We have received the world as an inheritance.
None of us has a right to damage it—
and everyone has the duty to leave it
in an improved condition.
Adapted from Joseph Joubert

Soil organic matter is derived from dead plant and animal remains and dead soil organisms. Thus, the compounds concerned are those which were part of living tissues: the carbohydrates and related substances, the lipides and related substances, and the proteins. In general, these compounds are either oxidized to their end products or they are changed to humus. Accordingly, organic matter in soils consists of compounds which become completely oxidized and compounds which become humus.

COMPLETELY OXIDIZED COMPOUNDS

In general, compounds which become completely oxidized are the relatively simple forms—the sugars, starches, hemicelluloses and related compounds, and simple proteins. These compounds are decomposed by the heterotropic organisms in soils—most bacteria, all fungi, and all actinomycetes. Like all living things, these organisms must have a source of energy for their vital needs. They obtain this energy from the organic compounds originally made by green plants. This decomposition is biochemical and is illustrated as follows:

Sugars $+ O_2 \longrightarrow CO_2 + H_2O +$ **heat and other forms of kinetic energy**
Simple proteins $+ O_2 \longrightarrow CO_2 + H_2O + NH_3$
$+$ **heat and other forms of kinetic energy**
Complex proteins containing sulfur $+ H_2O + O_2 \longrightarrow CO_2 + H_2O$
$+ NH_3 + H_2S +$ **minerals** $+$ **heat and other forms of kinetic energy**

Note that oxygen is needed for the decomposition of the sugars and simple proteins, that both oxygen and water are needed for the decomposition of the complex proteins, and that carbon dioxide, ammonia, hydrogen sulfide, and certain minerals are the end products. As previously explained, carbon dioxide is an essential raw material, ammonia changes to nitrate-nitrogen, hydrogen sulfide changes to sulfate-sulfur, and the minerals, particularly calcium and magnesium, combine with certain anions in the formation of salts. Thus, compounds which are completely oxidized have at least two important uses in crop production: (1) They provide the heterotropic organisms in soils with a source of energy; and (2) they supply crop plants, either wholly or in part, with essential raw materials.

RATE OF DECOMPOSITION

Important factors influencing the rate of decomposition are (1) soil temperature, (2) soil aeration and moisture, (3) soil reaction, and (4) the initial chemical composition of organic matter.

Soil Temperature.   The effect of temperature on the rate of respiration of heterotropic soil organisms and the consequent rate of decomposition of organic matter follows rather closely the van't Hoff law. This law states that for every increase of 10°C from 0 to 35°C the rate of a process increases two or more times. Thus, the rate of decomposition of organic matter will be at least twice as rapid at 30°C (86°F) as at 20°C (68°F), and twice as rapid at 20°C (68°F) as at 10°C (50°F). How can this effect of temperature be applied to the rate of decomposition of organic matter in the various parts of the United States? Inasmuch as for any particular season higher soil temperatures exist in warm climates than in cool climates, the rate of decomposition will be greater in the southern regions. Numerous investigations have shown this to be the case. Consequently, with other factors comparable, applications of organic matter in warm climates should be more frequent than in cool climates, and in the same climate they should be more frequent in greenhouses than outdoors.

Soil Aeration and Moisture.   The decomposition of organic matter in soils requires free oxygen and water. The oxygen is needed for the respiration of the heterotropic organisms, for the nitrifiers in changing ammonia to nitrate-nitrogen, and for the sulfur bacteria in changing hydrogen sulfide to sulfate-sulfur. Water is needed for cell division of these organisms and for the absorption of essential raw materials, such as nitrate-nitrogen and phosphate-phosphorus. As previously explained, oxygen is a component of the soil air, and this air, together with water, occupies the pore spaces of the soil. Thus, if the pore spaces are full of water, the oxygen supply will be low and the rate of decomposition will be accordingly low. On the other hand, if the pore spaces contain very little available water, the rate of decomposition will be low also. In general, saturated soils have inadequate quantities of oxygen and dry soils have inadequate quantities of water, whereas moist soils have adequate quantities of both oxygen and water.

Soil Reaction.   Soil reaction refers to the degree of acidity. In general, soils may be very acid, moderately acid, slightly acid, or slightly alkaline. As stated in Chapter 7, the degree of acidity of the soil solution markedly influences the growth and activity of many kinds of soil organisms. For example, the heterotropic soil organisms and the chemosynthetic soil organisms, such as the nitrifying bacteria, are more active and abundant in moderately acid and slightly acid soils than they are in strongly acid or slightly alkaline soils. Thus, with other factors favorable, the rate of decomposition is most rapid in moderately acid or slightly acid soils.

The Chemical Composition of Organic Matter.   Green-manuring crops, crop residues, and organic mulches vary greatly in chemical composition. In general, green-manuring crops in the early stages of growth contain relatively large quantities of sugars, starches, and simple proteins—compounds which decompose rapidly; green-manuring crops in the mature stages contain relatively low quantities of sugars and simple proteins and relatively large quantities of cellulose—a compound which decomposes less rapidly; and stubble, raw straw, or sawdust consists largely of lignocellulose and lignin—compounds which decompose slowly. Thus, succulent crops or residues may be expected to decompose more rapidly under favorable conditions than mature green-manuring crops, stubble, raw straw, or sawdust.

NATURE AND VALUE OF HUMUS

Humus is a synthetic compound; that is, it is made by living organisms, e.g., the bacteria in the digestive tract of dairy and beef animals and bacteria in the soil. The individual particles of humus are in the colloidal state, they are relatively stable, and they are closely related chemically to the lignoproteins. Humus is important in connection with cation exchange, phosphate availability, aluminum toxicity, water-holding capacity, and soil aeration.

Cation Exchange.   The humus particles absorb the colloidal clay particles and form a humus-clay colloidal complex. These particles have a large external and internal surface which contains numerous negative charges. As would be expected, these charges attract positively charged ions; and most of these ions are essential for plant growth. Thus, the humus-clay colloids serve as a storehouse for certain essential ions.

The essential ions adsorbed on the surface of the colloids are calcium, magnesium, potassium, ammonium, and possibly others. In fertile soils these essential ions are present in optimal amounts for plant growth, and this situation is shown in simplified form in Fig. 10.1. As plants absorb these essential ions, they exchange them for hydrogen ions. For example for the exchange of 1 calcium ion or 1 magnesium ion, 2 hydrogen ions are needed; and for the exchange of 1 potassium ion or 1 ammonium ion, 1 hydrogen ion is required. Thus, as the plants absorb these essential cations, the surfaces of the colloidal particles contain more and more hydrogen ions. This explains why the removal of crops tends to make soils more acid in humid climates and why these essential ions are supplied in the form of commercial fertilizers.

Plants require energy for the exchange of hydrogen ions and the essential cations on the colloidal surfaces. This energy comes from the sugars which are decomposed in respiration. Thus, photosynthesis and respiration are both needed for the intake of essential ions on colloidal

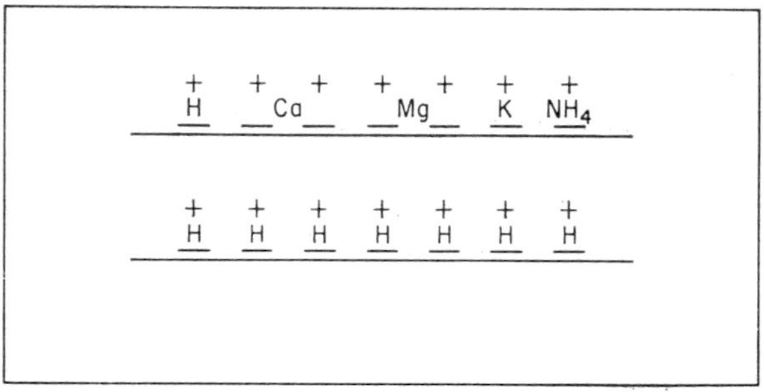

Fig. 10.1. The absorption of essential cations from colloidal surfaces. Note that hydrogen ions are exchanged for these cations.

surfaces. This explains why plants with high rates of photosynthesis and normal rates of respiration have a greater capacity for the absorption of essential ions than plants with low rates of photosynthesis and normal rates of respiration; why plants with dark green or healthy leaves have a greater capacity for the absorption of essential ions than plants with light green or diseased leaves; and why the root systems of most crops require well-drained soils, since carbon dioxide given off by respiration should diffuse rapidly from the roots and oxygen required by respiration should diffuse rapidly to the roots.

Phosphate Availability.   In general, phosphate ions remain in the available form between pH 5.5 and 7.0. In very acid soils, usually less than pH 5.0, compounds containing aluminum and iron become soluble and, as a result, high concentrations of aluminum and iron ions exist in the soil solution. Tests have shown that humus forms humic acids which in turn combine with aluminum and iron ions in the formation of aluminum and iron humate. These substances are relatively stable. In this way, the aluminum and iron ions are taken out of solution and the phosphate ions, which would otherwise form the relatively insoluble aluminum and iron phosphate, remain available to plants. In other words, under the foregoing conditions, humus reduces the amount of phosphate fertilizer that is combined in an unavailable state in the very acid soils, and hence greater quantities are available for the crop. Humus, therefore, is beneficial for crops which for some reason or other require very acid soil.[1]

Aluminum Toxicity. When a relatively large concentration of aluminum ions exists in the soil solution, horticultural plants grow slowly and yield poorly. As stated previously, the concentration of these ions is dependent largely on the degree of acidity of soils. In many soils aluminum ions begin to appear in toxic concentration when the pH is at or slightly below 5.0. Studies at the Virginia Truck Station show that humus reduces the concentration of aluminum ions in very acid soils. For example, Norfolk fine sand at pH 5.0 with 1 per cent organic matter had 875 milligrams of Al_2O_3 per 100 grams of soil, whereas the same soil with 5 per cent organic matter had only 0.2 milligrams. Plants growing in the soil with 1 per cent organic matter failed to grow normally, whereas those growing in the soil with 5 per cent organic matter made satisfactory growth. Evidently, humus is very helpful in reducing or entirely preventing aluminum toxicity. Manifestly, the humus unites with the aluminum ions to form a relatively stable colloid. In this way, toxic concentrations of aluminum ions are taken out of solution and rendered harmless to crop plants.

Water-holding Capacity. Humus particles possess a large surface in proportion to their size. This surface is hydrophilic. Thus, humus possesses the ability to adsorb considerable quantities of water. In fact, tests have shown that humus has four times the water-holding capacity of clay colloids. This explains why soils high in humus have a relatively high water-holding capacity; why the addition of humus, particularly to sandy soils, is likely to increase the water-holding capacity; and why crop plants growing in soils high in humus withstand short periods of drought without the application of irrigation water.

Aeration. Aeration refers to the amount of air in the soil. As stated in Chapter 4, the air and water of a soil occupy the spaces between the soil particles. If a soil is fully saturated, no air is present; hence the quantity of air in the soil is inversely proportional to the water content. The principal gases of soil air are nitrogen, oxygen, and carbon dioxide. In general, this air is comparatively high in carbon dioxide (0.5 to 10.0 per cent) and low in oxygen (5.0 to 19.0 per cent). The oxygen supply must be constantly renewed since root systems and most soil organisms require abundant oxygen for their respiration. Tests have shown that

[1] In the potato belt of eastern Virginia, the soils are kept at pH 5.0 to 5.5 because of the presence of scab—a serious disease.

organic matter increases the pore space of soils, and hence it increases the aeration capacity of soils. Thus, mineral soils high in organic matter are likely to have greater aeration capacity than soils low in organic matter.

THE CARBON:NITROGEN RATIO OF ORGANIC MATTER

When organic matter is incorporated with soil, its ratio of carbon to nitrogen is usually quite wide. As decomposition proceeds, relatively large quantities of carbon dioxide are liberated, and relatively small amounts of ammonium-nitrogen and nitrate-nitrogen are formed. Decomposition continues until the ratio of carbon to nitrogen is rather narrow, on the average of 10 parts of carbon to 1 part of nitrogen. When this ratio has been attained, further decomposition results in parallel rates of carbon and nitrogen. In other words, organic matter in its final state of decomposition has a ratio of 10 parts of carbon to 1 part of nitrogen.[2]

How do green-manuring crops which vary in the proportion of carbon to nitrogen differ in the amount of carbon dioxide given off during their decomposition? Suppose two crops of the same tonnage but with different ratios are turned under. Lot A has a ratio of 80:1, and lot B has a ratio of 20:1. Which lot will give off the greater amount of carbon dioxide? Since the soil organisms will reduce each lot to the same ratio, about 10:1, they will decompose much more carbonaceous material in lot A than in lot B. Hence, lot B will supply more organic matter for the making of humus than lot A, and, in general, organic matter possessing narrow ratios will be more effective in building up the humus content of soils than will material with wide ratios. A classification of organic matter based on the

Table 10.1.   ORGANIC MATTER OF VARIOUS C:N RATIOS

Organic matter low in C, high in N (a very narrow ratio)	Organic matter high in C, high in N (a narrow ratio)	Organic matter high in C, low in N (a wide ratio)	Organic matter very high in C, low in N (a very wide ratio)
Liquid manure (10:1) Legumes in early stages of growth (15:1–20:1)	Legumes in late stages of growth (20:1) Nonlegumes in early stages of growth (20:1)	Rotted straw and rotted leaves (60:1) Nonlegumes in late stages of growth (60:1)	Straw (80:1) Stubble (80:1) Strawy manure (80:1) Leaves (80:1) Sawdust (400:1)

Source: Data from various sources.

[2] Some authorities state 12:1.

C:N ratio is shown in Table 10.1. Note that various types of organic matter possess different C:N ratios and that the same crop has a narrow ratio at the early stages of growth and a wide ratio at the later stages. At which stage of growth of a given crop would the more carbon dioxide be given off?

Soil Organisms and Plant Growth. Soil organisms compete with higher plants for available nitrogen and other essential elements. In fact, plant scientists believe that the needs of soil organisms are met first. This

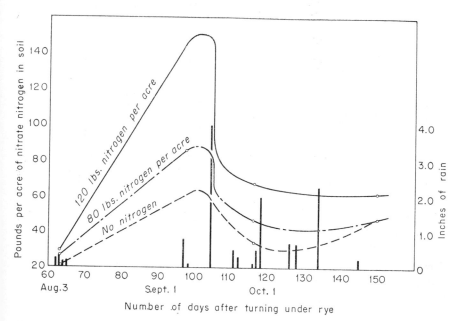

Fig. 10.2. The effect of applying available nitrogen to a green-manuring crop of mature rye on the formation of nitrates. Note the effect of the 4-inch rain on the leaching of nitrates. (Adapted from Fig. 248, Virginia Truck Exp. Sta. Bull. 94, 1937.)

ability of soil organisms to successfully compete with crop plants for available nitrogen may or may not be beneficial. If the plants are making slow growth due to an inadequate available nitrogen supply, the utilization of nitrate-nitrogen by soil organisms would be injurious. On the other hand, if the plants are making unduly vigorous vegetative growth because the available nitrogen supply is in excess, the utilization of the nitrogen by soil organisms would be beneficial. This behavior of soil organisms explains why symptoms of nitrogen deficiency occur on herbaceous crops which have been planted immediately after a mature green-manuring crop has been turned under; why mulching spring-planted herbaceous crops

Fig. 10.3. Effect of organic matter with a wide ratio on the growth of tomato plants. Left: plants growing in clay pots. Right: plants growing in paper pots. The plants are of the same variety and were started at the same time.

with raw straw or undecomposed sawdust is likely to retard vegetative growth and, in extreme cases, produce symptoms of nitrogen deficiency; why applications of sodium nitrate or ammonium nitrate will facilitate decomposition of mature green-manuring crops; and how a mulch of straw slows down vigorous vegetative growth of trees in the orchard or plants in the vineyard in the late summer or fall. Note the effect of applying available nitrogen to a green-manuring crop of mature rye on nitrate formation in Fig. 10.2 and the effect of paper pots on the growth of tomatoes in Fig. 10.3.

QUESTIONS

1. Name the two components of organic matter in mineral soils.
2. Write the equation illustrating the decomposition of proteins containing sulfur.
3. Show how nitrogen and sulfur in organic matter are made available by the activity of soil organisms.
4. In general, organic matter decomposes more rapidly in the southern United States than in the northern United States and more rapidly in greenhouses and hotbeds than outdoors. Explain.
5. If the soil is saturated, the rate of decomposition of organic matter is low. Explain.

6. If the soil is dry, the rate of decomposition of organic matter is low. Explain.
7. The rate of decomposition of organic matter is faster in well-drained soils than in poorly drained soils. Give two reasons.
8. Organic matter decomposes more rapidly in warm, moist soils than in cool, wet soils. Give two reasons.
9. The comparatively high rate of decomposition of organic matter in the southern United States should be considered an asset rather than a liability. Explain.
10. When a farmer says, "The soil has burned itself out," just what does he mean?
11. What is humus?
12. What is meant by cation exchange?
13. In general, plants with high rates of photosynthesis combined with normal rates of respiration have a greater capacity to absorb essential ions on colloidal surfaces than plants with low rates of photosynthesis combined with low rates of respiration. Explain.
14. In general, plants with dark green or healthy leaves have a greater capacity to absorb essential ions on colloidal surfaces than plants with light green or diseased leaves. Explain.
15. In general, plants growing in well-drained soils have a greater capacity to absorb essential ions than those growing in saturated soils. Explain.
16. How does humus increase the water-holding capacity and aeration of soils?
17. A grower wishes to plow under a mature crop of rye or oats in the spring on a well-drained sandy loam and plant a crop immediately afterwards. What would you advise that he do?
18. Just before a mature green-manuring crop is plowed under, growers frequently apply from 100 to 200 pounds of sodium nitrate or ammonium nitrate per acre. Explain.
19. Investigations at the Oklahoma Station have shown that potatoes planted immediately after the plowing under of a mature crop of rye showed symptoms of nitrogen deficiency. Explain.
20. Turnip greens grown on a soil immediately after the plowing under of a green-manuring crop are likely to show symptoms of nitrogen deficiency. Explain.
21. A college professor bought 12 tomato plants growing in cardboard bands for transplanting in his garden. He planted six with the bands and removed the bands from the remainder. The plants set with the bands became stunted and grew poorly, and those set without the bands grew satisfactorily. Explain.

PRODUCTION OF ORGANIC MATTER

Before organic matter is incorporated into the soil, it is produced by green plants. In general, it is incorporated in the soil in two forms: (1) as a crop or (2) as manure.

GROWING OF CROPS

Crops grown for the special purpose of adding organic matter to soils are called soil-improving crops. These crops have two prime functions: (1) to provide a cover for the soil and (2) to add organic matter. In certain horticultural enterprises, for example, in the production of apples or peaches, such a crop may be grown primarily to provide a cover for the soil. In other enterprises, for example, in the growing of potatoes or cabbage, the crop may be grown primarily to add organic matter. Soil-improving crops grown primarily to serve as a soil cover are called cover crops, and those grown primarily to add organic matter are called green-manuring crops. The student should remember that both types of crops provide a cover for the soil and add organic matter. They are called cover crops or green-manuring crops according to the main purpose for which they are grown.

Uses of Soil-improving Crops Other Than Supplying Organic Matter. Uses of soil-improving crops other than supplying organic matter are (1) conserving the supply of essential ions, (2) reducing erosion, (3) checking vegetative growth of crop plants, and (4) retaining snow and water in cold climates.

CONSERVING SUPPLIES OF CERTAIN ESSENTIAL ELEMENTS. The principal ions conserved are nitrate-nitrogen, phosphate, sulfate, calcium, magnesium, and potassium. Nitrate-nitrogen is conserved in the following manner: The crop absorbs the nitrates. In the plant these nitrates are changed to ammonium forms which combine with sugars to form proteins. These proteins are used for making protoplasm and reserve foods. Thus, the nitrogen in the absorbed nitrates becomes part of the plant body. When the soil-improving crop is turned under, decomposition sets in and the proteins are changed to nitrate-nitrogen by soil organisms. The conservation of nitrates is illustrated as follows:

$$NO_3\text{—}N \longrightarrow \underset{\substack{\text{plant body} \\ \text{conservation}}}{\text{protein—N}} \longrightarrow NH_3 \longrightarrow NO_3\text{—}N$$
$$\text{(in soil)} \qquad\qquad\qquad\qquad\quad \text{(in soil)}$$

The amount of nitrate-nitrogen conserved is quite marked. Lysimeter experiments at the West Virginia Station have shown that soils of orchards without a cover crop may lose as much as 100 pounds of nitrate-nitrogen per acre per year and that the same soil with a cover crop may lose only 10 to 20 pounds per acre per year.

Calcium, magnesium, and potassium are conserved when nitrates are conserved. The nitrate ion is negatively charged, is not held by soil colloids, and unites with positively charged minerals. In the soil these minerals are calcium, magnesium, and potassium. For every pound of nitrate-nitrogen leached, 0.7 pound of calcium, or 0.4 pound of magnesium, or 1.3 pounds of potassium, or equivalent parts of all three are also leached.

Phosphates and sulfates are conserved in much the same way as nitrates. The soil-improving crop absorbs phosphorus and sulfur in the form of phosphates and sulfates. In the plant, phosphorus and sulfur are used to make certain proteins. When the crop is turned under, the proteins containing phosphorus and sulfur decompose, and the phosphorus and sulfur are changed to phosphates and sulfates. Here again, the amount absorbed by soil-improving crops is quite marked. Investigations at the Virginia Truck Station have shown that a crop of sorghum yielding over 4 tons of dry matter per acre absorbs about 20 pounds of phosphorus. This is more phosphorus than an acre of potatoes or other horticultural crop requires.

RETARDING EROSION. Soil-improving crops reduce erosion in the following manner: Since the plants are grown close together, their roots ramify practically all the topsoil and a considerable part of the subsoil. In this way the roots serve as a fine, interlacing network which holds the soil together. In other words, they bind the soil. In addition, soil-improving crops reduce the packing effect of heavy rains, check the flow of water, spread it, and filter it from its load of silt. Thus, these soil-improving crops not only increase the fertility of the soil but also hold the soil.

CHECKING VEGETATIVE GROWTH OF CROP PLANTS. Soil-improving crops are used as cover crops in the production of apples, pears, peaches, grapes, pecans, and citrus fruits. When soil-improving crops are planted during the latter part of the growing season, they check the growth of the crop plants. The cover crop absorbs the nitrates, minerals, and water which may otherwise be used by the crop. This reduction in the essential-element supply, or in the water supply, or in both reduces the rate of cell division. This reduction in the rate of cell division correspondingly reduces the rate of carbohydrate utilization and facilitates carbohydrate accumulation. As stated previously, carbohydrate accumulation is necessary for resistance to adverse conditions of the winter and for growth of roots, flowers, leaves, and twigs the following spring. The planting of cover crops to check vegetative growth of trees in orchards and of vines in vineyards is a standard practice in many districts of the country.

RETAINING SNOW IN COLD CLIMATES. In general, a blanket of snow in the orchards or vineyards in the northern part of the United States is distinctly beneficial. The layer of snow keeps the soil comparatively warm, and, in this way, it protects the roots of orchard and vineyard plants from winter injury due to extremely low temperatures. Cover crops vary in their ability to hold snow. For example, in Michigan, amber sorghum and Sudan grass have been found more satisfactory than oats, vetch, rape, soybean, or buckwheat.

Selection of Soil-improving Crops. The selection of a soil-improving crop depends on many factors. Most important are (1) kind of crop (legume or nonlegume), (2) adaptation to soil and climate, and (3) type of horticultural enterprise.

KIND OF CROP. As previously stated, soil humus consists of lignin and a complex protein. Consequently, crop components high in these materials are more satisfactory as soil-improving crops than those comparatively low. In other words, crops which have comparatively narrow N:C ratios are better builders of soil organic matter than crops with comparatively wide ratios. In general, for the same state of maturity, legumes have narrow ratios and nonlegumes have wide ratios. In addition, the growing of legumes is a means by which nitrogen can be supplied to soils and plants.

ADAPTATION TO SOIL AND CLIMATE. Soil-improving crops differ in their acidity and temperature requirements. Some crops thrive in slightly acid soils only; others thrive in both moderately acid and slightly acid soils. Some thrive in warm weather, others in cool weather. A classification based on soil acidity and temperature requirements follows.

Crops Which Thrive on a Wide Range of Acidity (pH 5.0–7.0)

Cool Crops
    Legumes—crimson clover, vetch, Austrian winter pea, Caley pea, and Creole pea
    Nonlegumes—rye, oats, rape, and buckwheat

Warm Crops
    Legumes—cowpea, crotalaria, lupine, soybean, velvet bean, and lespedeza
    Nonlegumes—amber sorghum, Sudan grass, and millet

Crops Which Thrive on a Narrow Range of Acidity (pH 6.5–7.0)

    Legumes—alfalfa, sweet clover, red clover, white clover, Ladino clover

TYPE OF HORTICULTURAL ENTERPRISE. Practically all types of horticultural enterprises use soil-improving crops. For example, many tree fruits, such as apple, pear, peach, and citrus, are produced under the controlled–cover crop system of soil management. This system consists in growing a cover crop for a definite period and keeping its growth under control. With the apple, pear, and peach the cover crop is disked or mowed in the spring and summer and another crop is started the following fall. Disking or mowing the cover crop in the spring and summer eliminates competition for water and essential raw materials. Cover crops used are winter vetch, cowpea, rye, oats, Sudan grass, sorghum, millet, buckwheat, and turnip. With citrus in Florida the cover crop is grown in the summer and clean cultivation is practiced during the winter. During the summer the rainfall is sufficient for the growth of both the trees and the crop, but during the winter the rainfall usually is sufficient only for the growth of the trees. Cover crops used are beggar weed, crotalaria, and velvet bean. Note the cover crop in the peach orchard in Fig. 10.4.

Vegetable crops grown in the northern regions are produced in the summer, and the soil-improving crop is started in the fall. For example, in the market-garden district of Long Island, New York, potatoes, cauliflower, carrots, and other vegetables are planted in the spring and harvested in the fall. Rye or a mixture of rye and vetch is planted immediately after the crop is harvested and is plowed under in the spring. These soil-improving crops are particularly satisfactory in this district, since they grow well in cool weather and are adapted to moderately acid and slightly acid soils. On the other hand, vegetable crops produced in the winter-garden areas in the southern regions are produced in the late fall, winter, and early spring, and the soil-improving crop is grown in the summer. For example, in the Mobile Bay truck-crop district of southern Alabama, potatoes are produced in considerable quantity. The seed pieces are

Fig. 10.4. A cover crop of burr clover in a peach orchard of the Spartanburg-Inman district of South Carolina. (Courtesy, John T. Bregger, Soil Conservation Service, U.S. Department of Agriculture.)

planted in February and the tubers are harvested in May and June. Crotalaria or some other warm-season crop is planted immediately after the potatoes are harvested and allowed to grow until the fall and early winter.

PRODUCTION OF MANURE

There are two types of manure: (1) animal manure and (2) artificial manure.

Animal Manure.   Animal manure, just like organic matter, consists of a heterogeneous mass of organic compounds in various states of decomposition. Some of these compounds decompose quickly; others decompose slowly and finally change to humus. Thus, the application of manure supplies essential ions to soil organisms and crop plants. However, it is extremely low in these ions when compared with the commercial fertilizer mixtures on the market. For example, a ton of horse manure of average composition contains about 10 pounds of nitrogen, 5 pounds of phosphoric acid, and 10 pounds of potash. This has the analysis of 0.5 per cent nitrogen, 0.25 per cent phosphoric acid, and 0.5 per cent potash. Moreover, only about one-half of the nitrogen, one-sixth of the phosphoric acid, and one-half of the potash are immediately available to plants. In addition, animal manure is not a balanced fertilizer since it is low in phosphorus.

Before the advent of the automobile industry, many growers of horticultural crops, particularly market gardeners near large cities, obtained large supplies of manure from the many livery stables. In fact, this manure was the only material used to supply the fertilizer requirements of the crops. However, the development of the fertilizer industry has enabled growers to depend less on manure and more on commercial fertilizers. Many experiments with vegetable crops have shown that applications of moderate amounts of manure (10 to 15 tons per acre), combined with the use of commercial fertilizers (500 to 1,000 pounds per acre), have produced greater yields than the use of heavy applications of manure alone (20 to 40 tons per acre).

Artificial Manure.   Artificial or synthetic manure consists of the decomposition of organic matter under more or less controlled conditions. Various types of organic matter may be used, e.g., straw, hay, cornstalks, weeds, lawn clippings, and leaves. The organic matter is treated layer by layer with commercial fertilizers and lime and may or may not be wetted down by artificial applications of water. As previously stated, organic matter is decomposed by fungi and bacteria. Many factors influence their activity. For the making of manure important factors are (1) nature of the plant material, (2) amount of available nitrogen and other fertilizer materials, (3) moisture supply, and (4) temperature. In general, crop residues high in nitrogen, green material, or warm, moist material will decompose more rapidly than residues low in nitrogen, dry material, or cool, wet material, respectively. Of these factors, the water supply seems to be particularly important. In fact, experiments have indicated that moisture supply seems to be a limiting factor more frequently than temperature. For example, in June of 1933 two lots of straw were prepared for synthetic manure production at the Michigan Experiment Station. One lot, A, was wetted down at frequent intervals throughout the summer, and the other lot, B, was wetted by the rain only. Lot A produced a well-decomposed lot of manure by November of the same year, whereas lot B did not produce a satisfactory manure until July of the following summer. In other words, the annual rainfall of Michigan was sufficient to produce a good grade of synthetic manure in 12 months, but the addition of water produced manure in about 5 months. Thus, regions of comparatively high rainfall should facilitate more rapid decomposition than regions of low rainfall.

USE OF PEAT

The commercial florist is finding the use of peat advantageous in the production of certain greenhouse crops. As sold commercially, peat is a brown, spongy, semigranular material which is dry and easy to handle. It is comparatively free from disease pests and has a high water-holding capacity. Tests at the Ohio State University have shown that soils with peat as a mulch produced larger and better flowers of most greenhouse flower crops than soils without peat as a mulch. When peat was applied with suitable amounts of manure, 1 part to 20 by volume, it served as a very suitable material for the growing of flower crops in the greenhouse.

QUESTIONS

1. Soil-improving crops have many uses other than that of supplying organic matter. Explain.
2. Show how cover crops conserve the essential-element supply.
3. On the basis of the West Virginia results, growers of apples could well afford to raise cover crops in their orchards. Explain.
4. How do cover crops reduce soil erosion?
5. Show how cover crops planted in the orchard in the late summer and fall promote "conditioning" of the trees against the low temperatures of the winter.
6. Cool-season cover crops which thrive on a wide range of acidity are well adapted for use in the apple orchard. Explain.
7. Rye is a popular cover crop among market gardeners in the northern

United States, whereas soybeans, cowpeas, and crotalaria are popular among truck growers in the southern United States. Explain.

8. Could weeds be used as a cover crop? Give your reasons.
9. In the southern regions a crop should be growing on a given area of land at all times. Explain.
10. In your opinion, which is more important: the accumulation of organic matter in soils or its efficient utilization? Explain.
11. How does the decomposition of organic matter compare with the burning of leaves?
12. Many home owners and tenants, particularly in urban areas, burn leaves in the fall. In your opinion, is this a good or a bad practice? Explain.
13. The rate of synthetic manure production is dependent largely on the rainfall. Explain.
14. Explain how to make leaf mold. Give all the necessary instructions.
15. A farmer has a large amount of straw at his disposal. Show how he may use this straw for synthetic manure production.
16. The organisms that decompose organic matter are extremely beneficial. Explain.

11

USE OF COMMERCIAL FERTILIZERS

There is a way to do it better. Find it.
Thomas A. Edison

As explained in Chapter 7, the green plant is a biochemical factory. Certain raw materials are needed in the manufacture of the foods, fibers, enzymes, hormones, and vitamins. Many of these raw materials are deficient in soils, and they are usually supplied in the form of commercial fertilizers.

Commercial fertilizers are frequently called plant foods. In reality, they are not plant foods. *Plant foods are organic substances which supply plants with a source of energy and with compounds for making and maintaining living tissues.* As previously explained, these compounds are sugars, starch, hemicellulose, fats, and stored proteins, and the energy is liberated by the process of respiration. Since commercial fertilizers cannot supply plants with energy, they should not be called plant foods. Actually, commercial fertilizers are raw materials which contain one or more essential elements for the making of the all-important foods and fibers and other manufactured compounds.

MIXED FERTILIZERS

Most commercial fertilizers which are used in the United States and elsewhere are mixed fertilizers. As the name suggests, mixed fertilizers are mixtures of chemical compounds. In general, they contain relatively large amounts of the carriers of nitrogen, phosphorus, and potassium and relatively small amounts of the carriers of magnesium, manganese, copper,

197

zinc, and boron, depending on whether any one or a combination of these elements is deficient for any given crop in any given locality. In the United States, nitrogen, phosphorus, and potassium are deficient in most soils; and magnesium, manganese, copper, zinc, and boron are deficient in soils in certain areas. For example, magnesium is deficient in certain soils of the Atlantic Coastal Plain; manganese is deficient in certain soils in Rhode Island, Florida, and Virginia; boron is required in many soils east of the Mississippi River; zinc is necessary for certain crops in Florida and California; and copper is required for certain crops growing on muck soils in Florida, Indiana, Michigan, and New York.

MIXED-FERTILIZER TERMINOLOGY

Three terms—formula, analysis, and ratio—are used in connection with the preparation, selection, purchase, and application of mixed fertilizers. Each term has a distinct meaning.

Fertilizer formula is a statement of what materials make up the fertilizer. Is the nitrogen supplied in the form of sodium nitrate, in the form of ammonium sulfate, or as a mixture of sodium nitrate, ammonium sulfate, and cottonseed meal, or some other nitrogen carrier? Is the phosphorus derived from 16, 20, or 40 per cent superphosphate? Is the potassium derived from potassium chloride, from potassium sulfate, or from a mixture of the two? A knowledge of the formula is useful from the point of view of the availability of the nitrogen carriers and the acid- or nonacid-forming properties of the mixture.

Certain nitrogen carriers are available immediately after they are applied; others become available a short time after they are applied; and others become available gradually. Sodium nitrate, calcium nitrate, and ammonium sulfate are available immediately; anhydrous ammonia, urea, and cyanamid become available in a short time; and tankage, fish scrap, and cottonseed meal become available gradually. As explained in Chapter 7, the rate of decomposition of the gradually available materials depends largely on the activity of soil organisms. In some states the amounts of water-soluble nitrogen, water-insoluble nitrogen, and insoluble nitrogen which can become available are shown on the fertilizer bag or tag.

Nitrogen carriers of various degrees of availability have their place in the growing of economic crops. In general, readily available forms are applied when the immediate absorption of large quantities of nitrate-nitrogen is necessary, and slowly available forms are applied when a continuous supply of relatively small quantities of nitrate-nitrogen is necessary. For example, fruit growers apply readily available nitrogen just before the trees blossom. At this time the trees begin to develop their twigs and absorbing roots; hence, abundant quantities of available nitrogen must be present to make the cells which constitute the twigs and roots. Without an abundant supply many growing points, many young fruits, vegetative buds, and root initials would fail to develop. On the other hand, vegetable and flower growers apply nitrogen in both readily available forms and in slowly available forms. The readily available forms are usually applied to seedling flower and vegetable crops when the weather is cold and wet and when the plants are producing large quantities of flowers and fruit. At these times, the natural supply of available nitrogen is likely to be below the requirements for satisfactory growth of the crop.

As previously explained, certain carriers make soils more acid, others make soils less acid, and others have little effect on soil acidity. For example, sodium nitrate, calcium nitrate, superphosphate, bone meal, and basic slag make soils less acid; and ammonium sulfate, leuna saltpeter, and acidulated fish scrap make soils more acid. In general, the carriers of nitrogen, phosphorus, and potassium used, at present, in the preparation of mixed fertilizers tend in the aggregate to make soils more acid. In some states, dolomitic limestone is added in sufficient quantity to neutralize the acidity. Such mixtures are called neutral, or nonacid forming.

Fertilizer analysis is a statement of the percentage of nitrogen, phosphoric acid, and potash in the mixture, e.g., 7-7-5, 5-10-5, and 15-30-15. The first figure denotes the percentage of *total nitrogen* (N); the second, the percentage of *available phosphoric acid* (P_2O_5); and the third, the percentage of *water-soluble potash* (K_2O). The analysis is usually printed on the fertilizer bag or on the authorized tag.

Fertilizer ratio indicates the proportion of nitrogen, phosphorus, and potassium in the mixture, or the analysis reduced to its lowest common denominator. For example, a 4-8-4 mixture has a 1-2-1 ratio, and a 4-16-4 mixture has a 1-4-1 ratio. Certain analyses used in the United States and their ratios are presented in Table 11.1.

Low Analysis versus High Analysis. As shown in Table 11.1 materials with the same ratio vary in percentage or concentration of nitrogen, available phosphoric acid, and water-soluble potash. For example, 1,000

Table 11.1.   COMMERCIAL FERTILIZER ANALYSES
         AND CORRESPONDING RATIOS

	Mineral soils				Muck soils		
Analyses	7-7-7	4-8-4	4-12-4	4-16-4	0-12-24	2-8-16	3-12-15
	8-8-8	5-10-5	5-15-5	5-20-5			
	10-10-10	6-12-6	6-18-6				
	14-14-14	8-16-8					
Ratio	1-1-1	1-2-1	1-3-1	1-4-1	0-1-2	0-4-8	1-4-5

pounds of a 7-7-7 mixture contains 70 pounds of nitrogen, phosphoric acid, and potash, respectively; and a 14-14-14 mixture contains 140 pounds of each of these substances. Thus, a given quantity of a low-analysis mixture contains less essential raw materials than the same quantity of a high-analysis mixture. This explains why high-analysis mixtures cost less per pound of essential raw materials, why they are required in relatively smaller amounts to supply a given quantity of these materials, and why they have a lower overhead with respect to cost of shipping, storing, and handling.

The Analysis versus the Ratio.   In general, recommendations are made in terms of the analysis or the ratio. An advantage in making recommendations in terms of the ratio is that different analyses of the same ratio may be used to supply the same quantity of nitrogen, phosphoric acid, and potash. For example, 4-8-4, 5-10-5, and 15-30-15 are mixtures with the same ratio. To supply 80 pounds of nitrogen, 160 pounds of phosphoric acid, and 80 pounds of potash, 2,000 pounds of a 4-8-4, or 1,600 pounds of a 5-10-5, or 533 pounds of a 15-30-15 will be required. Thus, for any particular ratio the grower may select moderately high- or high-analysis mixtures.

THE PRINCIPLES OF COMMERCIAL FERTILIZER PRACTICE

In the principles of commercial fertilizer practice three important questions are considered: (1) What commercial fertilizer should be selected? (2) When should the commercial fertilizer be applied? (3) How should the commercial fertilizer be applied?

What Commercial Fertilizer Should Be Selected?

The selection of a suitable fertilizer depends largely on (1) the essential-element level of the soil with respect to the contents of the fertilizer, (2) the essential-element requirements of the crop, and (3) the season of the year.

Essential-element Level of the Soil.   The many types of soil in the United States and other parts of the world vary in the relative amount of compounds which supply the essential raw materials. Thus, for the same crop grown under practically the same temperature level, under favorable supplies of water and light, the soils may require different mixtures. For example, the well-drained sandy loams given over to potato production in the Atlantic Coastal Plain are relatively high in nitrogen in proportion to phosphorus and potassium, and in general they require 1-1-1 or 1-1½-1 mixtures; 5-8-7 mixtures are used in Aroostook County, Maine, and 6-6-5 and 5-7-5 mixtures are used in the Tidewater district of Virginia and the truck-crop district near Charleston, South Carolina. On the other hand, the well-drained sandy loams given over to potato production in the Middle West are relatively low in nitrogen and potassium in proportion to phosphorus, and in general they require 1-3-1, 1-4-1, or 1-4-2 mixtures; 4-12-4, 4-16-8, or 4-16-4 mixtures are used in New York, Michigan, Pennsylvania, and Ohio, and 4-8-4 mixtures are used in southern Mississippi and Louisiana. As a second example, the well-drained sandy loams given over to the production of celery in New York and adjacent states are relatively high in potassium, and they require 1-3-1 or 1-4-1 mixtures; whereas muck soils for the same crop in the same area are very low in potassium, and they require 2-8-16, 2-8-24, or similar mixtures.

The Essential-element Requirements of the Crop. Different crops grown on the same soil also differ in fertilizer requirements. As previously explained, vegetable crops grown for their leaves, such as spinach and turnip greens, require relatively large quantities of nitrogen in the fertilizer; whereas crops grown for their fleshy roots, such as sweetpotatoes, require relatively small quantities. For example, tests on well-drained sandy loams in central Georgia have shown that turnip greens require 80 to 100 pounds of nitrogen, about 80 pounds of P_2O_5, and about 40 pounds of K_2O per acre; whereas sweetpotatoes require 30 to 40 pounds of nitrogen and the same quantities of P_2O_5 and K_2O in the mixture.

The Season of the Year. Principal factors concerned are temperature and light. As explained previously, with other factors favorable, the temperature of the soil markedly influences the amount of available nitrogen. In general, if the soil has been cold for a considerable period, the natural nitrate-nitrogen supply is likely to be low and artificial applications are necessary. On the other hand, if the soil has been warm for a considerable period, with other factors favorable, the natural nitrate-nitrogen supply is likely to be high. For example, tests at the Louisiana Experiment Station have shown that snap beans started in April on Lintonia silt loam generally require about 35 pounds of nitrogen in the mixed fertilizer, whereas the same crop growing on the same soil but started in August generally requires no nitrogen in the fertilizer. Evidently, the relative activity of soil microorganisms is responsible for the different amounts of available nitrogen.

The light supply is of concern in the growing of crops in greenhouses and similar structures. Fall crops in forcing structures are usually started under more favorable light conditions than spring crops. The longer light period and higher light intensity of the early fall promote high rates of photosynthesis, and this, combined with normal rates of respiration, provides relatively large quantities of carbohydrates for growth and development. Thus, with moderate quantities of available nitrogen not all the carbohydrates are used for the vegetative phase; some are allowed to accumulate for the initiation of the flower buds and the development of the flowers, fruit, and seed. If the same quantities of available nitrogen were supplied in early spring, practically all the carbohydrates would be utilized in vegetative growth and none would be left for reproductive growth. This explains, partially at least, why tomatoes started in greenhouses in early spring in regions of low light intensity frequently develop relatively few fruits of the first cluster. The low carbohydrate supply and the high available nitrogen supply combine to promote excessive vegetative growth. As a result, very few carbohydrates are available for the setting of the fruit.

When Should the Commercial Fertilizer Be Applied?

The time any given commercial fertilizer is applied depends largely on the time available nitrogen is needed and the supply of available nitrogen in the soil. There are at least two reasons for this: (1) the behavior of nitrate, phosphate, and potassium ions in the soil and (2) the marked and direct effect of available nitrogen on the development of the vegetative phase and the indirect effect on the development of the reproductive phase.

As previously stated, nitrate ions leach readily, whereas phosphorus and potassium ions do not leach readily. Further, relatively large quantities of available nitrogen are needed for the development of the vegetative phase. Thus, commercial fertilizers containing available nitrogen are usually applied just before the nitrogen is needed.

For example, in tests on the fertilization of turnip greens in Arkansas, applications at two different periods were compared: (1) just before the seeds were planted and (2) after the stand of plants was established. In all cases the commercial fertilizer applied just before the seed was planted produced the higher yield. Apparently, natural supplies of available nitrate-nitrogen were insufficient for the rapid growth of the seedling plants. This explains why commercial fertilizers are applied to woody plants when they are starting growth in the spring; why they are applied to vegetable and flower crops a few days before or at the same time the seeds are planted; why additional nitrogen is added to crops in the vegetative phase after a series of heavy rains; and why crops grown for their fruits, especially those which contain large quantities of seed, such as tomatoes, require large quantities of nitrogen during the period of fruit growth.

How Should the Commercial Fertilizer Be Applied?

Any given commercial fertilizer may be applied in various ways. Principal methods are (1) broadcast, (2) row, (3) side placement, (4) perforated, and (5) liquid.

The broadcast method consists in applying the fertilizer evenly over the entire surface of the soil. It is usually done after the land is plowed and just before it is harrowed, since harrowing mixes the fertilizer with the upper 3 or 4 inches of soil. In general, this method is used to apply the essential raw materials to crops which are grown close together, such as the small grains and cover crops, and to crops which are grown in narrow rows, such as spinach, carrot, lettuce, onion, lily, and gladiolus.

The row method consists in applying the fertilizers at the bottom of the furrow a week or 10 days before the seed or plants are planted. The fertilizers are either mixed or not mixed with the soil and usually the land is ridged. This places the fertilizer directly below the plants. At present this method is used to supply the essential elements to many vegetable and flower crops grown in the southern United States. A disadvantage of this method is that the roots of plants are likely to become injured by the fertilizer salts. This is particularly true on sands and sandy loams.

The side-placement method consists in applying the fertilizer in a continuous band on one or both sides of the row of seed or plants. Investigations at the Virginia Truck Experiment Station have shown that placing the fertilizer on the side and slightly below the level of the seed of many vegetable crops produces greater yields than placing the fertilizer below the seed. There are definite reasons for the greater yields. The fertilizer is placed a short distance from the seed or plants, and relatively large quantities of essential raw materials are available during the early stages of growth. In this way losses due to leaching are reduced to a minimum in all soils, and relatively small quantities of the available forms of phosphorus are changed to the relatively unavailable forms in soils which fix large quantities of phosphorus. When small quantities of fertilizer are used, the side-placement method is particularly advantageous. Figure 11.1 shows the side placement of commercial fertilizers to tomatoes grown for the cannery in New Jersey.

The perforated method is used to apply commercial fertilizers to ornamental trees. In general, the method consists in making small holes about 12 to 18 inches deep around the base of the tree and at the same time placing a definite amount of fertilizer in each hole. In this way, the fertilizer is placed close to the roots of the tree, and it does not influence the growth of grasses or other plants under the tree.

The liquid method consists in applying soluble fertilizers in solution with water. Three rather distinct methods are used: (1) direct to the soil, (2) as a foliage spray, and (3) with irrigation water.

Direct to Soils. In general, liquid fertilizers applied directly to soils are used to supply relatively large quantities of essential raw materials close to the plants' roots or to supply a relatively cheap source of nitrogen. Examples are the so-called starter solutions and anhydrous ammonia.

*Fig. 11.1. The side dressing of tomatoes grown for the cannery in New Jersey.
(Courtesy, Jackson B. Hester, Elkton, Md.)*

Starter solutions frequently used in the transplanting of herbaceous crops
are sodium nitrate, ammonium phosphate, monopotassium phosphate,
and potassium chloride. Tests by the New York (Geneva), Florida, New
Jersey, and other experiment stations have shown that starter solutions
markedly increase the recovery rate of seedling plants of many vegetable
crops. The solution promotes rapid recovery and early growth by providing the plants with an adequate supply of readily available essential
ions and by stimulating the rate of root regeneration.

The anhydrous ammonia enters the soil as a gas. The ammonia is
adsorbed by soil colloids, and under warm, moist conditions it changes
rapidly to nitrate-nitrogen. Many experiments have shown that anhydrous
ammonia is a profitable source of nitrogen, and at present large quantities
are used to supply the nitrogen needs of many crops.

As a Foliage Spray. In general, foliage sprays are used (1) to correct
a deficiency of some essential element in a relatively short time and (2)
to supply essential raw materials which, if applied to soils, would for
some reason or other become unavailable to the plants. For example,
sprays containing magnesium sulfate have corrected magnesium deficiency
of apple trees in England and cantaloupe plants in Maryland; sprays
containing certain iron chelates have corrected iron deficiency of citrus
trees in central Florida; and sprays containing borax have corrected
boron deficiency of rutabagas in southern Ontario.

With Irrigation Water. As previously stated, the essential ions fixed by soils are applied most advantageously at the time of soil preparation. This particularly applies to the phosphate and potassium ions. On the other hand, ions which are subject to leaching may be deficient at the time plants need them. In general, these are compounds which dissolve readily in water and which contain the nitrate ion or which change to nitrate in a short time, e.g., sodium nitrate, ammonium nitrate, ammonium sulfate, and urea. Note that the first two compounds contain the nitrate ion, and the last two change into nitrate rapidly in warm, moist soils. Since the nitrate ion leaches readily, the irrigation water containing the readily available nitrogen carriers should never penetrate beyond the zone occupied by the root system. Otherwise, large quantities of the expensive nitrogen carriers are likely to be wasted. Two general methods are used in applying commercial fertilizers with irrigation water. The first consists in placing the fertilizer in solution with water before it is pumped through the irrigation system, and the other consists in forcing a concentrated solution of the fertilizer into the irrigation lines at the time the water is being pumped.

CHEMICAL QUICK TESTS

Chemical quick tests have been developed to determine the essential-element requirements of economic plants. They are of two types: (1) soil and (2) plant.

Soil tests consist of a quick chemical analysis of essential elements in a small sample of soil solution. The soil sample is extracted with a weak acid or with the salt of a weak acid. Aliquots of the extracted solution are treated with chemical reagents. Diphenylamine is used to test for nitrates; ammonium molybdate is used for phosphorus; and sodium cobaltinitrite is used for potassium. The object of the soil tests is to determine the degree of fertility of the soil. If the soil is well supplied with essential raw materials, it gives a good test; if it is moderately supplied, it gives a fair test; and if it is poorly supplied, it gives a poor test. Investigations at the Virginia Truck Experiment Station have shown that the soil tests for phosphorus and potassium agree fairly well with responses and yield of many vegetable crops grown in the area.

Plant tissue tests consist of a quick chemical analysis of a small portion of a few plants. In general, a portion of the stems or petioles is used. The sample is extracted with a weak acid, and the essential raw materials in the extract are determined with the same reagents and in practically the same manner as those in soil extracts. The plant tissue tests show the essential elements which are lacking or unavailable in soil and those which are sufficient for abundant yields. Experiments show that the soil and plant tissue tests have a useful function, provided representative samples of the soil and plant are used and the tests are done by persons who have a working knowledge of the characteristics of the soil and the needs of the crop under consideration.

In general, most states maintain one or more soil or plant tissue testing laboratories. What type of tests, soil or plant or both, are used to determine the commercial fertilizer needs of the crops grown in your community?

QUESTIONS

1. What are commercial fertilizers?
2. In a strict sense commercial fertilizers are not plant foods. Explain.
3. The foods of plants and of animals are the same substances. Explain.
4. What is a complete, or mixed, commercial fertilizer?
5. Differentiate between fertilizer formula, fertilizer analysis, and fertilizer ratio.
6. Give two reasons why growers should have a working knowledge of the fertilizer formula.
7. In general, readily available forms of nitrogen are required for a rapid development of the vegetative phase and slowly available forms are required for a moderately rapid development of this phase, particularly when the soils are warm and moist. Explain.
8. One thousand pounds of a 5-10-5 equals 500 pounds of a 10-20-10. Explain.
9. Fertilizer recommendations may be made on the basis of pounds of N, P_2O_5, and K_2O required per acre rather than on the basis of pounds of any particular analysis. Explain.
10. Given two complete mixtures. Mixture A contains 20 units (5-10-5), and mixture B contains 16 units (4-8-4). On the basis of current prices of each mixture, determine the cost of each unit in A and B.
11. In general, high-analysis mixtures cost less per pound of essential raw materials than low-analysis mixtures. Explain.
12. What is the advantage of making commercial fertilizer recommendations by the ratio rather than by the analysis?
13. In commercial fertilizer practices the essential-element level of the soil, the essential-element requirements of the crop, and the season of the year should be considered. Explain.
14. With other factors equal, the proportion of available nitrogen in the fertilizer should be higher for vigorous vegetative growth than for moderately vigorous growth. Explain.
15. In general, crops in the vegetative phase of growth can use more available nitrogen on sunny days than on cloudy days. Explain.
16. Tomatoes started in January and grown in the greenhouse frequently

set very few fruits of the first cluster, whereas the same variety started in August generally sets many fruits of the first cluster. Explain.

17. In general, the time that complete mixtures should be applied depends largely on the time available nitrogen is needed. Explain.

18. When ammonia forms of nitrogen are applied to soils, they require from one to several weeks to change into the nitrate form. Explain.

19. Applications of commercial fertilizer 2 to 3 inches above the seed piece of potatoes generally produce injurious effects. Applications 3 to 4 inches away and to the side of the seed piece generally produce beneficial effects. Explain.

20. In general, small quantities of commercial fertilizer, 100 to 300 pounds per acre, should be applied as side dressings or in hills, whereas applications varying from 1,500 to 2,000 pounds per acre should be applied broadcast. Explain.

21. What are starter solutions? How do they promote the growth of transplanted herbaceous crops?

22. In general, foliage sprays may be used to correct a deficiency of certain essential elements in a relatively short time. Explain.

23. Irrigation water containing commercial fertilizers should never penetrate beyond the zone occupied by the plants' roots. Explain.

24. What are chemical quick tests? What are their uses?

25. In order for farmers to obtain full returns on their investment in commercial fertilizers, they should control all insect, disease, and weed pests and maintain (for most crops) moderately acid to slightly acid soils. Explain.

26. If tomato fruits contain 0.50 per cent N, 0.17 per cent P_2O_5, and 0.87 per cent K_2O, calculate the amount of N, P_2O_5, and K_2O removed by a crop yielding 10 tons of fruit per acre.

27. In general, essential elements removed in harvested products should be systematically replenished. Explain.

PLANT–GROWING STRUCTURES

12

Quiet! Plants at Work
A sign in one of the greenhouses
at Mississippi State University

Many kinds of horticultural plants are grown in various plant-growing structures. In general, these structures provide a more favorable environment for growth and development than is available in the immediate outdoors. For example, the low temperatures of the winters in the northern United States preclude the growing of crops outdoors, and the high temperatures, combined with the high light intensity, of the summers in the southern United States are injurious to many valuable ornamental plants. Thus, the growing of crops in structures has at least the following advantages: (1) Plants can be protected from adverse environmental conditions; and (2) products can be placed on the market earlier or later than those produced outdoors.

GREENHOUSES

The production of crops in greenhouses is sometimes called plant forcing. In many communities forcing is an important industry. Three types exist: flower production, vegetable production, and a combination of the two.

Nature of Crop Forcing.   The growing of plants in forcing establishments is a most intensive type of agriculture. Plants are grown close together, and crops follow each other in quick succession. The initial capital required and costs of production are higher than for other forms of crop production. However, the water supply and the essential-element

208

supply are under the control of the grower at all times; with the advent of air conditioning, the temperature level is under his control at all times; and he can modify the light supply, particularly with respect to the intensity and to the length of the light and dark periods, according to the needs and requirements of the crop. In other words, the grower of greenhouse crops can regulate the plants' environment to a greater extent than the grower of outdoor crops. For this reason, the grower of greenhouse crops usually produces large yields of high-quality products.

Types of Greenhouses. The main types of greenhouses are (1) lean-to and (2) even-span. Lean-to houses consist of a single span. This type is built usually on the south or east side of a wall or house for the growing of crops, or on the north side of a wall or house for the rooting of cuttings. Even-span houses consist of two spans equal in width and pitch which may run from north to south or from east to west. Of the two types the even span is the more widely used. This type may be built as a single unit or separate from adjacent units, called detached houses, or in two or more units and gutter-connected, called ridge and furrow houses. Detached houses provide more ventilation and light exposure, but because of the greater glass area, they lose more heat, an important factor, during the winter. On the other hand, ridge and furrow houses are more difficult to keep in repair and tend to hold excess quantities of snow in northern climates. In general, detached houses are used for the simultaneous production of crops which have different temperature requirements, whereas ridge and furrow houses are limited to the simultaneous production of crops with the same temperature requirements. Figure 12.1 is an airview of the range of the J. W. Davis Company of Terre Haute, Indiana. Note that all the houses are of the even-span type, but that some are detached and others are gutter-connected.

Parts of a Modern Greenhouse. The parts of a modern greenhouse are the foundation wall, side posts, side glass bars and sash, eave plate, roof glazing bars, columns or purlin posts, roof ventilating sash, ridge and ridge cap, gable glazing bars and sash, and glass. Study the position of the various parts in Fig. 12.2. The foundation wall and side posts support the entire house; the columns and posts support the roof; the eaves carry water into the drainage system; the ventilating sash admits cool air and releases warm air; the glazing bars support the glass; and the glass admits the light. Two grades of glass are available for greenhouses: single strength, weighing 21 ounces per square foot and measuring 12 lights to the inch, and double strength, weighing 26 ounces per square foot and measuring 8 lights to the inch. Of these grades the double strength is needed in regions of heavy snowfall. Both the rectangular shape, usually 18 × 24 inches, and the square shape, usually 20 × 20 inches, are used. Of these the square shape is recom-

Fig. 12.1. The greenhouse range of the J. W. Davis Company, Terre Haute, Ind. This range, the largest vegetable-forcing establishment in the country, covers 25 acres and is given over to the production of vegetable crops, particularly greenhouse tomatoes and cucumbers. (Courtesy, W. Keith Owen, J. W. Davis Company.)

mended, since it requires fewer glazing bars to cover a given area and withstands stress and strain to a greater extent than the rectangular shape. For example, actual counts of broken panes of two adjacent houses in New Jersey after a heavy hail storm showed that two out of three panes, or 67 per cent, had broken in the 18 × 24 inch shape and only one out of four panes, or 25 per cent, had broken in the 20 × 20 inch panes.

Framework Material.   In general, the framework consists of redwood, aluminum alloys, and steel. Clear-heart, densely grained redwood, or specially constructed aluminum alloys are used for the glazing bars, ventilating sash, and ridges and sills, since these parts are constantly exposed to the weather and to wide fluctuations in temperature. Steel is used for the side posts, inside columns, purlins, and eave plates, since these materials do not excessively shade the plants. Thus, from the standpoint of framework materials two types of houses are used: (1) wood-steel frame and (2) aluminum or steel frame.

Methods of Heating.   Greenhouses are heated either by hot water or by steam. In the hot-water system, the boiler is on the same level as the greenhouse, and the hot water is circulated through heating coils by means of an electric pump which is controlled by a mercury tube thermostat. In general, two methods are employed. The first consists in maintaining a high and fairly constant temperature (180 to 220°F) at the boiler by means of an aquastat, the thermostat being connected to the pump only. When the temperature of the house approaches the lower limits of the optimum range for any given crop, the thermostat starts the pump which forces hot water through the coils; and when the temperature approaches the upper limit of the optimum range, the thermostat shuts off the pump. By this method hot water is always available for circulation into the houses. However, unless the temperature of the

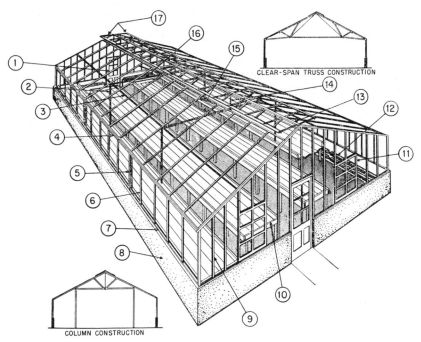

Fig. 12.2. Parts of a greenhouse: (1) roof bar, (2) column or purlin post, (3) roof purlin, (4) eave plate, (5) side post, (6) side sash, (7) wall sill, (8) masonry wall, (9) gable glazing bar, (10) bench, (11) gable casement sash, (12) fin for radiation, (13) ridge and ridge cap, (14) tie rod, (15) strut, (16) crosstie, (17) roof vent sash. (Courtesy, Alex Laurie et al., "Commercial Flower Forcing," 6th ed., New York, McGraw-Hill Book Company, Inc.)

water is maintained at a moderately low level (less than 180°F) during mild weather, the temperature of the house is likely to go beyond the upper limits of the optimum range. The second consists in connecting the thermostat to both the pump and the boiler. When the temperature of the house approaches the lower limits of the optimum range, the thermostat simultaneously starts the pump and then turns on the burner in the boiler. Thus, if the water in the boiler is cold, some time will elapse before warm water begins to circulate in the heating coils; and if the weather is cold, the temperature of the house is likely to drop below the optimum range. With efficient management the disadvantages of each method can be reduced to a minimum.

In the steam system, the boiler is also on the same level as the greenhouse, and steam varying from 212 to 250°F, depending on the pressure at the boiler, is admitted through the heating coils. When the temperature approaches the lower limits of the optimum range, a thermostat opens a valve at the head of the house; and when the temperature approaches the upper limits, the thermostat closes the valve. Various types of thermostatically controlled valves can be used. Some types open fully and close completely to admit or shut off the steam; other types open and close gradually. Of these types the latter is the more likely to keep the temperatures within a specified range.

Air Conditioning of Greenhouses.   A recent development is air conditioning or air cooling of greenhouses during the light period of the summer months. In general, air conditioning (1) lowers the temperature either to within or just above the optimum range, (2) increases the relative humidity, and (3) permits the use of relatively high light intensity. How does the lowering of the temperature, combined with increasing the relative humidity and increasing the light intensity, promote growth and development of crops in greenhouses during the summer months? The lowering of the temperature, combined with increasing the relative humidity, lowers the rate of transpiration. This allows the rate of absorption to keep up with it. As a result, the guard cells maintain turgor, the stomates remain open, carbon dioxide diffuses rapidly into the leaves, and the rate of photosynthesis is high, even in the presence of relatively high light intensity. In addition, the lowering of the temperature lowers the rate of respiration. Thus, abundant carbohydrates are available for growth and, if the plants are managed properly with respect to the vegetative and reproductive phases, high yields of high-quality products are obtained.

At present two methods are in operation: (1) using washed and cooled air and (2) using a high-pressure mist. In general, the use of washed and cooled air requires water-absorbing material to provide a large evaporating surface; a pump, pipes, and a shallow tank or well to circulate water through the water-absorbing material; and exhaust fans to pull the cooled, humidified air through the greenhouse. As water evaporates, it absorbs heat. This absorption of heat lowers the air temperature, increases the relative humidity, and permits the use of relatively high light intensity. The extent to which the temperature of the air can be lowered during sunny weather is quite marked. For example, at State College, Mississippi, during the months of June, July, and August, the temperature of non-air-conditioned houses frequently reaches a maximum of 105 to 120°F, whereas the temperature of adjacent air-conditioned houses with very little shade on the roof attains a maximum of 85 to 90°F. According to Laurie et al., the degree of cooling that can be obtained is about 80 per cent of the difference between the readings of the outdoor wet-bulb and dry-bulb thermometers. Thus, the greater the difference between the two readings, or the greater the evaporating power of the air, the greater will be the reduction in temperature.

In general, the use of a high-pressure mist requires a supply of water under high pressure, usually not less than 600 pounds per square inch, nozzle lines to break the water into a fine mist, and water relatively free of mineral solutes. The fine mist facilitates the evaporation of water. This in turn lowers the air temperature, increases the relative humidity, and permits the use of high light intensity. Of the two methods the use of washed and cooled air is the more effective in promoting favorable conditions and is more widely used.

PLASTIC HOUSES

Certain light-transmitting plastics are now available for greenhouse use, e.g., polyethylene, polyvinyl, cellulose acetate, and Polyflex. The main advantage of these materials is their low initial cost. The main disadvantage is their short duration, since ultraviolet light rapidly decom-

Fig. 12.3. A plastic house at Mississippi State University. Note how this type of house is ventilated. (Courtesy, E. L. Moore, Mississippi State University.)

poses the materials. In addition, unless proper precautions are made, the wind easily tears them. On the other hand, glass for greenhouses is quite durable and with proper care lasts indefinitely. Thus, the rate of depreciation, an important factor in any business enterprise, is much greater for light-transmitting plastic. Consequently, they are likely to be more expensive in the long run than glass. For this reason, plastic houses are not intended to take the place of greenhouses, but rather to help the prospective grower get started in the greenhouse business.

Several experiment stations in the United States and elsewhere are conducting tests with plastic houses. In most of these houses, the frame consists of wood, the fuel is natural or bottled gas, and the pitch of the roof is steeper than that for commercial greenhouses. Figure 12.3 shows the exterior of a plastic house being tested at Mississippi State University.

CLOTH HOUSES

Cloth houses have straight sides and a flat top. Their construction is relatively simple. The frame consists of wood or iron posts, and the cover consists of cloth or a light-transmitting plastic. Principal crops grown in cloth houses are chrysanthemums and asters. Under conditions of high temperature and high light intensity, these crops in cloth houses usually produce longer stems, larger leaves, and larger and brighter flowers than comparable crops grown outdoors. How is the more satisfactory growth secured? The fundamental process concerned is transpiration and the principal environmental factors concerned are (1) temperature, (2) light intensity, (3) relative humidity, and (4) wind velocity. Experiments at the Ohio Experiment Station have shown that cloth slightly lowers maximum daily temperatures and slightly increases the relative humidity. However, it markedly lowers light intensity. Study the data in Table 12.1. Note that the greater the intensity of light, the

Table 12.1. EFFECT OF CLOTH ON REDUCTION OF LIGHT INTENSITY

	In a laboratory		In sunlight outdoors	
Treatment	Ft-c	Reduction, %	Ft-c	Reduction, %
No cloth	45		11,500	
Cloth	37	17	7,474	35

Source: Adapted from Alex Laurie, D. C. Kiplinger, and Kennard S. Nelson, "Commercial Flower Forcing," 6th ed., New York, McGraw-Hill Book Company, Inc., 1958.

Fig. 12.4. Greenhouse roses growing in a cloth house at the Ohio State University. (Courtesy, Alex Laurie et al., "Commercial Flower Forcing," 6th ed., New York, McGraw-Hill Book Company, Inc.)

greater is the reduction. The decrease in light intensity in cloth houses during the summer undoubtedly lowers the temperature of the leaves, which in turn lowers the rate of transpiration and permits the rate of water absorption to keep up with it. As a result, the guard cells remain turgid, the stomates remain open, and a high rate of photosynthesis takes place throughout the light period. Note the greenhouse roses growing in the cloth house in Fig. 12.4.

LATHHOUSES

Lathhouses have straight sides and a flat top also. The frame is similar to that of cloth houses, but the cover consists of movable lath sash,

Fig. 12.5. A lathhouse made of Flexwood supported by iron rods. (Courtesy, A. C. Oelschig and Sons, Savannah, Ga.)

"snow fence," or nailed down 2×2 inch strips placed 2 inches apart. In the southern United States lathhouses are required to protect many ornamental plants which are sensitive to high light intensity, such as hydrangaes and azaleas, and are used to grow and maintain stock plants for the foliage industry. Note the lathhouse used for the protection of azaleas in Fig. 12.5.

HOTBEDS

Hotbeds consist of three parts: the frame, the cover, and the heating material or system. In general, the frame is made of wood, concrete, brick, or Transite and is usually 24 to 36 inches high on the north or west side, and 12 to 24 inches high on the south or east side. The covers consist of glass, light-transmitting plastics, or cloth. The glass and light-transmitting plastics are usually set in wooden frames 3 feet wide and 6 feet long, and cloth covers, usually muslin, canvas, or burlap, are used without frames. Hotbeds are heated by various materials and systems and are classified accordingly.

Manure. The manure-heated bed is the oldest type and the least efficient. Fresh horse manure is used and may be placed on or below the surface of the land. In general, the depth of manure varies with the climate and the temperature requirements of the crop. For example, in the South in average weather depths of 8 to 18 inches will suffice; whereas in the North greater depths, 18 to 36 inches, are required. The function of the manure is to produce heat. The process concerned is fermentation— a type of respiration. Note the equation.

$$\text{Manure} + \text{H}_2\text{O} + \text{O}_2 \xrightarrow{\text{(soil organisms)}} \text{CO}_2 \text{ and other gases} + \text{H}_2\text{O} + \text{heat} + \text{other forms of energy}$$

(organic matter)

As in the decomposition of organic matter, warm-moist manure decomposes more rapidly than cool-moist manure, warm-wet manure, or

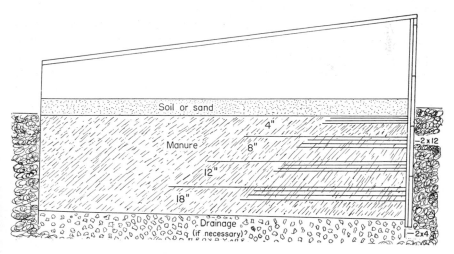

Fig. 12.6. Cross section of manure-heated hotbed. Note varying depths of manure depending on the climate and temperature requirements of the crop.

warm-dry manure. With warm-moist manure the principal environmental factors—temperature, oxygen, and water—are most favorable for rapid decomposition and heat production. When the manure is cold, wet, or dry, temperature, oxygen, and water, respectively, become the limiting factors. The necessity for rapid decomposition and rapid liberation of heat explains why growers turn the manure pile inside out at frequent intervals; why they prefer manure from grain-fed animals; why they apply hot water when the weather is cold; and why they see that the manure does not become saturated with water. Figure 12.6 shows a cross section of a manure-heated hotbed.

Hot Air.   The hot-air-heated bed contains sets of flues which carry the heat and products of combustion from the furnace, usually situated at one end of the bed, to the chimney, usually situated at the other end. The reaction concerned is combustion which, like respiration, liberates heat and other forms of energy. Note the equation.

Gas or coal or wood + oxygen $\longrightarrow$ CO_2 and other gases + H_2O
$$+ \text{ heat } + \text{ other forms of energy}$$

Flue-heated beds are usually used when growers have plentiful supplies of cheap wood. In general, the direction of the prevailing wind and the length and size of the flue are important considerations. For example, in the production of sweetpotato plants in the South, beds 9×12 feet wide and 50×60 feet long, underlined with two to four rows of 6- or 8-inch tile, have produced satisfactory results.

Hot Water.   The hot-water-heated bed has pipes under the bed or along the sides of the frame. The size of the pipes, position of the boiler, and slope of the floor are primary considerations in this type of bed. The heaters are usually thermostatically controlled. Thus, they maintain uniform temperatures with little waste of fuel and are economical and efficient. This type of hotbed is very popular among market gardeners in New Jersey.

Electricity.   The electric bed is heated by lead-covered resistance coils placed on or under the soil or along the inside walls of the frame or by lamps placed over the bed. This system is automatic, always available, more or less permanent, and reliable. At present, the cost of electricity for the growing of plants is a prime consideration. Thus, many experiments have been made to determine production costs. For example, in 1938 the cost of the electricity was about 2.8 cents per week per sash at the Washington and Pennsylvania Stations and about 1.5 cents per week per sash at the Maryland Station. At the Minnesota Station the combined use of the heating cable and lamps produced better plants than the use of the heating cable alone. This is to be expected, since light is usually the limiting factor in growing plants under glass in the early spring in northern climates.

COLD FRAMES

Cold frames are used to protect plants from frosts, hard rains, and heavy winds. In regions characterized by mild winters herbaceous crops are started in these structures. Later, as the weather becomes warm, the covers are removed. Two types exist: (1) temporary and (2) permanent. The temporary type is usually made of wood (cedar, locust, or chestnut). Permanent types are made of concrete, concrete block, or brick.

PLANT PROTECTION IN THE FIELD

Many kinds of economic crops grown in the field are given protection. Light frosts and heavy winds are the principal environmental factors concerned. Research workers and growers have developed many ways by which plants may be protected from these adverse environmental conditions. The various types of protectors are classified according to function: (1) those which protect individual plants and (2) those which protect plants in groups.

Individual Plant Protectors. They include, for example: (1) small, boxlike structures with an adjustable pane of glass on the top, sometimes called forcing boxes, (2) chemically treated paper made in the form of a cone, and (3) light-transmitting plastics. The profitable use of the cone-type protector seems to depend on weather conditions. For example, from 1925 to 1931, the influence of 10 different types of cone protectors on the growth of seedling tomatoes and peppers was investigated at the Michigan Experiment Station. Under conditions of the experiment, the protectors were found to be of decided value in 1925, of doubtful value in 1926 and 1928, and of no value in 1927, 1930, and 1931.[1] The investigators found weather conditions so variable that it was impossible to assert that the protectors were beneficial in all years. From 1932 to 1935, the effect of five different types of plant protectors on the growth of seedling cantaloupes was investigated in southern Arkansas. Under the conditions of the experiment, all plant protectors hastened germination and seedling emergence from one to four days and gave a more complete stand. Some types actually increased earliness of yield and total yield. Thus, positive results may be obtained in one part of the country, and doubtful results in another. Other types of plant protectors are shingles, newspapers, and brush. Note the cone-type protectors in Fig. 12.7.

At present the use of light-transmitting plastics for the protection of plants in the field is in the experimental stage. Preliminary tests at the Kentucky Experiment Station and the Plant Industry Station, Beltsville, Maryland, indicate that these materials may protect nonhardy plants against subfreezing weather. For example, in northern Kentucky tomato plants were set in the field on April 5, 1955, and covered with polyethylene plastic. Sometime later the temperature dropped to 25°F, but the plants were not damaged. Although the total yield of the protected plants was lower than that of plants which were set later and thus needed no protection, the returns were greater because the protected plants produced ripe fruit earlier when prices were relatively high.

[1] No outdoor tests were conducted in 1929.

Fig. 12.7. Plant protectors over tomatoes in South Carolina.

Group Plant Protectors. The kind of protection depends largely on the kind of enterprise. For example, *hedge protection* is used by the growers of slicing cucumbers in the vicinity of Norfolk, Virginia. Cedar hedges on the west, north, and east sides of small tracts (1 to 5 acres) give the necessary protection from cold winds. *Building protection* is used by market gardeners and florists, particularly in the North, where protection from cold north and northeasterly winds is essential. *Protection by V-shaped troughs* is used by growers of cucumbers in Florida. These troughs are placed on the north side of the rows of cucumbers. In this position protection is given from wind, and the reflection of sun rays from these troughs helps germination and growth of the young plants. If frosts are likely to occur, the troughs are placed over the plants. *Protection by strip cropping* is used by growers of onions in New York and Michigan. Strips of barley or oats protect the young plants from the injurious action of the rather heavy winds. *Southerly or southeasterly slopes* are used by market gardeners, since these slopes warm up earlier in the spring than do northerly or northwesterly slopes.

PLANT CONTAINERS

Plant containers have two rather distinct functions: (1) the growing of plants to full maturity and (2) the growing of plants for transplanting to the field, garden, greenhouse bench, or bed. They are classified as follows: (1) plant containers used to raise plants in groups and (2) plant containers used to raise plants individually.

Group Containers. The principal type of group container is called a flat. The flat is essentially a shallow tray. Its width varies from 6 to 24 inches, its length from 18 to 36 inches, and its depth from 2 to 6 inches. Commercial growers usually use flats of standard dimensions—12 × 24 × 3 inches. Their use facilitates standardization of other crop-growing operations, and more efficiently utilizes greenhouse, hotbed, and cold-frame space. In general, durable, nonwarpable wood is used. Recently, metal flats with holes in the bottom for drainage have become available. Note the two general methods of planting seed in flats in Fig. 12.8.

Individual Containers. Individual plant containers are (1) pots and (2) bands. Pots are round and may or may not have a hole in the bottom for drainage. Bands are square and are open at the bottom. Pots are either porous or nonporous. Porous pots are made of clay or peat fiber, and nonporous pots are made of metal, concrete, rubber, or plastics. Bands are made of wood or paper.

Principal factors concerned in the growing of plants in pots or bands are (1) water supply and (2) nitrogen supply. The water supply pertains particularly to porous and nonporous pots. Investigations at the Massachusetts Experiment Station have shown that, under the same conditions, plants in nonporous pots required less moisture than those in porous pots. Consequently, failures through the use of nonporous pots are likely to be due largely to overwatering, whereas failures through the use of porous pots are likely to be due to excessive drying out or underwatering. If moist soil is constantly maintained in either case, either type of pot should be equally satisfactory.

The nitrogen supply pertains particularly to new clay pots and to paper and peat fiber pots. Tests have shown that new clay pots absorb nitrates. Thus, unless adequate available nitrogen is supplied in the irrigation water, rapidly growing plants are likely to be deficient in nitrogen. Tests also

Fig. 12.8. Two standard flats. Left: seed broadcast. Right: seed planted in rows. (Courtesy, K. H. Buckley, Mississippi Agricultural Extension Service.)

Fig. 12.9. Examples of individual containers. Front row: standard clay pots of various sizes. Second row: notched clay pot, veneer band, paper pot for growing, paper pot for shipping, plastic pot, and rose pot. Third row: orchid pot, pan, standard pot showing single hole for drainage. Fourth row: large clay pot, cypress tub. (Courtesy, E. W. McElwee, University of Florida.)

have shown that microorganisms decompose paper pots. Here again, unless adequate available nitrogen is supplied, rapidly growing plants are likely to become deficient in nitrogen. In general, applications of available nitrogen at the rate of 1 ounce of sodium nitrate or ammonium sulfate to 1 gallon of water at intervals of 1 week or 10 days will suffice to supply the nitrogen requirements of the plants and the decomposing bacteria.

USES OF POTS AND BANDS. *Pots* are used to raise transplants or to raise plants to full maturity, and bands are used to raise transplants only. Of the many types of pots on the market, clay pots are the oldest and most popular. Many sizes are available, varying from 2, $2\frac{1}{4}$, $3\frac{1}{4}$, 4, 5, 6, and 7 inches in diameter. Other types of pots are innovations. The metal type, for example, is quite ornamental and somewhat adapted to the growing of plants in the home or conservatory. *Bands* are made of either wood veneer or paper. The most popular sizes are $2 \times 2 \times 3$, and $4 \times 4 \times 5$ inches. Figure 12.9 shows various types of pots.

Ornamental Plants and Pot Size. The amount of growth a plant will make and the time it will flower depend largely on the immediate and potential available nitrogen supply. This in turn depends on the volume of soil in which the plant is growing. In general, plants growing in small pots produce less vegetative growth and flower earlier than plants growing in large pots. Plants growing in small-sized pots naturally deplete the nitrogen supply earlier than plants growing in large-sized. The earlier depletion permits earlier accumulation of carbohydrates and flower-forming substances, which in turn are associated with flower-bud formation, flowering, and fruiting.

Growing Seedling Vegetable Plants. Certain vegetable crops, particularly tomatoes, cabbage, and onions, are raised during the seedling stage in relatively cool weather in the southern United States and shipped as transplants to market gardeners and canners in the northern United States. Because of the necessity for strict control of diseases, the raising of these crops is a highly specialized industry. The seedling plants are grown in open fields of 1 to 100 acres or more. Relatively infertile, well-drained sandy loams and loams are used. In general, the seed is drilled in rows 6 to 12 inches apart. On many plant-growing farms the amount of seed used is numbered in tons and the number of plants produced is counted in millions.

Two important plant-growing districts are the Rio Grande Valley of Texas and the Tifton-Valdosta of south Georgia. The Rio Grande Valley produces annually some 160 million sweetpotato plants, 100 million tomato plants, 400 million cabbage plants, and 900 million onion plants.

Fig. 12.10. A field of tomato transplants in the Tifton-Valdosta district of Georgia. In general, the plants are "lifted" when they are 6 to 10 inches tall and are shipped by express train or plane to growers of tomatoes in the Northeast and Middle West. (Courtesy, Otis Woodard, The Coastal Plain Experiment Station, Georgia.)

The Tifton-Valdosta area comprises about five counties and produces approximately 100 million sweetpotato plants, 500 million tomato plants, 400 million cabbage plants, and about 20 million onion plants. Small quantities of pepper, eggplant, and cauliflower seedlings are produced also. Figure 12.10 shows a field of tomato transplants in the Tifton-Valdosta district.

QUESTIONS

1. How does the growing of crops in plant-forcing structures differ from the growing of crops outdoors?
2. Higher yields and higher quality generally result when a given crop is planted in greenhouses instead of outdoors. Explain.
3. Compare detached or separate units and ridge and furrow units from the standpoint of ventilation, light exposure, heat loss, and maintenance.
4. State the function of the following parts of a greenhouse: the foundation wall, the columns and posts, the eaves, the ventilating sash, and the glazing bars.
5. In general, how are the optimum temperature ranges maintained by each of the two hot-water heating systems and by the steam heating system?
6. Show how air conditioning of greenhouses during the summer months promotes the production of high yields and high quality.
7. Give an advantage and a disadvantage of light-transmitting plastics for greenhouses.
8. Under conditions of high light intensity and high transpiration, pompon chrysanthemums and asters grown under cloth or light-transmitting plastic produce longer stems, larger leaves, and larger flowers than comparable plants grown outdoors. Explain.
9. How do lathhouses protect plants which are sensitive to high light intensity?
10. Draw a cross section of a manure-heated hotbed.
11. What difference is there, if any, between the decomposition of organic matter in soils and the decomposition of manure in hotbeds?
12. Give an advantage and a disadvantage of manure-heated, hot-air-heated, and electrically heated hotbeds.
13. How would you change an electric-heated hotbed into a cold frame?
14. The grower of crops for early market frequently protects his plants. Explain.
15. Cantaloupe growers in the Imperial Valley, California, place brush on the north side of the furrows in early spring. Explain.
16. Explain how to protect tomato plants just set in the home garden. Outline a practical measure.
17. In your opinion how do hedge protection and strip cropping influence the photosynthesis of the protected crop?

18. How does planting on a southeast slope promote earliness?
19. Flats and pots should be set level on beds and benches. Explain.
20. The soil in a porous pot drys out more quickly than that in a non-porous pot. Explain.
21. Recommend a type of pot which should be used for growing plants in the living room. Give reasons for your choice.
22. Given two plants. Plant A is grown in a porous pot; plant B is grown in a nonporous pot. Both plants are grown side by side in a greenhouse and are given the same (moderate) supplies of water. In your opinion, which plant would make the better growth? Give your reasons.
23. Your mother has a vigorously vegetative geranium plant growing in rich soil. She gives the plant optimum supplies of water. She wants the plant to produce flowers at the earliest possible moment. What would you advise? Give reasons.
24. Tomato and cabbage plants grown in the southern United States for shipment to the Middle West are raised in relatively infertile, well-drained sands and sandy loams. Explain.

13

TRANSPLANTING, CONTROLLING WEEDS, IRRIGATING

Work is the essence of a man's life.

TRANSPLANTING

Transplanting is a most important practice. Many thousands of deciduous fruit trees, evergreen fruit trees, nut fruit trees, and many millions of ornamental trees and shrubs in this country and throughout the world have at one time or another been transplanted. Moreover, many millions of vegetable and flower plants are transplanted annually. By transplanting, many deciduous fruit orchards, citrus fruit orchards, grape vineyards, and small fruit, vegetable, and flower crop plantations are established; and parks, streets, lanes, highways, factories, business buildings, recreational areas, and homes are made more beautiful.

There are many terms used in transplanting: potting, repotting, or shifting, balling and burlapping, and setting out. In general, potting is the transplanting of seedlings from a seedbed or flat to a pot. Repotting, or shifting, is the transplanting of a plant from one pot to another, usually to a larger one. Balling and burlapping is the transplanting of plants, chiefly evergreens, with a ball of soil supported by burlap or similar material. Setting out is the transplanting of plants, usually herbaceous kinds, from pots, flats, or beds to the garden or field.

TRANSPLANTING HERBACEOUS PLANTS

Influence on Plant Behavior. How does transplanting influence the growth of herbaceous plants? What are the fundamental processes concerned? The student should remember that *herbaceous plants always have leaves,* that *most of the water is lost through the leaves,* and that *transplanting destroys part, if not all, of the region of absorption.* Thus, during transplanting operations the amount of water going into a plant is reduced, and this amount is usually less than the amount going out. As a result, a water deficit is likely to take place within the tissues. This deficit produces at least two effects: (1) *a reduction in the size of the cells in the region of elongation and* (2) *a reduction in the rate or cessation of photosynthesis.* In the first case the region of enlargement fails to receive sufficient water for normal size of the cells; and in the second, the guard cells lose turgor, the stomates partially or completely close, the rate of diffusion of carbon dioxide into the leaves is reduced, and the manufacture of the primary food substances is accordingly reduced. This in turn reduces the amount of growth which would otherwise be made. Therefore, transplanting herbaceous plants reduces their growth and development, and, in general, the extent of the injury or reduction in growth is more or less directly proportional to the severity and duration of the water deficit within the tissues.

Factors Influencing Rate of Recovery

Size and Age of Plant.   Since size and age are positively associated, these factors may be considered together. In general, the greater the size or age, the lesser the ability of the plant to recover from the check in growth incident to transplanting. Why do large or old plants recover less rapidly? Usually large plants have an extensive root system, and, in transplanting, the younger portion, the tips, is not retained. In this way the region of absorption is reduced considerably. In addition, large plants have more leaves. Thus, the amount of water absorbed in proportion to the amount of water transpired is likely to be materially reduced in the case of the large or old plant. For this reason, whenever it is possible and practical, herbaceous plants should be transplanted in the seedling stage. Growers who transplant large numbers of plants—truck gardeners, market gardeners, florists, and nurserymen—generally transplant seedling plants when they are small. In general, the first transplanting is usually done just before or immediately after the first true leaves begin to develop, and the second transplanting, when necessary, is usually done three to six weeks later.

Age of Absorbing Region When Suberization Takes Place.   Suberization of the roots involves the laying down of suberin in the walls of the endodermis or cortex or both. Since suberin is impervious to water, suberization of the walls of the endodermis or cortex in the root-hair zone prevents the passage of water from the root hairs to the xylem. Thus, that portion of the root in which suberization has taken place is useless for water absorption. Plants differ in the time they deposit suberin in the walls of the water-absorbing region. For example, in beans, cucumbers, and sweet corn, suberization becomes evident in the three-day-old portion of the root system, whereas in tomatoes and cabbage it becomes evident in the five- to six-week-old portion. Naturally, crops in which suberization takes place relatively early (just back of the tips) are likely to recover less rapidly than those in which suberization takes place relatively late (at a considerable distance from the tips).

Rate of Root Regeneration.　A direct relation exists between the rate at which the new root system is formed and the rate of recovery. In other words, the faster the new root system is formed, the faster is likely to be the rate of recovery. The rate at which the new root system is formed is largely dependent on a supply of reserve carbohydrates within the tissues at the time transplanting takes place. Thus, with other factors favorable, plants with large quantities of reserve carbohydrates in their tissues may be expected to recover more rapidly than plants with small quantities.

Classification

On the basis of differential rate of recovery, a classification of herbaceous crops is possible. Three groups are presented in Table 13.1. In general, plants of group 1 develop new roots at a rapid rate and lay down suberin relatively late in the life of the root system; plants of group 2 develop new roots at a moderately rapid rate; and plants of group 3 develop new roots at a slow rate and lay down suberin relatively early in the life of the root system. This explains why plants of group 2 and 3 require more care in transplanting than those of group 1. In fact, experience has

Table 13.1.　CLASSIFICATION OF HERBACEOUS PLANTS BASED ON RATE OF RECOVERY FROM TRANSPLANTING

Group 1 Crops recovering rapidly	Group 2 Crops recovering slowly	Group 3 Crops recovering very slowly
Cabbage, cornflower, lettuce, petunia, stock, sweetpotato, verbena	Aster, Canterbury bell, celery, larkspur, onion, pansy, pepper	Bean, cantaloupe, cucumber, poinsettia, pumpkin, squash, watermelon

shown that relatively large plants of group 3 should be grown in pots or bands if they are to be transplanted.

Hardening off of Herbaceous Plants

As stated previously, the rate of new root formation is dependent on a supply of reserve carbohydrates within the tissues. To promote rapid accumulation of carbohydrates in the tissues, high rates of photosynthesis, combined with low rates of respiration and low rates of cell division, are necessary. With high rates of photosynthesis large quantities of carbohydrates are made per unit time; and with low rates of respiration and cell division small quantities of carbohydrates are used. As a result, large quantities of carbohydrates are stored in the tissues in a relatively short time. Thus, sunny weather, combined with optimum day temperatures and relatively low night temperatures, would promote a rapid accumulation of carbohydrates within the tissues. The sunny weather, combined with optimum day temperatures, makes possible high rates of photosynthesis; and the low night temperatures maintain low rates of respiration and low rates of cell division. Any deviation from these favorable conditions, as for example cloudy days combined with warm nights, would correspondingly reduce the rate of carbohydrate accumulation within the tissues. This explains why growers transfer plants from greenhouses to hotbeds or cold frames usually during late spring and why they keep plants relatively cool just before the plants are to be set in the field. How long should plants be hardened-off to facilitate rapid recovery? In general, about four to six days of favorable conditions as described are sufficient to provide the carbohydrates necessary for the rapid development of the new root system.

With certain plants, this accumulation of carbohydrates permits the making of the hydrophilic colloids—the substances which bind water so that the protoplasm can withstand subfreezing temperatures, intense sunshine, and dry winds. With other plants, the carbohydrates which accumulate do not form the colloids which bind water readily. In general, the cool-season crops possess the ability to bind water, whereas the warm-season crops do not. This explains why the tops of most cool-season crops can be hardened-off to withstand relatively low temperatures, and those of warm-season crops cannot. For example, investigations at the Missouri Station and elsewhere have shown that hardened-off cabbage plants can withstand temperatures as low as 20°F, and hardened-off tomato plants cannot withstand freezing temperatures. This does not mean, however, that tomato plants should not be hardened-off. As stated previously, an advantage of hardening off is the accumulation of carbohydrates within the tissues, and these carbohydrates are used for the development of the new root system.

Transplanting and the Weather

As previously explained, low rates of transpiration facilitate rapid recovery from the check in growth incident to transplanting. Thus, environmental factors which induce low rates of this process should be utilized whenever they are available. These environmental factors are relatively low temperature, low light intensity, still air, and high relative humidity. This explains why a light, misty rain is almost ideal for rapid recovery; why cloudy days facilitate recovery to a greater extent than sunny days; why still air is more favorable than rapidly moving air; and why transplanting in late afternoon, particularly in regions of high light intensity, is likely to promote a faster rate of recovery than transplanting in early morning.

Use of Water in Transplanting

Most herbaceous crops are transplanted with water. In fact, growers believe that the application of water at transplanting is essential to rapid recovery and full stands. The water settles the soil around the roots, thus eliminating air pockets, and is available for immediate absorption.

As discussed in Chapter 11, starter solutions are used in the field transplanting of certain kinds of vegetable plants, as for example tomatoes, peppers, and sweetpotatoes. In general, these solutions contain compounds which supply nitrogen, phosphorus, potassium, and other essential elements. According to tests at the Louisiana and other experiment stations, starter solutions are likely to promote rapid recovery and increase yields when the plants are grown on relatively infertile soil, when light applications of commercial fertilizers are made, and when the commercial fertilizer is placed some distance away from the roots of the seedling plants.

Transplanting Machines

Many herbaceous crops—celery, cabbage, cantaloupe, tomato, pepper, eggplant, and sweetpotato—grown on a commercial scale are transplanted by machine. These machines set plants at definite intervals and depths and release a definite amount of water or starter solution to the roots. In this way, plant setting and watering take place simultaneously. Note the machine transplanting scene in Fig. 13.1.

Fig. 13.1. Machine transplanting of tomatoes in New Jersey. (Courtesy, Jackson B. Hester, Elkton, Md.)

TRANSPLANTING EVERGREEN TREES AND SHRUBS

Influence on Plant Behavior. How does transplanting influence the growth of evergreen trees and shrubs? As with herbaceous plants, the student should remember that *evergreen trees and shrubs always have leaves and that most of the water is lost through the leaves.* Thus, during the transplanting operation the amount of water absorbed is likely to be less than the amount of water transpired. As a result, a water deficit is likely to take place within the tissues with a reduction in the size of the cells in the region of elongation and a reduction in the rate of photosynthesis.

Factors Influencing Rate of Recovery

Size and Age of Plant. As with herbaceous plants recovery varies indirectly with size and age. Thus, under the same conditions small evergreen trees and shrubs recover more rapidly than large trees and shrubs. In fact, in the establishment of wood lots and forests certain species of pines are usually transplanted bare-rooted; that is, the plants are removed for transplanting without a mass of soil around the roots. However, evergreen trees and shrubs for landscape use are usually transplanted when they are large. In other words, at the time the plants are transplanted they have a large number of leaves or transpiring surface and the amount of water lost is relatively great. To replace the amount of water lost per unit time a considerable portion of the root system must be retained. This is done by balling and burlapping the roots or by growing the plants in containers. In balling and burlapping, field-grown plants are dug with a large portion of the roots set in a ball of soil which is held together by burlap or similar material. This practice has certain disadvantages: (1) With large plants the severe pruning of the root system removes carbohydrates that have been made; and (2) the operation requires considerable labor. To overcome these disadvantages many nurserymen are now growing ornamental plants in containers. In this way, the root system is not pruned as in balling and burlapping, and it is injured only slightly, if at all, in the transplanting operation.

Season of the Year.   The transplanting of evergreen trees and shrubs is usually done in the fall and winter in warm areas and in early spring in cold areas. In general, during these seasons the rate of transpiration is lower than during the summer, and the deficit of water within the tissues is likely to be mild and of short duration. However, in southern Florida trees and shrubs are transplanted during the summer. During this season the rainfall is higher than during the winter. Because of the high rainfall, the light intensity is relatively low, the relative humidity is high, and, as a result, the rate of transpiration is correspondingly low.

TRANSPLANTING DECIDUOUS TREES AND SHRUBS

How does transplanting influence the growth of deciduous trees and shrubs? The student should remember that, unlike herbaceous plants and evergreen trees and shrubs, *deciduous trees and shrubs shed their leaves in the fall or early winter and develop a new set of leaves in the spring.* Since most of the water is lost through the leaves and since during the period of recovery transpiration should be low, it follows that deciduous trees and shrubs are transplanted most advantageously when they are without leaves, that is, during the nongrowing season. During this period transpiration is at a minimum, a water deficit within the plants does not take place, and the root system has an opportunity to become established before stem and leaf growth begins.[1] In general, the time of transplanting during the nongrowing season for any given region depends on the temperature of the soil. Thus, in regions characterized by mild winter temperatures, as for example in the southern United States, transplanting can be done in late fall and early winter, since the soil temperature is sufficiently high for the development of the new root system during the latter part of the winter and air temperature and light intensity in-

[1] Roots do not have rest periods.

crease rapidly in the spring. On the other hand, in regions characterized by severe winter temperatures, for example in the northern United States, transplanting should be done in the early spring only, since soil temperature inhibits root growth during the winter and air temperature and light intensity increase slowly during spring and early summer. However, regardless of the region or climatic condition, if the trees or shrubs are very large, they should be removed with the ball of soil around the base of the plants.

Use of Waxes

Investigations have shown that the use of emulsified waxes facilitates the rate of recovery of trees and shrubs in full leaf. These emulsified waxes are soluble in water, nontoxic to plant tissues, relatively permeable and colorless, and can be applied to plants in the form of a spray. The principal purpose of the wax is to reduce the rate of transpiration without reducing the rate of photosynthesis or interfering with the rate of respiration. Thus, the outgo of water is reduced, wilting is avoided, photosynthesis takes place, and recovery from transplanting is facilitated. Applications of these emulsions to trees at the time of digging and again after setting facilitate recovery. For example, in 1934 a nursery in Michigan transplanted 22 moderately large elms in full leaf. Of these trees 11 were sprayed with wax emulsion and 11 were sprayed with water only. Of the 11 trees sprayed with wax emulsion, 10 recovered, and of the 11 trees sprayed with water, only 1 survived the transplanting operation.

QUESTIONS

1. What are the immediate and subsequent effects of transplanting herbaceous plants?
2. Show how transplanting is likely to reduce size of the cells in the region of elongation.
3. Since transplanting herbaceous plants is likely to reduce the rate of photosynthesis, why transplant? Give two reasons.
4. Tomatoes grown for early market in the northern United States and for long distance shipment in the southern United States are usually transplanted. Are they or are they not transplanted in both regions for the same reason? Explain.
5. In the same environment a plant with a large leaf surface has a greater outgo of water than a plant with a small leaf surface. Explain.
6. Whenever feasible, herbaceous plants should be transplanted in the seedling stage. Explain.
7. Pots and bands are used for cantaloupes and cucumbers, and pots are

used for poinsettias, but they are unnecessary for cabbage, tomatoes, and stocks. Explain.

8. In general, plants with a rapid rate of root regeneration recover more rapidly than plants with a slow rate of root regeneration. Explain.

9. How does hardening off herbaceous crops facilitate recovery from transplanting?

10. Show how hardened-off cabbage plants withstand subfreezing temperatures, whereas hardened-off tomato plants cannot.

11. In your opinion, which method would be more effective in hardening off herbaceous plants: (a) maintaining night temperatures just below the optimum range and keeping the soil moist or (b) maintaining night temperatures within the optimum range and keeping the soil relatively dry with plants not wilting? Give reasons.

12. Describe ideal weather conditions during and immediately after transplanting which promote rapid recovery incident to transplanting. Give two reasons.

13. Foggy weather or a light, misty rain is ideal transplanting weather for plants with leaves. Explain.

14. Given two comparable or identical lots of herbaceous plants. Lot A is transplanted in the morning; lot B is transplanted in late afternoon. Which lot is likely to recover the more rapidly? Explain.

15. Given two lots of plants transplanted to flats in the greenhouse. Lot A was shaded three or four days; lot B was not shaded. In your opinion which lot would recover the more rapidly from transplanting? Explain.

16. Show how the use of water facilitates recovery from transplanting.

17. Large evergreens are usually transplanted with a ball of earth. Explain.

18. The use of containers in growing ornamental plants for transplanting is likely to take the place of balling and burlapping. Explain.

19. In general, the deciduous orchardist transplants his trees when they are without leaves. Explain.

20. In your opinion, which time of the year would be better for transplanting deciduous or evergreen trees or shrubs in your community: (a) the fall or (b) early spring? Explain.

21. Show how water-soluble wax emulsions facilitate recovery of trees and shrubs in full leaf from the check in growth incident to transplanting.

CONTROLLING WEEDS

What Is a Weed?   A weed is a plant growing in a place where it is not wanted. It may belong to an economic crop, for example, corn plants in fields of cotton; or it may have no economic importance, for example, henbane in fields of spinach or wild onion in lawns. In any case, weeds markedly decrease growth and yields of crop plants. They use carbon dioxide, water, and the essential raw materials, particularly the available nitrogen; and if the weeds are taller than the crop plants, they use the light. According to recent surveys, weeds cause farmers and gardeners in the

United States a loss of 3 to 4 billion dollars each year. Thus, the practical importance of weed control is obvious.

METHODS OF CONTROLLING WEEDS

Cultivation

Cultivation is the intertillage of a crop, and its primary purpose is to control weeds. Study the data in Table 13.2. Note the extremely low yields of the garden beets in the weed plots. The tests were conducted at Cornell University from 1920 to 1925 inclusive. In one set of plots the weeds were allowed to grow, and in another comparable set they were controlled by cultivation. Experiments with other crops (carrot, cabbage, onion, celery, potato, and tomato) produced similar results. Many crop-plant scientists believe that even a small growth of weeds reduces yields from 20 to 50 per cent. Successful growers keep their gardens and fields practically free from weeds.

The question arises: Is cultivation beneficial in the absence of weeds? An important factor is the relative extensiveness of the root systems of crop plants. Note that the marketable yields of the cultivated and scraped plots as presented in Table 13.3 are practically the same for all crops except those of celery and onion. What is the explanation for the similarity of yield of both the cultivated and the scraped plots of cabbage, carrots, and tomatoes, and what is the explanation for the marked increase in yield for the cultivated plots of celery and the moderate increase for the cultivated plots of onions? The investigators studied the root systems of each of these crops. They found that cabbage, carrots, and tomatoes develop extensive root systems, whereas celery and onions develop sparse root systems. Thus, under the conditions of the experiments, only sparsely rooted crops may be expected to respond to cultivation in the absence of weeds. In fact, cultivation in the absence of weeds of extensively rooted crops, particularly during the later stages of growth, is likely to severely prune most of the absorbing roots just below the surface. The severe

Table 13.2. **EFFECT OF WEEDS ON THE YIELD OF GARDEN BEETS GROWN AT ITHACA, NEW YORK, 1920–1925**

Number of roots per plot		Average weight of roots, lb	
Cultivated plot	Weed plot	Cultivated plot	Weed plot
381	149	60.6	9.3

Table 13.3. MEAN YIELDS PER PLOT FOR SIX YEARS
(1920–1925) OF VEGETABLE CROPS ON
CULTIVATED AND SCRAPED SOILS WITH
WEEDS ABSENT IN BOTH CASES*

Kind	Product	Cultivated		Scraped		Increase in favor of cultivation, %
		Number	Weight, lb	Number	Weight, lb	
Celery	Plants	145	145	143	116	24
Onion	Bulbs	269	78	270	72	8
Beet	Roots	381	61	382	58	4
Carrot	Roots	611	87	637	84	3
Cabbage	Heads	50	119	50	119	0
Tomato	Fruit	699	188	714	186	1

* All crops except tomatoes were grown in a gravelly fine loam, and tomatoes were
grown in a soil containing a large amount of clay.
Source: Adapted from Tables 1–6, Cornell Agr. Exp. Sta. Mem. 107, 1927.

pruning reduces carbohydrates already made and the area of absorption.
This reduces the amount of water going into the plant per unit time, and
this in turn is likely to lead to a water deficit within the plant, with a
resulting decrease in cell enlargement, photosynthesis, and marketable
yield.

Another factor is whether soils crust after a rain. Certain soils form a
crust after a rain, whereas other soils do not. Theoretically, the crust limits
the flow of oxygen to and the flow of carbon dioxide away from the roots
and the beneficial bacteria. This in turn is likely to reduce the growth
and the absorbing capacity of the roots and to decrease the available
nitrogen supply. For example, experiments in Ohio with Brookston sandy
loam, a noncrusting soil high in organic matter, and with Miami sandy
loam, a crusting soil low in organic matter, and with corn as the test crop,
showed that cultivation of the Brookston soil had no value other than
the control of weeds; but cultivation of the Miami soil, in addition to
weed control, increased the nitrate and water supply of the soil and the
yields of the crop.

Cultivation Tools. Cultivators are fitted with various types of attach-
ments, depending on the kind of cultivation to be done. In general, there
are two types: (1) scraper and (2) toothed. The toothed types cultivate
relatively deep, and the scraper types cultivate relatively shallow. Each
type has its specific purpose. Examples of the toothed type are the cultivator steels. These vary in width from 1 to 4 inches. In general, narrow
steels are used for fine work, and broad steels for coarse work. Examples

of the scraper type are one-sided sweeps, two-sided sweeps, and horizontal blades.

The Cultivation Program

The frequency and depth of cultivation of any particular crop depends largely on the following factors: (1) frequency with which crops of weeds become established, (2) amount of top and root growth of the crop plants, and (3) soil type.

Weed Establishment. The best time to kill weeds is when they are young. During the seedling stage most weeds are easily displaced or covered with soil, and they have not become sufficiently large to seriously compete with the crop for carbon dioxide, light, water, and essential raw materials. Obviously, with other factors equal, the number of cultivations will depend on the frequency with which crops of weeds become established. For this reason, a continuously moist soil usually requires a greater number of cultivations than a continuously dry soil.

Amount of Top and Root Growth. A direct relation exists between the amount of top growth a crop is making and the amount and extent of the root system. Thus, during the seedling stage the root system of any given plant is relatively small and inextensive. As the plant continues to grow, the root system continues to grow also, and with most crops it gradually becomes very extensive. Consequently, the first and second cultivations of any given crop may be relatively deep, particularly if the crop has been transplanted. Succeeding cultivations should be relatively shallow and proceed further from the plants to avoid cutting the feeding roots just beneath the surface. Certain authorities believe that if weeds are absent when herbaceous annual crops are half grown, cultivation should cease.

Using Herbicides

Herbicides are chemical compounds which are used to control weeds. They fall into two groups: (1) compounds which are nonselective in action and (2) compounds which are selective.

Nonselective compounds are toxic to all plants, e.g., lead arsenate, calcium arsenate, borax, sodium chloride, and ammonium sulfamate, called Ammate. As would be expected, each of these nonselective compounds has advantages and disadvantages; one compound may be more effective and desirable for use under one set of conditions, and another compound may be more effective and desirable under another.[2]

[2] For further information on the use of nonselective herbicides, the student is referred to Weed Control Recommendations, *Mississippi Agr. Exp. Sta. Bull.* 556, **1958.**

Fig. 13.2. Effect of a petroleum product on control of weeds in carrots. (Courtesy, W. H. Lachman, University of Massachusetts.)

Selective compounds kill certain kinds of plants and do very little, if any, damage to other kinds. Thus, selective compounds for any given crop should kill all or practically all the weeds in that crop and do no damage to the crop plants (see Fig. 13.2). These compounds may be placed in two groups: (1) the toxic and (2) the growth regulators. In general, toxic compounds kill the protoplasm by direct chemical action, and the growth regulators induce an abnormal development of certain tissues. Examples of toxic compounds and growth regulators used in the control of weeds, together with the preferred type of application and the weeds found in the crop which are not usually controlled by the chemical, are presented in Table 13.4.

Preemergence and Postemergence Treatments.   As shown in Table 13.4 both preemergence and postemergence treatments are used. In general, preemergence treatments are made before the seedling plants emerge. The land is prepared to receive the seed, the weed seeds are allowed to germinate, and then the seed is planted and the chemical is applied. The main advantage of this method is that the chemical is applied when the weed seedlings are very susceptible to injury, that is, when the seedlings are in the germination stage; and the main disadvantage is that heavy rains may leach the chemical to the vicinity of the seed and thus retard or prevent its germination. In general, postemergence treatments are made after the seedlings of the crop plant have emerged. The land is prepared to receive the seed, the seed is planted immediately afterwards, and the chemical is applied when the crop plants are in the seedling stage. The

Table 13.4.   EXAMPLES OF SELECTIVE HERBICIDES

Type of compound	Common or trade name	Crop	Recommended type of application	Weeds not usually controlled
Toxic compounds:				
Dinitro	DNPB	Snap bean	Preemergence	Late weeds
		Lima bean	Preemergence	
		Garden pea	Postemergence	
		Sweet corn	Preemergence	
		Potato	Preemergence	
Carbamates	Chloro IPC	Onion	Pre- and postemergence	
		Spinach	Preemergence	
		Southern pea	Preemergence	
		Sweetpotato	Postemergence	
Petroleum products	Stoddards	Carrot	Postemergence	Ragweed
Cyanates	Cyanamid	Onion	Preemergence	Grasses
Substitute ureas	CMU	Asparagus	Before and after harvest	Lamb's-quarters
		Grape		Milkweed
Other	NPA or Analap	Vine crops	Preemergence	
Growth regulators:				
Phenoxyacids	2, 4-D	Gladiolus	Postemergence	Most
		Lawns	Postemergence	grasses
		Sweet corn	Postemergence	

Source: Data from various sources.

main advantage of this method is that possible injury to the germinating seed is avoided. The main disadvantage is that the weed plants are likely to be quite resistant to the effects of the chemical, since mature tissues are more resistant than immature tissues.

Flaming

Flaming consists in directing jets of flame on weed plants. The practice is actually selective in action. In other words, crops vary in ability to withstand extremely high temperatures. Thus, for successful flaming, the basal stem of the crop plants should be resistant to these temperatures, and the unwanted plants, the weeds, should be susceptible. In general, flaming machines use butane or propane or mixtures of both, and both hand- and power-operated types have been developed. According to tests at the Mississippi Delta Experiment Station, satisfactory performance of the machine flamer requires that the crop plants be in straight rows on fairly level land and that the burners be adjusted in order to direct the flame to the weeds with little or no damage to the crop. At present, the use of the flaming machine in the control of weeds in horticultural crops is in the experimental stage.

Combinations with Cultivation

Cultivation combined with the use of selective herbicides and/or the flaming machine may be necessary or more desirable for certain crop industries. For example, compact soils may require cultivation even though selective chemicals satisfactorily control the weeds. Study the data in Table 13.5. Note the two weed-control treatments and the marked decrease in yield of carrots due to the compactness of the soil. Evidently, compact soils are unfavorable for the growth and development of carrot roots. As previously stated, compact soils are likely to limit the flow of oxygen to and carbon dioxide away from the absorbing roots and the nitrifying and nitrogen-fixing bacteria. This would seriously interfere with normal respiration and functioning of the root system and the respiration of the bacteria.

Further, combinations with cultivation may be necessary because of the

Table 13.5. **EFFECT OF TWO WEED-CONTROL TREATMENTS ON THE YIELD OF CARROTS, 1948***

Weed-control treatment	Condition of soil at harvest	Yield, lb marketable roots/acre	
		Woodstown sandy loam	Steinburg silt loam
Cultivation and hand weeding	Not compact	11,126	11,658
No cultivation, but hand weeding and oil spray	Compact	7,007	1,204

* A 5-10-10 mixture was applied to each soil at the rate of 1,000 pounds per acre and disked in immediately after plowing.
Source: Science, Dec. 3, 1948.

scarcity of hand labor. According to research at the Mississippi Delta Experiment Station, the use of selective herbicides markedly reduced hoe-labor requirements in cotton. But, it did not always result in corresponding reduction in weed-control costs. In many cases the cost of the chemicals and their application offset the savings made in reducing hoe labor.

The use of both nonselective and selective chemicals in the control of weeds is in a state of flux. The U.S. Department of Agriculture and many experiment stations and chemical companies have active research projects. For this reason, the student should consult a local experiment station for the latest information.

Mulching

The primary purpose of mulching is to promote growth and development and the production of high yields. For the most part, the beneficial effects vary with the season of the year. In general, mulches during the summer particularly in hot climates (1) reduce the rate of evaporation of water from the surface of the soil, thus conserving soil moisture; (2) keep the upper layer of soil from getting extremely hot during the midportion of sunny days, thus keeping soil temperatures close to or within the optimum range for root growth; (3) protect the soil from the bulletlike impact of intense rain, thus reducing soil erosion; (4) eliminate light from the surface of the soil, thus preventing the germination of many kinds of weed seed; and (5) prevent the splashing of soil particles on fruit close to the surface of the soil.

In general, mulches during the winter particularly in cold climates (1) reduce the loss of heat from the surface of the soil, thus keeping the soil comparatively warm; (2) prevent heaving of the soil, thus keeping the root system intact; (3) reduce the absorption of heat in the early spring, thus delaying the growth and, in some plants, the opening of the flowers until the last killing frost; (4) keep the fruit clean, as do summer mulches.

Organic materials usually used are straw, pine needles, peat, leaves, chopped corn cobs, and sawdust. The use of certain plastics as mulches is in the experimental stage.

QUESTIONS

1. What is a weed?
2. Weeds markedly decrease yields. Give four reasons.
3. Cabbage has an extensive root system. When the heads begin to form, the roots occupy all the fertile soil. Outline a cultivation program for your particular section of the country.

4. Celery has a sparse root system. The roots occupy soil not more than 6 inches from the basal portion of the plant. Outline a cultivation program for your particular section of the country.

5. In general, rains are light in intensity in the North and heavy in intensity in the South. Would the cultivation program for a crop of tomatoes be the same for each region? Give reasons.

6. Given two types of soil. Soil A is self-mulching; soil B is self-crusting. Which soil requires cultivation after a rain? Explain.

7. In general, the toothed type of cultivator is used when the crop is in the seedling stage. The scraper type is used when the crop is more than half grown. Explain.

8. A deep cultivation (2 to 3 inches) during the fruiting period of a crop of tomatoes or cantaloupes is likely to reduce the yield. Explain.

9. Given a wet season during the period of head formation of a cabbage crop. Show how deep cultivation would reduce the bursting of the heads.

10. Under what conditions would deep cultivation lower the rate of photosynthesis of a crop, and under what conditions would it have little effect? Give reasons.

11. What are herbicides?

12. State the main difference between nonselective and selective herbicides.

13. How do toxic compounds and growth regulators differ in their action on plants?

14. How are preemergence treatments made? Postemergence?

15. In general, preemergence treatments should be very effective in weed control. Explain.

16. What is flaming?

17. Compact soils may require cultivation even though the use of selective herbicides satisfactorily controls the weeds. Explain.

18. State the beneficial effects of mulching during the summer. During the winter.

IRRIGATING

THE WATER SUPPLY

Photosynthesis and Yield.   When the living cells of plants are in a state of turgor, they are fully stretched. The guard cells are fully expanded, and the size of the stomates is at a maximum. With other factors favorable, the diffusion of carbon dioxide into the leaves is rapid and the rate of photosynthesis is accordingly rapid. To maintain this condition, the rate of water absorption must, in general, equal the rate of transpiration. If, for any reason, the rate of absorption is lower than the rate of transpiration, a chain of events is initiated which finally results in decreased photosynthesis, growth, and yield. The guard cells become flaccid, the stomates decrease in size, and the rate of diffusion of carbon dioxide into the leaves is reduced. As a result, the rate of photosynthesis is reduced, while the rate of respiration continues at its usual level, and very few carbohydrates are available for growth and yield. Thus, when the intake of water is less than the outgo per unit time, the water supply becomes the limiting factor in plant growth. Note the relation of the amount of available water to yield in Fig. 13.3.

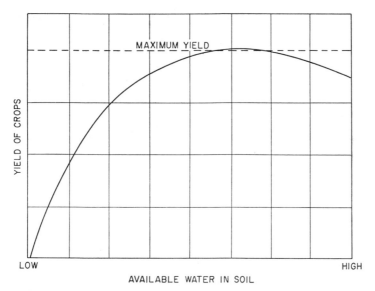

Fig. 13.3. Relation of amount of available water to yield. (Courtesy, D. W. Thorne and H. B. Peterson, "Irrigated Soils," New York, McGraw-Hill Book Company, Inc.)

Natural Supplies of Water. The principal sources of water for irrigation are rain and snow. The annual amount and distribution of rain and snow in the continental United States vary greatly from region to region within any given season and from season to season within any region. Based on the average annual precipitation, the continental United States may be divided into three more or less overlapping regions: (1) arid—less than 10 inches, (2) semiarid—from 10 to 30 inches, and (3) humid—from 30 to 100 inches or more. The arid region is a relatively small area and, in general, comprises the Salt River Valley of Arizona, the Coachella Valley of California, and parts of Nevada and southern Idaho. The semiarid region includes the western part of Kansas, Oklahoma, and Texas; the eastern part of Washington and Oregon; most of Idaho and California; and practically the whole of Montana, Wyoming, Colorado, Utah, North Dakota, South Dakota, Nebraska, and Minnesota. The humid region is the largest area and comprises the eastern half of the United States and the coastal section of Washington, Oregon, and northern California. Within the eastern half of the country, the mean annual precipitation varies from 30 inches in Maine to 60 inches in southern Louisiana, Mississippi, Alabama, and parts of Florida and to 80 inches in the mountain section of western North Carolina and northern Georgia. Within the coastal section of Washington, Oregon, and northern California, the mean annual rainfall varies from 30 to 120 inches or more. In fact, the wettest places in the country are certain areas in the Puget Sound district of Washington, which has an annual precipitation of approximately 120 inches. Study the precipitation data in Fig. 13.4. Note the marked differences in annual rainfall in many places of the country.

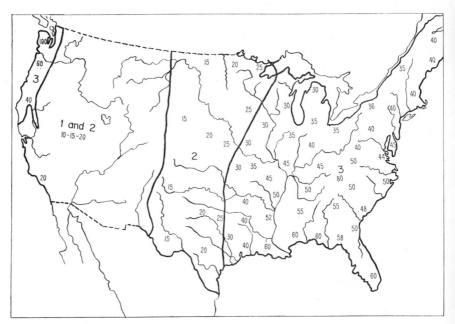

Fig. 13.4. Arid, semiarid, and humid regions of the continental United States. 1–2: mostly arid (about 10 inches per year with semiarid districts scattered throughout the area). 2: semiarid (15–30 inches per year). 3: humid (30–120 inches per year).

Is the rain from year to year adequate for the growth of crops in each of these regions? Since from 10 to 30 inches of water is necessary for the growth and development of most horticultural crops, the rain in the arid and semiarid regions is entirely inadequate. Hence, applications of irrigation water are necessary. In fact, irrigation of the crops of these regions is considered the most important cultural practice, and the value of the land is determined by its accessibility to an abundant source of suitable water. In these regions, laws and regulations governing the use of irrigation water have been established. In general, these laws, usually known as water rights, have been established so that any given individual grower of any given producing district obtains his proportionate share of irrigation water from any given source.

What is the situation in the humid regions? The records show that the rainfall in these regions for the most part is adequate. However, crops growing in these regions frequently suffer from lack of water. In other words, the rains do not always come when they are needed. Every year in some districts there is likely to be a droughty period. This period may last for only one or two weeks; yet it may come at a time when crops require a high moisture content of the soil for satisfactory growth. In general, these droughty periods occur quite frequently. For example, there were 127 droughts in the eastern part of the country from 1919 to 1939. This is an average of six droughts per year. To look at the situation in another way, a study of the annual rainfall at State College, Mississippi, from 1919 to 1949, a period of 30 years, showed that on the average 42 per cent, or 95 days, of the 226-day frost-free growing period did not receive sufficient rain for abundant plant growth. As previously stated, droughts induce water deficits within the plant. This in turn decreases the size of the cells in the region of elongation, lowers the rate of photosynthesis, and decreases yield and quality. As a result, the money spent in buying seed, commercial fertilizers, and other materials and the time spent in preparing the soil, planting the seed, applying the commercial fertilizers, and controlling the weeds are wasted.

Results of Experiments with Irrigation. Since the annual rainfall in the humid regions is usually sufficient in quantity, many growers store the water when it is not needed and apply it when needed. What are the increases in marketable yield due to applications of irrigation water during periods of insufficient rainfall? The results of two tests are set forth to give the student some idea of the possibilities and the potentialities of using irrigation water.

In 1937 the Illinois Experiment Station irrigated 4 acres of tomatoes by the furrow system and allowed a similar area to remain unirrigated. (The growing season for tomatoes in central Illinois extends from June to October.) The rainfall during the period of the test was well distributed, and only one irrigation was given to the irrigated area. The harvest season extended from August 18 to October 4. The irrigated plot produced 521 baskets of marketable tomatoes, and the nonirrigated plot produced 311 baskets. Thus, the increased yield due to the one irrigation was 210 baskets of tomatoes. These tomatoes had a market value of $51.20. The costs of irrigating the 4-acre plot, including labor, fuel, and equipment, was $16.91, leaving a net gain of $34.29. Thus, irrigation was profitable during one of the most favorable seasons from the standpoint of the rainfall for growing tomatoes in Illinois.

Table 13.6.   **EFFECT OF TWO FURROW IRRIGATIONS ON YIELD OF SNAP BEANS, CRYSTAL SPRINGS, MISSISSIPPI, 1951**

Water supply	Marketable yield, bu/acre			Value*	Cost of irrigation†	Net profit
	First harvest	Second harvest	Total harvest			
Natural plus irrigation	177	122	239	$585	$125	$269
Natural only	37	41	78	191		

* *According to actual prices at local market.*
† *Includes depreciation of pump, cost of fuel and labor in applying the water, cost of picking and hauling, and cost of hampers for the additional 161 bushels.*

In 1951, the Truck Crops Branch Experiment Station in Crystal Springs, Mississippi, irrigated certain plots of a field of Contender snap beans. The results are presented in Table 13.6. Note the marked increase in marketable yields and the increased returns due to the application of water. As a result of numerous tests with irrigation, applications of water within the humid regions are becoming increasingly common in orchards, vegetable crop plantings, flower gardens, lawns, parks, and so forth.

Sources of Irrigation Water.   The principal sources of irrigation water are large springs, streams, lakes, wells, ponds, reservoirs, and municipal water supplies. In the arid and semiarid regions, the source of water is generally above the land to be irrigated and the water is carried over the land by gravity.[3] This water is derived from snow precipitated on the mountains by the moisture-laden winds from the west and northwest. Thus, growers of horticultural crops are vitally interested in the annual snowfall of these regions. In the humid regions, the source of water is usually below the level of the land to be irrigated and pumps are necessary to lift the water. Like growers in the arid regions, growers in this region are interested in the annual precipitation, since this rainfall maintains the lakes, streams, ponds, reservoirs, and surface wells.

Water suitable for irrigation is moderately to slightly acid and free from appreciable quantities of salts, particularly sodium chloride which ionizes, forming sodium and chlorine ions. In districts where the water is quite alkaline, it is acidified to prevent the formation of highly alkaline

[3] The western half of the San Joaquin Valley of California and the winter-garden area and Rio Grande Valley of south Texas are exceptions.

soil with its resultant deficiency of available nitrogen, phosphorus, and other essential elements. Chemicals generally used are sulfuric acid and phosphoric acid. The Ohio and Michigan Experiment Stations have developed machines for the acidification of water for greenhouse use.

The right to use water in the humid regions is now assuming the same importance as that in the arid and semiarid regions. In fact, many states have made surveys of water resources and are now considering the development of codes embodying water rights and the use of irrigation water by growers of crops.

METHODS OF APPLYING IRRIGATION WATER

Three more or less distinct methods by which water is applied to the land and crops are (1) surface irrigation, (2) subirrigation, and (3) spray irrigation. Each method has advantages and disadvantages.

Surface irrigation is the application of water directly over the surface of the land. In general, this method requires a gentle slope, a deep, compact, uniformly textured soil, and plentiful supplies of water. Thus, it is not adaptable on rolling land or on fields which contain shallow topsoils. Two systems of surface irrigation are used: (1) border, or basin, and (2) furrow.

For border irrigation the land is leveled, if necessary, and bordered. The borders vary from 6 to 8 inches in height, generally follow the contours, and run in both directions. This method is commonly used to irrigate orchards in California and spinach in south Texas.

For furrow irrigation the land is leveled or ridged. The furrows vary from 4 to 10 inches in depth and follow the contours of the land. This method is commonly used to irrigate most row crops in the arid and semiarid regions. In fact, the many horticultural crop industries of the West have been made possible by the use of man's engineering skill in applying water to the land in this region. Note the position of the water stream in the furrow-irrigated orchard in Fig. 13.5.

Subirrigation is the application of water below the surface of the land. In general, this method requires relatively large quantities of water and specific soil strata: (1) an impervious lower layer to hold the water against the force of gravity (clay or hardpan), (2) an open, porous, intermediate layer to serve as a reservoir for water (sand or sandy loam), and (3) a finely textured top layer to facilitate capillary action (fine sandy loam, silt loam, or peat). Subirrigation is used extensively in certain vegetable districts in Florida and in the celery and onion districts of Michigan and New York. In Florida the water is obtained from artesian wells and is conducted through lines of 3-inch drain tile placed 18 inches deep and 24 feet apart. In Michigan and New York the soil—a slightly acid, highly

Fig. 13.5. Furrow irrigation of a peach orchard. The water is applied in the terraced channels (below the trees) and in the contour furrows (above the trees). (Courtesy, Soil Conservation Service, U.S. Department of Agriculture.)

decomposed muck—is drained by ditches, and the height of the water table is controlled by a series of dams in the ditches.

Spray irrigation is the application of water on the surface of the land in the form of spray similar to a gentle rain. This type of irrigation is adapted to all types of soils and to both level and rolling land and generally requires less labor and less water than surface irrigation. The types of spray irrigation systems are classified according to the materials which carry and apply the water. These are (1) the stationary nozzle, (2) the portable sprinkler, and (3) the perforated pipe.

The stationary nozzle consists of nonportable parallel lines of galvanized iron pipes. The lines are usually placed 50 feet apart and are supported on low posts 3 to 4 feet high, on high posts 10 to 20 feet high, or on a cable supported by posts 12 to 20 feet high. The high-post system is more popular than the low-post, since it allows teams, tractors, and workers to pass under the pipelines and utilizes the land to better advantage. Each line of pipe is equipped with nozzles and an oscillator. The nozzles are of two types: (1) those which deflect and thus break the water into a fine mist (generally used in greenhouses) and (2) those which discharge the water in the form of a small stream (generally used outdoors). When water is running through the system, the oscillator turns the pipe through an arc of 60 to 90°. Thus, pipes equipped with oscillators require less attention and facilitate a more uniform and steady application of water than pipes not so equipped. This system of irrigation is used extensively by market gardeners and florists throughout the country. A trip to any of the large market-garden districts in the United States will convince the student of its profitable use and application. Its main disadvantage is the high initial cost.

The portable sprinkler consists of feed lines with joints which are quickly assembled and taken apart. The sprinklers are mounted on the pipes and are spaced 20 to 40 feet apart, depending on the type of nozzle and the water pressure used. The main advantage of the portable pipe system is the relatively low initial cost. This type of irrigation is becoming popular in different regions of the country. Note the portable sprinkler system in operation in Fig. 13.6.

The perforated sprinkler consists of the same type of feed lines as that of the portable rotary system, but instead of rotary sprinklers perforated pipes are used. In general, these pipes are laid on the surface of the land with the perforations on the upper side. This system is adaptable to all crops and to all soils which have high infiltration rates.

Amount of Water per Application and Time Interval between Applications. In general, the amount of water that should be applied for any given irrigation depends on (1) the stage of growth of the crop, (2) the depth of the absorbing system, and (3) the field capacity of the soil. Since capillary water moves for short distances only, the amount of water applied at any given time should fill the rooting zone and no more. Thus, crops in the early stages of growth require less quantities per application than crops in the later stages. In like manner, mature crops which develop

Fig. 13.6. Spray irrigation in a potato field. The water is applied by means of a portable sprinkling system.

shallow root systems require less quantities per application than crops which develop moderately deep or deep root systems. For example, most of the roots of mature strawberry, celery, and onion plants are within 6 to 12 inches from the surface. For this reason, nothing is gained by applying more water than is needed to go to these depths. Further, under the same climatic conditions soils with low field capacities, the sands and sandy loams, require less quantities per application than soils with high field capacities, the silt loams and clay loams.

In general, the time interval between applications depends on (1) the area of transpiring surface, (2) the rate of transpiration, (3) the rate of evaporation of water from the soil, and (4) the field capacity of the soil. Thus, under the same conditions plants with a large transpiring surface (large leaf area) need more frequent irrigations than plants with a small transpiring area (small leaf area). In the same type of soil and at the same stage of growth, plants with high rates of transpiration require more frequent applications than plants with low rates. In this manner, soils with high rates of evaporation require shorter intervals between irrigations than soils with low rates. Finally, soils with low field capacities require more frequent applications than soils with high field capacities.

Cost of Irrigation.   Important factors are (1) type of system, (2) length of time the equipment is used each season, and (3) source of water. In general, the furrow system has a low initial cost, but it requires more attention when water is applied; the longer the time the equipment is used, the lower the cost; and water from shallow wells or ponds costs less than water from deep wells. According to studies at the Mississippi Experiment Station, the cheapest system is the contour-check, or furrow, with water from a lake or stream slightly below the level of the land to be irrigated. With this system the cost may be as low as $1 per acre-inch. On the other hand, the spray system with water from a deep well may cost as high as $5 or more per acre-inch. In 1954 the Georgia Experiment Station obtained data on returns from the irrigation of 32 fields growing many kinds of vegetables. These fields averaged 20 acres in size; the crops were given an average of 6 inches of water in 4.5 applications; and although the returns and the costs varied widely with the crop and with the operator, the returns on the average were $163 per acre and the cost of applying the water on the average was $42 per acre.

QUESTIONS

1. The amount of water needed for the actual combination of carbon dioxide and water in photosynthesis is very small compared with the amount required to keep the living cells turgid. Explain.

2. Increases in yield by irrigation depend largely on the rate of water absorption keeping up with the rate of transpiration. Explain.
3. For the same crop grown in comparable soils more water would be needed in the Southeast than in the Northeast or Middle West. Explain.
4. The mean rainfall in the humid East is sufficient for the growth of horticultural crops, yet these crops frequently produce low yields. Explain.
5. Investigations in apple orchards in the Cumberland Shenandoah Valley have shown that drought during the period of fruit growth decreases fruit size and that irrigation has increased fruit size. Explain.
6. Many orchardists in the humid region of the continental United States have found that irrigation pays. Explain.
7. Growers of vegetable crops for early market frequently irrigate their high-cash crops. Explain.
8. Irrigation systems are part of the necessary equipment of the commercial florist. Explain.
9. What are the principal sources of irrigation water in your community?
10. Distinguish between surface irrigation, subirrigation, and spray irrigation
11. State the three requirements for successful surface irrigation.
12. In furrow irrigation, the slope for sandy loams should be from 10 to 12 inches per 100 feet, and for clay loams from 1 to 3 inches per 100 feet. Explain.
13. Draw a soil profile of a mineral soil which is particularly adaptable to subirrigation.
14. Compare furrow irrigation and spray irrigation from the standpoint of adaptability to the region east of the Mississippi River.
15. Given two crops. Crop A develops a relatively shallow and nonextensive root system; crop B develops a deep and extensive root system. With the same soil and environment, how would the irrigation of these crops vary from the standpoint of number of irrigations and amount of water applied at each irrigation? Give reasons.
16. In general, growers who are inexperienced in irrigation should start in a small way and "grow" with the practice. Explain.
17. In general, any given farm is an irrigation problem within itself. Explain.
18. From your own observation and experience, describe how the home grounds are supplied with irrigation water.

PRUNING

14

They shall beat their swords into plowshares,
and their spears into pruning hooks.

Isaiah 2:4

Pruning is a major horticultural practice. It is necessary for the successful production of tree fruits, grapes, small fruits, nut fruits, and many flower and ornamental plants. In general, pruning consists in the removal of parts of the top or root system of plants. Woody tissues are usually removed by means of sharp cutting instruments in order to make clean, non-jagged wounds. Succulent tissues are usually removed by hand.

The object of pruning varies with the viewpoint of the pruner. Commercial orchardists, gardeners, and florists are interested primarily in profits. In other words, they consider such factors as size, color, shape, or quality of flower or fruit only as these factors influence profits. On the other hand, amateur gardeners place costs and profits in a secondary category. They consider such factors as size, color, shape, or quality as important in themselves.

Both the stem and the root systems of plants are pruned. Since pruning the stem and pruning the root influence growth and development differently, they are discussed separately.

PRUNING THE STEM

All plants respond to removal of the top in two definite ways. Pruning the top (1) always reduces the total amount of growth which could otherwise be made and (2) always influences the vegetative-reproductive balance of the plant.

252

Total Amount of Growth Made. Numerous investigations have shown that pruning the top dwarfs the tree or plant. The removal of twigs of trees or stems of herbaceous plants reduces the amount of carbohydrates and other materials already made and reduces the number of leaves which would have contributed to further food manufacture. In other words, the removal of stems and leaves or of stems containing buds which would later develop into leaves reduces the machinery for food manufacture. This removal in turn reduces the total amount of food that can be made in any one season. For example, consider two branches of an apple tree. Each branch has four twigs of equal size and vigor, and each twig has 50 leaf buds which later develop into 50 leaves. Suppose we remove one twig from branch A and none from branch B. Although the individual leaves on branch A will be somewhat larger than those on branch B, with other factors favorable, the 200 leaves on branch B will make more food during the season than the 150 leaves on branch A. Thus, at the end of the growing season branch B will have made a greater amount of growth than branch A. As a second example, consider two tomato plants. Plant A is pruned to a single stem; that is, the laterals on the main axis are "pinched off" as soon as they begin to develop. Plant B is allowed to grow the natural way; that is, no stems are removed. During the fruiting period plant B will have the greater leaf area. This greater leaf area will manufacture a greater quantity of food, and because of this greater quantity of food, plant B will produce the greater number of tomatoes. As a third example, consider two chrysanthemum plants. Plant A is pruned to a single stem, and plant B is allowed to grow in the natural way. Plant A will produce one large flower at the top of the stem, and plant B will produce a small flower at the top of each of several stems. The total weight of the several small flowers produced by plant B will exceed the weight of the single large flower produced by plant A. Clearly, the removal of healthy stems and leaves reduces plant size and yield and the total amount of growth that can be made.

Vegetative-Reproductive Balance. What is the relative effect of pruning the top on the disposition of the carbohydrates and the vegetative-reproductive balance of plants? In general (1) pruning the top reduces the number of growing points of any given plant; (2) this increases the supply of available nitrogen and other essential elements to the growing points which remain; and (3) this in turn increases the number of cells which can be made. Pruning the top, therefore, promotes the making of cells and the utilization of carbohydrates. Accordingly, it promotes the vegetative phase and retards the reproductive phase. The stimulation of the vegetative phase and retardation of the reproductive phase may or may not be desirable. Much depends on the vigor of growth any given plant is making. If, for example, orchard trees are young and vigorous, pruning, if necessary, should be extremely light, since heavy pruning of the top delays flower-bud formation. On the other hand, if orchard trees are old and weakly vigorous, severe pruning of the top helps to promote vigor and rejuvenation.

Kinds of Top Pruning. There are two kinds of top pruning: (1) heading back and (2) thinning out. In *heading back,* the terminal portion of twigs, canes, or shoots is removed, but the basal portion is not. In *thinning out,* the entire twig, cane, or shoot is removed. In general, heading back stimulates the development of more growing points than a corresponding thinning out. How does heading back stimulate the development of more growing points? The student should remember that terminal buds on shoots secrete growth-inhibiting hormones which are translocated to the lateral buds. These growth-inhibiting hormones prevent the development of the lateral buds. When the terminal bud is removed, as in heading back, the formation and translocation of the growth-inhibiting substances cease and one to several lateral buds develop. Usually, the lateral buds just below a cut develop more, and they in turn manufacture the growth-inhibiting hormones which prevent the development of the lateral buds farther down. Thinning out does not have this effect as much as heading back. Thus, heading back induces the compact, dense, or much-branched type of growth and thinning out induces the open or rangy type of growth.

PRUNING THE STEM OF WOODY PLANTS

TREE TRAINING AND TREE FORMS

Training is a type of top pruning. It is particularly important in the many tree-fruit industries. Young trees are trained to develop a frame of scaffold limbs sufficiently strong to bear large crops of fruit without breaking. Thus, the development of strong crotches and well-spaced limbs is essential. Furthermore, since even a light pruning of young trees lengthens the time from planting to flowering and fruiting, the practice should be efficiently performed. The various forms to which trees are trained are of three general types: (1) central leader, (2) open center, or vase, and (3) modified leader.

Central Leader. The central-leader type of tree has a main branch and a series of well-spaced "subordinate" lateral branches. Its main advantage is the development of strong crotches due to the interlacing of fibers at the junction of the limb and the trunk. Its main disadvantage is shading the interior of the tree. This shading weakens the central leader and thus shortens the life of the tree. Authorities state that trees of some varieties, such as the Wealthy apple, are trained rather easily to this form, but trees of other varieties, such as the Rhode Island Greening apple, are trained to this form with difficulty.

Open Center, or Vase. The open-center, or vase, type of tree has no main or central branch but a series of well-spaced "coordinate" lateral branches. These laterals are given the same dominance by cutting them back equally each year. Practically the same number of leaves will develop on each branch. Thus, all the coordinate branches make the same growth

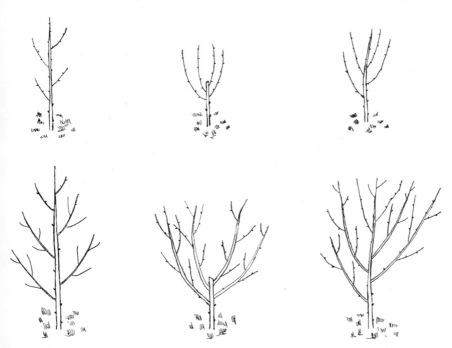

Fig. 14.1. Outline of scaffold branches of the three tree forms. Left: central leader. Center: open center. Right: modified leader.

each year. The main advantages of this tree form are that light penetration becomes sufficient for the fruiting of inner branches and that a low-headed tree develops, which facilitates pruning, thinning, spraying, and picking operations. Its main disadvantage is that the tree develops weak, crowded crotches which frequently break under severe stress and strain, such as bearing a heavy crop of fruit.

Modified Leader. The modified-leader type of tree is a happy medium between the central leader and open center. During the period of training the central leader is cut back slightly and not allowed to become dominant. The process of cutting back and selecting laterals is repeated until the proper number and distribution of branches have been obtained. The central leader is then discontinued, and the tree assumes a more or less rounded, open top. In this way the modified-leader type of tree has low and well-spaced limbs, well-distributed fruiting wood and is sufficiently close to the ground to facilitate the many orchard operations. Of the three types the modified leader is the most desirable for many tree fruits because it combines the most important advantages of the other types. Note the relative dominance of the main and lateral branches of each of the three types in Fig. 14.1.

TOP PRUNING SPECIFIC CROPS

Pome Fruits (Apple and Pear)

Fruiting Habit. A working knowledge of the flowering and fruiting habits of crop plants is essential to a proper understanding of pruning requirements. In general, the fruit of the apple and pear is produced

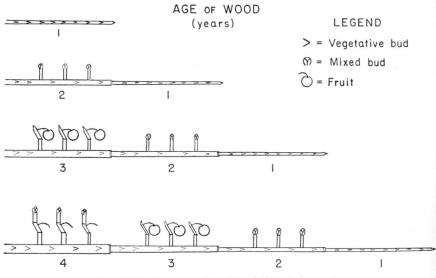

Fig. 14.2. Diagram of fruiting habit of the apple.

from mixed buds which are borne on short lateral branches called fruiting spurs. These spurs develop in the following manner. Certain laterally situated vegetative buds on the second season's wood make a short growth, usually ½ to 3 inches or more, and in late summer they develop a terminally situated mixed bud (see the second-year wood in Fig. 14.2). The following spring each mixed bud develops into a cluster of flowers, makes a short vegetative growth, and develops one or more fruits (see the third-year wood in Fig. 14.2). During the third spring a laterally situated vegetative bud on any given individual spur makes a short growth, and in late summer it develops a terminally situated mixed bud. This sequence continues throughout the life of any given spur. Thus, an individual spur lays down a mixed bud one year and produces fruit the next.

In the ideal situation half the spurs lay down flower buds while the other half bear fruit, which makes the tree an annual bearer. However, should a frost, freeze, or some other adverse condition destroy most of the blossoms in any given year, large quantities of carbohydrates accumulate in the tops. As a result, a large number of flower buds are laid down and a heavy crop of fruit is produced. This exhausts the carbohydrate supply, and, as a result, a small number of flower buds are laid down and a light crop of fruit is produced the following year. In this way the so-called alternate, or biennial, habit is established. Study the diagram of the fruiting habit of the apple in Fig. 14.2.

Vegetative Period (1 to 4 years). During the vegetative period the trees are trained usually to the modified-leader type. Briefly, training consists in (1) heading back to promote the development of lateral branches and a low-headed tree, (2) selecting well-spaced laterals to form the framework and removing the others, and (3) pruning the remaining limbs to regulate their growth so that they may occupy a relative proportion of space without interference. In general, one-year-old trees consist of a single stem called a whip. This whip is headed-back to a height of 42 to 48 inches immediately after planting, and laterals are selected about three or four weeks after they have started growth in the spring or during the next winter. In either case, four to six well-spaced lateral shoots are selected and the others are removed. The uppermost lateral usually achieves the greatest

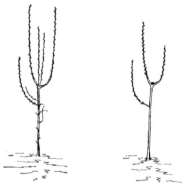

Fig. 14.3. Training of a young apple tree. Which limbs were removed, which were allowed to remain, and which were headed-back? (Redrawn from Training Young Fruit Trees, Iowa Agr. Ext. Serv. Pamphlet 102, 1945.)

growth and is called the leader. In general, two-year-old trees have well-developed lateral branches. Immediately after the trees are planted, three to four well-spaced laterals are selected and the remainder are removed. Adequate spacing of the laterals is essential in order to keep them well distributed around the trunk (see Fig. 14.3).

Transitory Period (5 to 8 Years). In the transitory period the trees are changing from an entirely vegetative phase to a period of alternating vegetative and reproductive phases. During this period the plants are pruned lightly, since heavy pruning delays the onset of the fruiting period. In general, this pruning consists in removing undesirable water sprouts and dead or diseased wood and lightly thinning out the top.

Fruiting Period (8 to 40 Years).   This period is divided into two stages: (1) early and (2) late. During the early period the young bearing trees are vigorous, and in general only corrective pruning is necessary. Corrective pruning consists in the removal of dead or diseased wood or undesirable parallel branches and in the regulation of the growth of the branches to permit the development of strong crotches. As the trees become older the development of small, weak branches become evident. Investigations at the Michigan Experiment Station have shown that a direct relation exists between the diameter of the four-year-old wood and the number, size, and quality of the fruit which it bears. In Michigan orchards, four-year-old wood $\frac{1}{2}$ inch or more in diameter produced an average of 10 fruits of good size and color; four-year-old wood from $\frac{3}{8}$ to $\frac{1}{2}$ inch in diameter produced an average of seven fruits of medium size and poor color; and four-year-old wood less than $\frac{1}{4}$ inch in diameter produced only three small, poorly colored fruits. Thus, the pruning of mature bearing trees consists largely in the removal of four-year-old wood less than $\frac{1}{4}$ inch in diameter. Most of the thin, unproductive branches are found on the inside of the trees. The apple grower, therefore, in pruning his trees leaves the thick, productive branches and removes the thin, unproductive ones.

Drupe Fruits (Peach, Apricot, Almond, Plum, and Cherry)

Fruiting Habit.   The fruit of the peach, apricot, and almond is borne on the second season's wood, which is itself developed during the previous season. During the first part of the first season this wood, called shoots, grows in length, and during the latter part it develops the laterally situated flower buds (see the first and second seasons' wood in Fig. 14.4). Scientists have found a remarkably close relation of vigor of shoot growth to productivity the following year. In fact, the fruiting wood of the peach may be classified as follows: (1) weakly vigorous, (2) moderately vigorous, and (3) excessively vigorous. In general, weakly vigorous shoots make a short growth, 3-6-8 inches, and develop relatively few flower buds; moderately vigorous shoots make a moderately long growth, 6-12-18 inches, and develop a large number of flower buds; and excessively vigorous shoots make an extremely long growth, 18-24-26 inches, and develop relatively few flower buds. Obviously, the moderately vigorous wood is the most productive.

The fruit of the plum and cherry is produced from simple laterally situated buds also. These buds are laid down on the current season's growth and on spurs. Vegetative buds always terminate shoot and spur growth; therefore, the spurs are usually straight. Like the peach, moderately vigorous growth of the plum and cherry increases the number of nodes, the number of flower buds, and fruitfulness; whereas scant or overvigorous growth decreases the number of flower buds and fruitfulness.

The Peach. VEGETATIVE PERIOD (2 TO 3 YEARS). In general, the peach is trained to the open-center form. In the spring the newly planted trees are headed-back to a lateral branch or bud 24 to 36 inches from the ground line, and lateral branches are allowed to grow for two to three years before the scaffold limbs are selected. Thus, during the

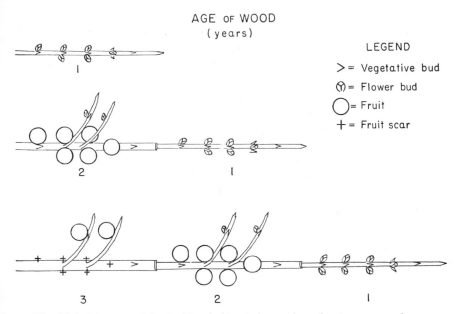

AGE OF WOOD
(years)

LEGEND

> = Vegetative bud

= Flower bud

= Fruit

+ = Fruit scar

Fig. 14.4. *Diagram of the fruiting habit of the moderately vigorous peach tree.*

first two or three years very little pruning is required. The branches which are obviously out of place, broken, or diseased are removed. If any lateral branch becomes overdominant, it is pruned back to an outside branch. This mild pruning during the first two or three years provides for a maximum leaf area and hence a rapid development of the tree. After the tree has grown for two or three years, three to five lateral branches, preferably four, are selected. These should be arranged spirally around the trunk 4 to 6 inches apart. These lateral branches become the main scaffold limbs of the tree.

The secondary laterals in the center of the tree are removed or cut back to a lateral branch. In this way, the open-center type of tree is de-

Fig. 14.5. Training of the young peach tree.

veloped, which exposes the leaves to full sunlight and facilitates spraying, harvesting, and pruning operations (see Fig. 14.5).

TRANSITORY PERIOD (3 TO 4 YEARS). During the transitory period, moderate pruning is necessary. If any branch becomes dominant, it is cut back to an outside lateral branch. The branches in the center portion are pruned to maintain the open-center type. The objectives are (1) to maintain strong, evenly distributed scaffold limbs, (2) to expose all parts of the tree to adequate sunlight, and (3) to maintain a relatively low-headed tree with well-distributed fruiting wood.

FRUITING PERIOD (5 TO 20 YEARS). Since the moderately vigorous tree is the most productive, the main objective is to establish, if necessary, and maintain the moderately vigorous condition. Thus to establish moderate vigor, weakly vigorous trees will require relatively severe pruning, and excessively vigorous trees will require light, if any, pruning. To maintain moderate vigor two facts should be kept in mind: (1) The moderately vigorous tree develops more flower buds than it can develop into marketable fruit; and (2) the fruiting wood is borne on relatively young wood. Thus, to reduce the number of flower buds and to keep the fruiting wood close to the frame of the tree, heading back is required. In general, this is done by removing one-third to one-half of the terminal portion of the past season's growth or by removing four to five shoots at the terminal of each branch and heading back the remainder of the current season's growth of each branch. Of the two methods the latter requires less time and stimulates the development of shoots close to the frame of the tree. For these reasons it is generally recommended.

Cherry and Plum.   Like the apple and pear, the many kinds of cherries —sour, sweet, and Dukes—and the many kinds of plums—European, Japanese, and American—are trained to the modified-leader tree form. In general, training involves the selection of three or four laterals and a leader. The laterals should be at least 4 to 6 inches apart and arranged around a main stem to prevent girdling of the trunk. During the transitory period light pruning, mostly of the thinning-out type, is necessary. With upright-growing varieties attention is given to the development of lateral branches. During the bearing period the amount of thinning out and heading back varies with the species. In general, cherries require the least pruning, since direct light is unnecessary for the development of the fruit, and the crop is seldom heavier than the tree can bear. The European plum requires more pruning than the cherry, but less than the Japanese plum, which requires less than the peach. In any case old trees are pruned more severely than young trees in order to renew the fruiting wood.

The Grape

Fruiting Habit. The fruit of the grape comes from mixed buds which are borne on one-year-old shoots called canes, which are developed during

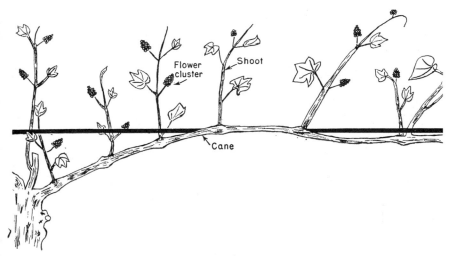

Fig. 14.6. *Fruiting habit of grape. The fruit-bearing shoots have just started their growth in the spring. Note the flower clusters opposite the leaves. (Redrawn from H. J. Sefick and J. Harold Clark, Pruning Grapevines, New Jersey Agr. Exp. Sta. Circ. 423, 1942.)*

the previous season. Investigations have shown that fruiting of the grape is positively associated with vigor of the cane. In general, medium-thick (moderately vegetative) canes are more fruitful than thin (weakly vegetative) or thick (vigorously vegetative) canes. For example, in Michigan and elsewhere canes of the Concord variety $\frac{1}{4}$ inch or slightly more in diameter at the fifth or sixth node are more productive than greater or smaller sizes at the same position. Thus, size of cane is an important consideration in productivity. Note the fruiting habit of the grape shown in Fig. 14.6.

Pruning the Young Vine. Although grapes are pruned to various systems, the pruning requirements of the vine for the first, second, and third years are practically the same for all systems. The main operations are (1) cutting back the most vigorous cane to two or three buds and removing the remainder, (2) setting the plants in the vineyard, (3) tying the canes to a stake to permit close cultivation during the growing season, and (4) cutting back the most vigorous cane to two or three buds and removing the remainder during the dormant season. After the next season the vines are trained to the system desired.

Some systems used in training and pruning grapes are the six-arm, the fan, the wire canopy or overhead, but a common system is the single trunk and arm. In general, this system, or frame, consists of a permanent trunk with lateral branches called arms. The length and number of arms depend largely on the size of the individual fruit clusters produced, and this in turn depends on the kind of grape grown.

In the labrusca, or northern, grape the individual fruit clusters are large, and, as a result, only a relatively small number of clusters can develop into marketable fruit and only relatively short arms are required. Four arms are usually used, and this requires a two-wire trellis with the arms, one to the right and the other to the left, at the level of each wire (see Fig. 14.7). In pruning for each arm a moderately vigorous cane is selected for the production of fruit and is headed-back to 8 or 10 buds, and, in addition, one or two canes near the arm are selected for renewal purposes and cut back to two or three buds. In this way, the fruiting wood is kept reasonably close to the trunk of the vine.

In the muscadine, or southern, grape the individual fruit clusters are small, and, as a result, a relatively large number of fruit clusters can develop into marketable fruit. Thus, a relatively large number of canes are required, and in order to support these canes the arms are extended

Fig. 14.7. Pruning the labrusca grape, variety Portland. Left: before pruning. Right: after pruning. (Courtesy, H. J. Sefick, Clemson College.)

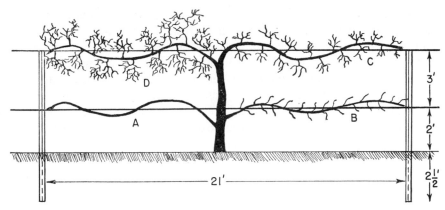

Fig. 14.8. Pruning the muscadine grape. A: one-year-old arm. B–D: two-, three-, and four-year-old arms with fruiting branches. (Courtesy, M. Aubrey Owen, Gay, Ga.)

(see Fig. 14.8). In pruning for each arm all the canes are headed-back to two, three, or four buds, depending on the vigor of each individual cane.

The Brambleberries (Black, Purple, and Red Raspberry, Blackberry, and Dewberry)

Fruiting Habit.   Like the grape, the fruit of the brambleberries develop from mixed buds borne on one-year-old canes. The canes develop the first season, fruit, and then die the second season (except the everbearing raspberries and the Himalaya blackberries). Pruning of the canes before they have fruited depends on the variety and method of training.

Black and Purple Raspberry.   The black and purple raspberry usually set more fruit than the canes can adequately develop, hence they are pruned heavily. The kind and amount of pruning depend on the training system. If the canes are grown with support, the tips of the young shoots of the black varieties are "pinched-off" when they are 12 inches high if grown in California and when they are from 18 to 24 inches high if grown in the Northeast and South. The tips of the purple varieties are pinched-off when they are from 30 to 36 inches high. The pinching off induces the development of lateral branches and prevents the canes from becoming top-heavy. Just before growth starts in the spring the laterals are headed-back. The student should keep in mind that the fruit is borne on branches developed from the laterals. Investigations have shown that the number and size of the fruit can be regulated by the number of buds left. In general, if the canes are small, two buds per lateral are sufficient; if they are vigorous, from 8 to 10 buds per lateral can be left (see Fig. 14.9).

Red Raspberry. The red raspberry produces tall, erect stems. Pruning, other than removing the canes which have fruited, consists in thinning out small or extra canes. In the Pacific Northwest excess canes are removed in the spring and the remaining canes are cut back in the winter. A Y-trellis is used to support the canes. In the central and eastern states the plants are pruned according to the method of planting. Under the hill system the plants are set 4 × 8 feet, and pruning consists in removing all but about seven of the most vigorous canes per plant. Under the hedge system the plants are set 2½ × 8 feet, and pruning consists in removing

Fig. 14.9. Pruning the black raspberry. Left: before pruning. Right: after pruning. (*Redrawn from Fig. 10, Kansas Agr. Exp. Sta. Circ. 239, 1947.*)

the small canes and leaving from three to four vigorous canes per linear foot of row (see Fig. 14.10).

Blackberry. The blackberry is of two types: (1) erect and (2) trailing. The erect varieties produce suckers like the red raspberry and are pruned and trained in much the same manner. In general, the plants are thinned from five to seven canes per hill in hill culture and from two to three canes per linear foot of row in hedge culture. The tips of the young canes may be pinched-off when they are from 24 to 30 inches high. The pruning of the laterals is done in the winter. The amount of wood removed depends on the fruiting habit of the variety. Investigations have shown that some varieties produce most of their mixed buds at the base of the laterals and others produce most of them at the tips. In the former case the laterals are pruned to leave three or four buds; with the latter only the tips of the laterals are removed. The trailing varieties are trained to stakes or on horizontal or vertical trellises. Pruning, other than cutting out canes which have fruited, consists in reducing the number of canes per plant to facilitate the development of berries of large size and the production of vigorous canes for the following year.

Dewberry. The dewberry is trained on trellises, on stakes, or is allowed to grow on the surface of the land. All canes, both young and old, are removed after the harvest, and the canes which develop later are used

Fig. 14.10. Pruning the red raspberry. Left: before pruning. Right: after pruning.

for the next year's crop. These canes are tied to stakes the following spring or are allowed to run along the surface of the land.

Other Small Fruits

Blueberry. Like other small fruits, the blueberry produces fruit on one-year-old wood. Two important considerations are kept in mind in pruning: (1) Without pruning most varieties tend to overbear and produce small fruit; and (2) the largest fruit is produced on the most vigorous wood. Consequently, the purpose of pruning is to induce the development of vigorous new wood and to reduce the number of flower buds. This is accomplished by removing weak, slender, and small branches throughout the body of the plant and by cutting back the fruiting branches. The amount of heading back varies with the variety and growing conditions. Rancocus, Concord, and Rubel varieties require little heading back; whereas Cabot, Pioneer, and others require cutting back to about three to six buds per shoot. Usually, little pruning is necessary for the first two years; only the weak, slender wood is removed.

Currant and Gooseberry. The current and gooseberry form many stems. With no pruning the plants become dense and unproductive. Since the fruit is borne on one-year-old branches, and on one-year-old spurs on two- and three-year-old branches, and very rarely on one-year-old spurs on older branches, pruning consists largely in removing branches over three years old. Enough one-year-old branches are left to replace those removed. Usually from 8 to 10 branches, well distributed throughout the plants, produce the highest yields. The branches seldom need heading back.

QUESTIONS

1. Pruning a tree or plant reduces its top and root growth. Explain.
2. Given two limbs growing from a common point, having equal size and vigor. Limb A is pruned back severely; limb B is left unpruned. Which will become the dominant limb? Give reasons.
3. Given two lots of tomatoes. Lot A is pruned to a single stem and topped at the sixth cluster; lot B is allowed to grow in the natural way. For a harvesting season of eight weeks which lot would produce the greater total yield? Explain.
4. Show how pruning the top increases the supply of water and essential elements to the remainder of the growing points.
5. Pruning the top promotes vegetative processes and retards reproductive processes. Explain.
6. How does thinning out differ from heading back? Give an advantage and a disadvantage of each.
7. Name the tree forms to which fruit trees are trained.
8. Severe pruning of the top delays flower-bud formation in young deciduous fruit trees. Explain.
9. How is the thin-wood method of pruning applied to mature bearing apple trees?
10. The modified-leader type of apple tree produces stronger crotches and a more substantial frame than the open-center type. Explain.
11. Show the relation of vigor of the tree and number of flower buds formed to yield of peaches.
12. How does the pruning of bearing peach trees differ from that of bearing apple trees?
13. How does the pruning of bearing peach trees differ from that of bearing plum trees?
14. Describe the fruiting habits of grapes and brambleberries.
15. What is the relation of vigor of grape canes to fruitfulness?
16. How does the single-trunk, four-cane kniffin system of training differ from that of the fan system?
17. How does pruning the branches differ from pruning bearing apple trees?
18. How does pruning blackberries and black raspberries differ from that of red raspberries?

Nut Fruits (*Pecans, Walnuts, and Hazelnuts*)

Fruiting Habit. The pecan, walnut, and hazelnut are monoecious. The pistillate flowers are borne, usually in clusters, on the current season's growth and arise from terminal mixed buds. The staminate flowers are borne in catkins and arise from the base of the leaves on the second season's wood. The individual flowers of both sexes are inconspicuous, and the pistillate flowers are wind-pollinated. Because the pistillate flowers and thus the fruit are borne on terminal branches, except when the crop should be thinned and the trees invigorated, severe heading back would seriously reduce the production of nuts. Consequently, the pruning of vigorous bearing trees consists largely in removing interfering, broken, dead, or diseased branches.

Pecans and hazelnuts are trained to the central-leader type of tree, and walnuts are trained to the modified leader. In this way, higher branches will not excessively shade and thus retard the growth of the lower branches.

Citrus Fruits (*Orange, Lemon, and Grapefruit*)

Fruiting Period. Like other plants, citrus trees in any one year may produce (1) excessive stem and leaf growth and little fruit, (2) little stem and leaf growth and abundant fruit, and (3) moderate stem and leaf growth and moderately abundant fruit. Obviously, the moderately vegetative and moderately productive condition is the most desirable. Hence, the problem in pruning citrus trees is to maintain a balance between stem and leaf growth on the one hand and the flower and fruit production on the other. Since the fruiting wood declines in productivity after the second and third year, the proper balance is maintained by the production of a moderate amount of new wood at a uniform rate each year. How is this objective obtained? Experience with citrus trees shows that they need not be pruned heavily every year but just enough to keep the tree growing fairly vigorously. The removal of conflicting, dead, and broken branches, as well as suckers, each year is usually necessary. In addition it may be advisable to thin out some of the old wood in order to stimulate the growth of new wood.

Figs

Figs produce two crops of fruit each year. The first crop, or brebas, is borne near the end of the previous season's wood, and the second crop is borne in the axils of the leaves of the current season's wood. A number of weeks elapse between the ripening of the last fruit of the first crop and the ripening of the first fruit of the second crop.

The type of pruning required depends on the crop grown. For varieties which are grown primarily for the first crop or for both crops, the thinning out of the dead, broken, or diseased branches is all that is necessary. For varieties which are grown mainly for the second crop, such as the Kadota group in California, heading back rather severely is required in order to keep the trees low and thus make picking less expensive.

Ornamental Trees, Shrubs, and Vines

Ornamental Trees.   Two general types of pruning are required for ornamental trees: (1) removing dead, diseased, or injured branches and (2) keeping the trees within due proportion of the dimensions of the area. Evergreen trees, such as the junipers and arborvitae, must be pruned regularly to keep them within due bounds. Spruces, pines, and similar evergreens seldom require pruning.

Ornamental Shrubs.   In common with the brambleberries, the root system of ornamental shrubs is perennial in nature, whereas the stems

Fig. 14.11. Pruning flowering shrubs. Left: before pruning. Right: after pruning. (Redrawn from F. S. Batson and R. O. Monosmith, Care of Ornamental Trees and Shrubs, Mississippi Agr. Exp. Sta. Bull. 354, 1941.)

live for a relatively short time only, usually one to three or more years. From the standpoint of pruning, these shrubs are divided into three groups: (1) shrubs which grow slowly, (2) shrubs which grow rapidly and bear flowers and fruit on current season's wood, and (3) shrubs which grow rapidly and bear flowers and fruit on one-year-old wood. In group 1 only the dead stems are removed, and this should be done during the nongrowing season, e.g., flowering almond, flowering quince, pearlbush, and viburnum. In group 2 the two- or three-year-old stems are removed, and this should be done during the nongrowing season also, e.g., athea, butterfly bush, climbing rose, crepemyrtle, coralberry, honey-suckle, hydrangea, spirea, and ligustrum. In group 3 one-fifth to one-third of the previous season's wood should be removed, preferably immediately after flowering has taken place, e.g., barberry, dogwood, deutzia, forsythia, jasmine, spirea, winter honeysuckle, and weigela (see Fig. 14.11).

Woody Vines. Woody vines, such as English ivy, Virginia creeper, and the bittersweets, usually require little pruning. In general, only dead or in-jured branches are removed. However, some vines—bittersweet and grape —when comparatively old produce laterals from the upper stems only, thus leaving the base without foliage. To correct this situation the older stems are headed-back to the ground. As a result the top is renewed from the younger shoots.

Roses

The kind and severity of pruning of the rose depend on the kind of rose grown and the size of flower desired. Some kinds require severe

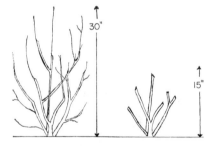

Fig. 14.12. Pruning the hybrid tea rose. Left: before pruning. Right: after prun-ing. The degree of heading back depends on the number of flowering stems de-sired and on the variety. (Redrawn from F. S. Batson and R. O. Mono-smith, Care of Ornamental Trees and Shrubs, Mississippi Agr. Exp. Sta. Bull. 354, 1941.)

annual pruning and other kinds require little or no pruning. Roses which require severe pruning are the hybrid perpetuals and the hybrid teas. These kinds are grown for cut flowers. In general, the weak stems are thinned-out and the sturdy stems are headed-back to varying heights depending on their vigor. In heading back all cuts are made to an outer bud to promote spreading of the plant. From 6 to 10 buds are usually left on each stem. The student should remember that cutting flowers is essentially a pruning operation. Usually, flower stems are cut so as to leave one to three nodes of the current season's growth on the stem (see Fig. 14.12).

Roses that require relatively little pruning are the climbing, rambler, and rugosa types. Climbers are pruned immediately after they have finished flowering. Stems that produced flowers are removed to facilitate the development of new shoots which produce flowers the following year. Ramblers require a small amount of heading back and removal of dead and weak wood. Rugosa types require the removal of old, weak, dead, or diseased wood only.

Hedges

Ideal hedges make uniform growth within any season and are dense from base to top. To accomplish uniformity of growth the plants must be subjected to a uniform environment—a uniform water supply, essential-element supply, and light supply. This is particularly true of the light supply. Clearly, with other environmental factors in favorable supply, that part of the hedge growing in shade will make less growth than that part growing in sun. To secure density and a compact type of growth from base to top, the frequent formation of lateral shoots throughout the life of the hedge is necessary. Thus, the heading-back type of pruning is used. In general, the plants are headed-back to a uniform height when they are set. As the new shoots attain a length of from 6 to 12 inches they are headed-back to a length of from 3 to 6 inches. This practice

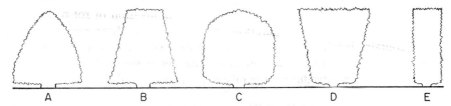

Fig. 14.13. Pruning the hedge. Satisfactory and unsatisfactory shapes. A, B: good. C: fair. D, E: poor.

is continued until a desired height is reached, after which a severe heading back is practiced. Naturally the number of trimmings in any one season depends on the amount of growth made. Heading back induces the development of lateral buds on the older wood, and as a result the body of the hedge is as dense as the top. Figure 14.13 shows satisfactory and unsatisfactory shapes for hedges.

PRUNING TOOLS FOR WOODY PLANTS

For the pruning of woody plants three kinds of tools are essential: (1) hand pruning shears for small cuts up to $\frac{1}{2}$ inch in diameter, (2) lopping shears with 24- to 30-inch handles for cuts between $\frac{1}{2}$ and 1 inch in diameter, and (3) pruning saws for larger cuts. All pruning tools should be sharp in order to make clean, nonjagged wounds.

Time of Pruning Woody Plants. Woody plants are generally pruned between the time of leaf fall and blossoming. Recent investigations have shown that pruning wounds made in early spring heal more quickly and effectively than those made at any other time of year. At this time the wound cork cambium forms readily and produces a layer of corky tissue rather quickly. Furthermore, the temperatures of the spring are more favorable for the activity of the wound cork cambium than those of the winter.

How Are the Cuts Made? Cuts involving the removal of entire shoots, twigs, and branches are made flush with the adjoining branch or limb. In other words there is no stub or projecting end of the cut branch. Observation shows that cut surfaces of stubs heal less rapidly than the cut surfaces of wounds close to the branch or limb. In fact, unless a shoot forms at the cut end, the surface of the stub rarely heals. Thus, pruning wounds will heal more rapidly if they are made close to the base of removed branches or limbs and parallel to the part from which it was taken.

Treatment of Pruning Wounds. Many preparations are available for coating the surface of pruning wounds on woody plants which are 1 inch or more in diameter. An ideal preparation should (1) facilitate the development of the callus tissue and (2) prevent the invasion of rot-producing organisms. There is no preparation that fully meets these requirements. Some contain disinfectants that retard the rate of callus formation; others retard or entirely prevent the flow of air into the wound; and others crack and thus allow rot-producing organisms to invade the tissue.

PRUNING THE STEM OF HERBACEOUS CROPS

Important herbaceous plants which are pruned are tomatoes in greenhouses, tomatoes outdoors, cucumbers in greenhouses, chrysanthemum, dahlia, zinnia, calendula, and mignonette.

Tomatoes in Greenhouses. Tomatoes grown in greenhouses are always trained and pruned. Individual plants are usually trained to a single stem which is supported by a stake or string. The laterals are pinched-off as soon as they arise in the axils of the leaves; thus the thinning-out type of pruning is employed. Pruning in the greenhouse permits close setting, development of fruit above the soil, and facilitates spraying of the plants and picking of the fruit. Since the water and fertilizer supply are under the control of the grower, competition between plants, particularly for water and essential elements, is reduced to a minimum and comparatively large yields per unit area are secured.

Tomatoes Outdoors. Tomatoes are pruned in certain commercial sections for the fresh market and in many home gardens. The plants are trained to one, two, or three stems and are topped at the fourth, fifth, sixth, or succeeding flower cluster. Stakes are usually used for support. The effect of pruning and training tomato plants outdoors on the production of fruit has been investigated by many experiment stations. Advantages and disadvantages of the practice as set forth in *New York (Cornell) Experiment Station Bulletin 580,* 1934, follow.

Advantages	Disadvantages
1. Permits close spacing of plants	1. Increases cost of production
2. Increases early yield of fruit per acre	2. Requires stakes and twine for training plants
3. Keeps fruit off the ground	3. Requires labor for setting stakes and pruning and tying plants
4. Facilitates spraying plants and harvesting fruit	4. Requires labor for removing and storing stakes

Cucumbers in Greenhouses.   Like tomatoes, cucumbers grown in greenhouses are always trained and pruned. Individual plants are trained to a single stem and are usually supported by string fastened to a single-wire

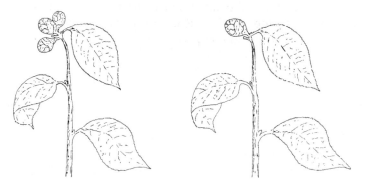

Fig. 14.14. Disbudding of camellia. Left: before. Right: after.

trellis from 4 to 8 feet above the level of the land. For about two months after the plants are set, the primary laterals are cut back to the first or second female blossom, and the secondary laterals are pinched-out. Thus, both heading back and thinning out are used. As in the case with tomatoes, the pruning and training of cucumbers in greenhouses permit close setting of the plants and the development of fruit above the ground.

Chrysanthemums.   Chrysanthemums, particularly the large flowering or standard types, are given a special type of pruning called disbudding. Chrysanthemums produce two types of flower buds: (1) crown buds and (2) terminal buds. Crown buds appear first and are surrounded by leaf buds, and terminal buds appear later and are surrounded by the flower buds. According to authorities at the Ohio Experiment Station, the use of crown or terminal buds depends largely on the variety. On early maturing varieties crown buds produce the most satisfactory type of flower, and on late maturing sorts terminal buds are the more satisfactory. In either case, only one flower is allowed to develop on each plant. In this way a large inflorescence is obtained. Other flower crops which are disbudded are camellia and dahlia. The disbudding of camellia is illustrated in Fig. 14.14.

The stems of many flowering plants are headed-back or pinched to produce the development of a large number of stems and flowers per plant. Examples of plants headed-back in this way are the pompon varieties of chrysanthemum, calendula, carnation, and mignonette.

PRUNING THE ROOT

Root pruning consists in the removal of part of the root system of plants. Root pruning, like top pruning, affects the total amount of growth made and the vegetative-reproductive balance.

Total Amount of Growth Made. Investigations have shown that root pruning dwarfs the tree or plant in much the same way, although not to the same degree, as top pruning. Root pruning removes certain portions of the root system. The roots require carbohydrates for growth, and primary and secondary roots of woody plants store carbohydrates also. Thus, root pruning removes some of the carbohydrates used for the growth and maintenance of the roots, and removes all those stored in the severed roots. To replace the removed roots the plants develop other roots. These new roots require carbohydrates which could be used for other purposes.

Vegetative-Reproductive Balance. What is the relative effect of pruning the root on the disposition of the carbohydrates and the vegetative-reproductive balance? In general, pruning the root reduces the area for the absorption of available nitrogen and other essential elements and water; this, in effect, reduces the amount of available nitrogen and other essential elements and water, which go to each of the growing points in the top; and accordingly, it reduces the number of cells which would otherwise be made. Pruning the root, therefore, decreases cell division and enlargement and the utilization of carbohydrates and promotes the accumulation of carbohydrates. In other words, root pruning favors reproductive processes more than it favors vegetative processes. The student will note that root pruning has the same effect as top pruning on the amount of growth that can be made, but it has the opposite effect of top pruning on the disposition of the carbohydrates and the vegetative-reproductive balance.

PRUNING THE ROOT OF WOODY PLANTS

Up to the end of the nineteenth century root pruning was practiced and recommended in Europe, particularly in England, for the culture of fruit trees. In England fruit trees were grown mostly on dwarf stock. A circular trench usually about 18 inches from the base of young trees and about 18 inches deep was made around the tree and all exposed roots were cut with a sharp knife. For each succeeding year the distance of the trench from the base of the tree was slightly increased so that the roots of any one year were pruned from 2 to 3 inches from the stubs of the previous year. It was generally recommended that the trenching be done in the fall. In this way the trees would show a reduced vegetative growth the following spring and an increase in flower-bud formation in the summer. The student should remember that heavy manuring was practiced also. In fact, the growers generally filled the trench with manure or compost. Since these materials stimulated vegetative growth and since root pruning reduced vegetative growth, the one practice had a nullifying effect on the other. Studies in American orchards during the early part of the twentieth century showed that root pruning markedly reduced the life and the yield of fruit trees. In this country orchards are not heavily manured, and lack of vigor is a more serious problem than excessive vigor. Consequently, root pruning by trenching is no longer recommended and practiced.

PRUNING THE ROOT OF HERBACEOUS CROPS

Certain vegetative plants, particularly tomato and cabbage, when grown in flats are blocked about a week or 10 days before they are set out in the field. Blocking consists in running a sharp knife or a hoe, with a straightened shank, down the middle of the rows in both directions. This operation cuts the root system of the plants, reduces water and mineral absorption, and thus reduces vegetative extension and permits carbohydrate accumulation. These carbohydrates are used for the development of a new root system within the blocked soil. Thus, blocking is essentially a root-pruning practice.

QUESTIONS

1. How does the pruning of mature citrus trees differ from that of peach trees?
2. Heavy heading back of pecan branches would greatly reduce the yield. Explain.
3. The heading back of figs grown for the first crop of fruit would seriously decrease the yield. Explain.

4. In what way are the pruning requirements of ornamental shrubs similar to those of the brambleberries?

5. Show how heading back a large spirea bush would reduce its aesthetic and ornamental value.

6. How is density secured in the development of a privet hedge?

7. How does the pruning of hybrid tea roses differ from that of rambler roses?

8. How do woody plants heal their cut surfaces?

9. Pruning wounds made in the early spring just before growth starts heal more quickly than those made in the winter. Explain.

10. Cuts made at the base of removed branches or parallel to the branch from which it was removed heal more effectively than cuts made away from the base. Explain.

11. State the two main requirements of preparations for the treating of wounds. Give reasons.

12. Certain flower crops are disbudded. What is the object of disbudding?

13. The pruning of tomatoes and cucumbers in greenhouse culture is a necessary practice for profitable production. Explain.

14. The removal of healthy leaves from the basal portion of young tomato plants grown in the greenhouse reduces the total yield of the plants. Explain.

15. State two advantages and two disadvantages of pruning and training tomatoes grown outdoors.

16. Show how heavy grazing of pastures or frequent cutting of the lawn shortens the productive life of the plants.

17. How does root pruning reduce the total amount of growth that would otherwise be made?

18. Root pruning orchard trees as a practice is injurious. Explain.

19. How does the blocking of seedling tomato plants facilitate recovery from the check in growth incident to transplanting?

15

CONTROLLING PESTS

Waste is unworthy of a great people.
Ezra Taft Benson

Three great groups of organisms—all animals, all fungi, and most species of bacteria—are dependent on the products of photosynthesis for their growth and development. Many kinds and species within each group are continually competing with man for these products. For example, man is constantly fighting certain insects which reduce plant yields and certain fungi and bacteria which cause disease. Since these organisms compete with man for the products of photosynthesis, they are called pests. This competition is so great that man has organized groups (entomologists, nematologists, and plant pathologists) to study the life cycle and habits of pests. He has developed many materials and many devices for their control. Growers of horticultural plants, like the growers of other crops, must devote a great deal of their time and energy to combat pests in order to obtain profitable crops. These pests are classified as follows: (1) those belonging to the animal kingdom, (2) those belonging to the plant kingdom, and (3) viruses.

PESTS BELONGING TO THE ANIMAL KINGDOM

Pests belonging to the animal kingdom are many kinds of insects, certain kind of mites, many kinds of nematodes, and a miscellaneous group.

276

INSECTS

Insects have three pairs of legs and three body regions. They may be classified according to the way they feed on plants. In general, there are two groups: (1) those with biting mouth parts and (2) those with sucking and/or rasping mouth parts.

Insects with Biting Mouth Parts. Insects with biting mouth parts are classified according to the part of the plant on which they feed. In general, there are four more or less distinct groups: (1) those that feed on leaves and/or stems, (2) those that feed on roots, (3) those that bore into stems, and (4) those that feed on fruits, seed, or fleshy storage structures.

Stem and Leaf Eaters. How do the stem and leaf eaters reduce photosynthesis? In general, they reduce the chlorophyll content of the leaves. This reduces the amount of light that can be absorbed per unit time, and this in turn reduces the amount of initial food substances which can be made. Examples of stem and leaf eaters are the caterpillars of certain butterflies and moths, e.g., cabbageworm, tomato worm, celery worm, cutworm, apple-tree tent caterpillar, and webworm; certain beetles and their larvae, e.g., Japanese beetle, blister beetle, asparagus beetle, common bean beetle, Colorado potato beetle, and rose chafer; grasshoppers, both adults and nymphs; and leaf miners, e.g., spinach leaf miner, rose slug, and arborvitae leaf miner.

Root Feeders. How do root feeders reduce photosynthesis? In general, they eat the younger portions of the root system and reduce the area for the absorption of water. This reduces the amount of water which can be absorbed per unit time, while transpiration is not reduced. As a result, as previously explained, a water deficit occurs within the plant, the guard cells lose turgor, the stomates close, carbon dioxide cannot diffuse rapidly into the leaves, and photosynthesis is accordingly reduced. Examples of root feeders are the larvae of the cucumber beetle and the white-fringed beetle, and strawberry rootworm and white grubs—the larvae of the May or June beetle.

Stem Borers. Stem borers may be placed in two groups: (1) herbaceous stem borers and (2) woody stem borers. How do herbaceous stem borers reduce photosynthesis? In general, they bore into the stems and eat the xylem (and other tissues). This stops the flow of water into the leaves above the damaged area, while transpiration continues. As a result, the guard cells collapse, the stomates close, carbon dioxide cannot diffuse into the leaves, and photosynthesis slows down or entirely stops. Examples of herbaceous stem borers are the squash vine borer and the corn borer.

How do the woody stem borers reduce photosynthesis? In general, they puncture or sever the secondary phloem. This reduces the flow of manufactured substances to the roots, and as a result these substances accumulate in the tops; and, in accordance with the law of mass action, photosynthesis slows down. In other words, the effect of the injury caused by woody borers is practically the same as that caused by girdling. Examples of woody stem borers are peach tree borer, apple tree borer, and raspberry cane borer.

Feeders on Fleshy Fruits, Seed, and Storage Structures.   These are usually the larvae of moths and beetles. These larvae eat large quantities

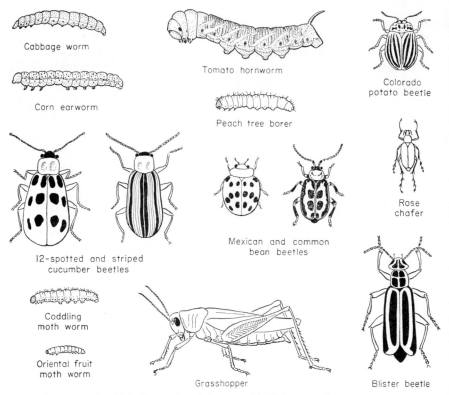

Cabbage worm

Tomato hornworm

Colorado potato beetle

Corn earworm

Peach tree borer

12-spotted and striped cucumber beetles

Mexican and common bean beetles

Rose chafer

Coddling moth worm

Oriental fruit moth worm

Grasshopper

Blister beetle

Fig. 15.1. Examples of insects with biting mouth parts.

of food and make the products unfit for human consumption. In a sense these insects have successfully competed with man for their food, e.g., sweetpotato weevil, bean weevil, pea weevil, tomato fruitworm, corn earworm, plum curculio, and Oriental fruit moth worm. Some of the more common insects with biting mouth parts are shown in Fig. 15.1.

Insects with Sucking or Rasping Mouth Parts.   How do insects with sucking or rasping mouth parts reduce photosynthesis? In general, they pierce the epidermis, suck the tiny chloroplasts, soluble foods, and vitamins from the leaves, and make the leaves incapable of making chlorophyll. This reduces the amount of light which would otherwise be absorbed and the amount of initial food substances which would otherwise be made. Examples of insects with sucking mouth parts are the many kinds of aphids, e.g., apple aphid, English pea aphid, cabbage aphid, and rose aphid; the bugs, e.g., squash bug, harlequin cabbage bug, and tarnished plant bug; thrips, e.g., onion thrips and citrus thrips; leafhoppers, e.g., potato leafhopper and aster leafhopper; and scales and mealybugs, e.g., oystershell scale, San Jose scale, grape mealybug, and taxus mealybug.

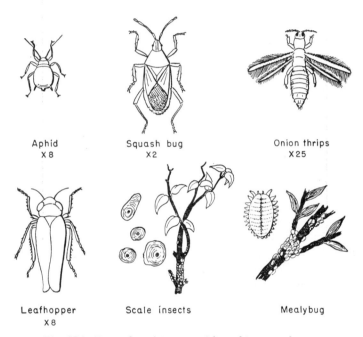

Aphid
X 8

Squash bug
X 2

Onion thrips
X 25

Leafhopper
X 8

Scale insects

Mealybug

Fig. 15.2. Examples of insects with sucking mouth parts.

Some of the more common insects with sucking or rasping mouth parts are shown in Fig. 15.2.

MITES

Mites have four pairs of legs and two body regions. They comprise the spiders, scorpions, daddy longlegs, and ticks. Of these kinds the most serious pests on plants are (1) the foliage mites and (2) the bulb mites. How do the foliage mites reduce photosynthesis? In general, they pierce the foilage, usually the underside of the leaves, with two pronglike projections, and cause the leaves to turn yellow at first and then brown. Thus, foliage mites reduce the amount of light which would otherwise be absorbed, and the amount of foods which would otherwise be made. Examples of foliage mites are the common red spider, cyclamen, or straw-

Fig. 15.3. Red spider injury on sweetpotato leaves. Upper: healthy leaf. Lower: moderately infested leaf. Note the yellow areas. (Courtesy, Ross E. Hutchins, Mississippi State University.)

berry mite, and citrus mite. Figure 15.3 shows red spider injury on the leaves of sweetpotato. Note the small and numerous yellowish-green spots.

Bulb mites, as the name suggests, feed on bulbs and similar structures, and in a sense they have successfully competed with man for their food. Examples of storage structures susceptible to infestation are bulbs of lily and onion, corms of gladiolus and crocus, and rhizomes of asparagus and peony.

PARASITIC NEMATODES

Parasitic nematodes are minute, mostly dioecious, unsegmented worms. In general, they suck the juices from plant tissues by means of a hollow tube called the stylet. Parasitic nematodes may be placed in two groups: (1) those which attack the roots and (2) those which attack the foliage. Nematodes which attack the root system are the root knot, the root lesion, and the root tip. How do these kinds reduce photosynthesis? Tissues invaded by the root-knot nematode form galls, but the cells are not killed; and tissues invaded by the root-lesion and root-tip nematodes do not form

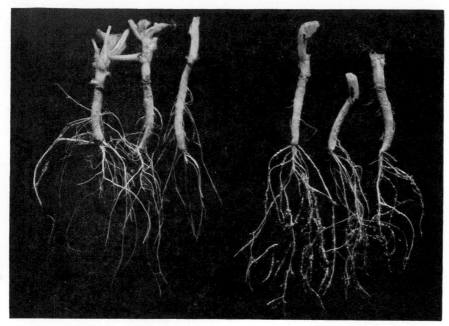

Fig. 15.4. Nematodes on roots of squash. Left: healthy. Right: nematode-infested. Note the formation of galls. (Courtesy, John T. Presley, U.S. Department of Agriculture.)

galls, but the cells are killed. In each of these three cases the water-absorbing capacity of the root system is reduced, and under conditions of high transpiration wilting takes place; the guard cells lose turgor, the stomates close, carbon dioxide cannot diffuse into the leaves, and photosynthesis is accordingly reduced. Most horticultural crops are susceptible to parasitic nematodes. In fact, only a few varieties are resistant; these belong to the following kinds: apricot, avocado, citrus, date, peach, plum, and snap bean. Note the formation of galls on the roots of squash in Fig. 15.4.

Nematodes which attack the foliage are known as foliar nematodes. How do these foliar nematodes reduce photosynthesis? In general, they move from leaf to leaf by films of water, enter the stomates, and feed on the tissue that makes the initial food substances. Thus, they reduce the chlorophyll content, and this in turn reduces the amount of light that would otherwise be absorbed and the amount of foods which would otherwise be made. Horticultural crops susceptible to the foliar nematode are potato, chrysanthemum, African violet, and begonia.

MISCELLANEOUS GROUP

The miscellaneous group includes rodents and certain birds. Rodents comprise ground moles, field mice, and rabbits. The *ground mole* frequently damages lawns and crops grown in the garden and occasionally damages crops grown in the field. These animals, searching for white grubs and other insects in the soil, make tunnels and thus loosen the soil and seriously disturb the root system. *Field mice* and *pine mice* are frequently troublesome during the planting season, since they eat the seed; this often necessitates replanting. These mice and *rabbits* frequently damage trees in the orchard by eating the bark at the base of the tree.

PESTS BELONGING TO THE PLANT KINGDOM

Plant pests are minute plants. They have no chlorophyll, hence they cannot manufacture their own food. They must live, as all animals must live, on the food that green plants have made. The student should remember that not all minute plants are harmful to green plants. Some are distinctly beneficial, such as the fungi which decompose organic matter and the bacteria which change ammonia to nitrates.

Many plant pests live on horticultural crops. They attack the plant in various ways. Some attack crop plants in the seedling stage and thus reduce the stand; others attack the leaves and thus reduce the plant's capacity to make food; others attack the stem and disrupt the food, water, and mineral transportation systems; and others attack the marketable product. In all instances profitable yields per plant or per unit area are decreased. Plant pests are classified as follows: (1) fungi and (2) bacteria.

FUNGI

Fungi consist of many cells. The body may be divided into two parts: (1) the fine threadlike strings of cells collectively called mycelia and (2) the fruiting bodies. The mycelia are the vegetative part and the fruiting bodies are the reproductive part. Fungi can multiply and spread by fragments of the mycelia or by germination of the spores. Under favorable conditions each type of structure is capable of growing into a new individual. The fungi which attack horticultural crops constitute a large group. Their mode of living and manner of feeding on the host plant vary greatly. They are classified as follows: (1) fungi with practically all their mycelia and all their fruiting bodies on the surface of the plant; (2) fungi with all their mycelia within the plant and fruiting bodies that break through the outer cover; (3) fungi with their entire bodies within the plant.

Fungi with practically all their mycelia on the surface of the host plant are external feeders. An example is the powdery mildews. On infected plants the mycelia can be seen as fine welts of grayish threads among which are interspersed small brown or black fruiting bodies. The fungus attacks the lower side of the leaves more than the upper side and thrives best in warm humid conditions.

Fungi with mycelia within the tissues of the plant and fruiting bodies that break through the outer cover are the lesion producers. They are divided into four groups: (1) anthracnoses, (2) downy mildews, (3) leaf spots, and (4) rusts. In general, the lesions are small at first and water-soaked. They gradually enlarge and assume a characteristic color, gray, brown, or black, depending on the color of the fruiting bodies of the fungus. Frequently the fungus grows so rapidly that the spots grow together (coalesce). The lesion producers attack many horticultural crops. Examples are presented in Table 15.1 and in Figs. 15.5 and 15.6.

Fungi with their bodies within the plant are the fusarium wilts. These minute plants live on organic matter in soils, enter the host plant body through the region of the root-hair zone, and attack the xylem. The xylem

Table 15.1. TYPES OF FUNGUS AND BACTERIAL AND VIRUS DISEASES

Group	Disease	Crops
Fungi	Powdery mildews	Grain, legume, cucurbit, chrysanthemum, rose, zinnia
	Anthracnoses	Bean, cowpea, cucumber, cantaloupe, watermelon
	Downy mildews	Grass, grain, cantaloupe, cucumber, lettuce, onion, spinach, tobacco, violet, pansy, grape
	Leaf spots	Apple scab, cherry leaf spot, rose black spot, black rot of sweetpotato
	Fusarium wilts	Cotton, sweetpotato, tomato, watermelon
Bacteria	Local infections	Fireblight of pear, bacterial blight of snap bean, soft rot of carrots
	Bacterial wilts	Sweet corn, carnation, ring rot of potato
	Galls	Crown gall
Viruses	Mosaics	Potato, tomato, raspberry
	Yellows	Peach, aster

Fig. 15.5. Leaf spot of strawberry. (Courtesy, John T. Presley, U.S. Department of Agriculture.)

Fig. 15.6. White rust of spinach. Left: upper side. Right: lower side. (Courtesy, S. S. Ivanoff, Mississippi Agricultural Experiment Station.)

becomes plugged, turns brown, and the host plant wilts. Examples are fusarium wilt of aster, cotton, sweetpotato, tomato, and watermelon.

BACTERIA

Bacteria are microscopic, one-celled, and reproduce by cell division. They vary in size and shape. Some are small and round; others are large and rod-shaped. In general, the bacteria which cause disease on plants are short rods. They possess the faculty to live on dead and living tissue, but they can enter plants only through natural openings, such as stomates, hydathodes, and nectaries, and through wounds. There are three more or less distinct groups: (1) those which cause local infection, (2) those which induce wilting, and (3) those which induce galls. Bacteria which cause local infection are rather specific in their action. Some produce lesions on stems and leaves, others produce cankers on woody stems, and others produce soft rots. Like the fusarium wilts, bacteria which induce wilting invade the xylem and thus disrupt the flow of water from the roots to the leaves, and bacteria which induce galls cause a rapid rate of cell division. Examples of each of the three types of bacterial disease are shown in Table 15.1.

VIRUSES

Viruses are considered to be large protein molecules. Under the electron microscope they look like short, slender rods. Inside the plant these molecules possess the ability to reproduce themselves. Outside the plant they do not possess this ability. For example, if a molecule of the tobacco virus

Fig. 15.7. Tomato mosaic. Left: mosaic-infected plant. Middle: healthy leaf. Right: mosaic-infected leaf. (Courtesy, John T. Presley, U.S. Department of Agriculture.)

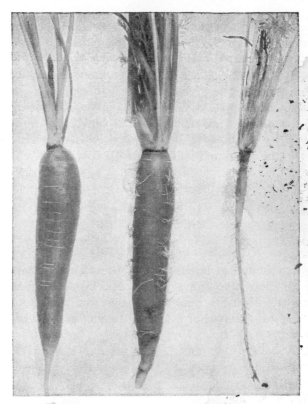

Fig. 15.8. Aster yellows on carrot. Left: healthy plant. Middle: moderately infected plant. Right: severely infected plant. (Courtesy S. S. Ivanoff, Mississippi Agricultural Experiment Station.)

is injected into a healthy tobacco plant, this molecule will multiply millions of times and produce the virus disease. On the other hand, if the molecule is placed in a test tube containing nutrient substances, it does not multiply and produce the disease. Two common types of virus diseases are (1) mosaics and (2) yellows. In the mosaics certain areas in the leaf blade become yellow, but the remainder remains green; and, in the yellows the entire leaf blade becomes yellow. In either case, since the chlorophyll content is reduced, photosynthesis and yields are correspondingly reduced. Examples of virus diseases are presented in Table 15.1 and illustrated in Figs. 15.7 and 15.8.

QUESTIONS

1. All animals, most fungi, and most bacteria are dependent on green plants for their existence. Explain.

2. Horticulturally speaking, what is a pest?
3. Man always has been seriously concerned about his food supply. Explain.
4. Distinguish between insects, mites, and nematodes.
5. How do the leaf eaters reduce photosynthesis, growth, and yield?
6. How do the root feeders reduce photosynthesis, growth, and yield?
7. How do woody stem borers reduce photosynthesis, growth, and yield?
8. How do foliar mites reduce photosynthesis, growth, and yield?
9. How do root nematodes reduce photosynthesis, growth, and yield?
10. How do foliar nematodes reduce photosynthesis, growth, and yield?
11. Given a tomato plant wilting from 10 A.M. to 4 P.M. only. Examination of the roots shows galls or swellings. State the pest.
12. Distinguish between fungi, bacteria, and viruses.
13. How do lesion-producing fungi and bacteria reduce photosynthesis, growth, and yield?
14. How do the fusarium wilts lower the rate of photosynthesis, growth, and yield?
15. How do virus diseases reduce photosynthesis, growth, and yield?

METHODS OF CONTROL

In order that any pest may grow and develop three conditions must be fulfilled: (1) The pest responsible for the damage must be present; (2) the environment must be favorable for the spread of the pest; and (3) the crop must be susceptible. Pests, therefore, may be controlled by practicing any one or more of the following methods: (1) eliminating or eradicating the causal organism, (2) using natural enemies of pests, (3) using chemical compounds, and (4) growing resistant varieties.

ELIMINATING THE CAUSAL ORGANISM

Eliminating the casual organism involves (1) removal of the organism from seed or plants, (2) crop rotation, and (3) crop sanitation.

Removal of the Organism. Removal of the organism may be secured with a specific lot of seed, a plant or tree, or a large group of plants. As an example, consider the control of black rot of cabbage. The causal organism is a bacterium which lives on the coat of the seed and on organic matter in the soil. Soaking the seed in hot water at a temperature of 122°F for 25 minutes followed by rinsing in cold water eliminates the bacterium from the coat of the seed. Unless the bacterium is present in the soil after the seed or seedlings have been planted, the crop will be entirely free of the disease. As a second example, consider the control of citrus canker. Citrus canker was at one time a serious disease of oranges, lemons, and related fruits in Florida. This disease was controlled permanently by promptly removing and burning all trees that showed the disease. As a result, citrus trees in Florida now are free from canker because the causal organism no longer is present. As a third example, take the production of certified potato seed. Many varieties of potatoes are susceptible to many kinds of virus diseases, e.g., mild mosaic, rugose mosaic, leaf roll, and spindle tuber. These viruses impair the capacity of the plant to make chlorophyll. As a result, the rate of photosynthesis is low. These viruses are present in the sap of infected plants and are carried from plant to plant by insects. Control of the virus diseases, therefore, consists in controlling the insect carriers, combined with prompt removal of plants showing symptoms of any of the virus diseases. Certified seed of the potato are tubers which are practically free from several viruses or mosaic diseases. During the growing season the plants which are raised for certification are inspected frequently, and all infected plants are removed and destroyed. The removal of infected plants prevents the disease from spreading to healthy plants and permits the raising of a crop of tubers which is practically free from the several virus diseases.

Crop Rotation.   Crop rotation consists in growing a group of crops in a definite sequence on the same land. In other words, a definite period is allowed to elapse before the crop is planted again. In this way, the insect or disease organism is starved out. In general, crop rotation is most effective in controlling pests which live in the soil for a short time only. It has little or no effect on organisms which live in the soil for a period of 10 to 25 years. For example, the spores of clubroot of cabbage can live in the soil for two years only. Consequently, if the land is kept free of crops and weeds of the cabbage family for two years after a cabbage crop has been grown, the land will be free of this disease. On the other hand, a short rotation is ineffective in the control of fusarium wilt of watermelons, since the wilt fungus lives in the same soil for a period of 20 to 25 years.

Crop Sanitation.   Crop sanitation consists in (1) removing promptly insect-infested and diseased plants and (2) plowing under refuse immediately after the harvest. Both methods of sanitation assist in controlling pests in the following way: Prompt removal of insect-infested and diseased plants assists in reducing and may, in many cases, entirely prevent the dissemination of the pest. It is particularly essential in controlling pests of crops which are grown close together and in quick succession, as in the raising of plants in greenhouses, hotbeds, and cold frames. Plowing under plant remains reduces the multiplication of fungi and bacteria in the plant and soil. It is generally practiced to control pests of crops grown in the field.

USING NATURAL ENEMIES

Using predators and parasites which are natural enemies of a given pest can be advantageous with some crops. Two examples of this kind of pest control follow. In 1869, cottony-cushion scale, a serious pest on citrus trees, was accidently introduced into California on a species of Australian acacia. Neither of its two natural enemies, the vedalia beetle and a parasitic fly, was introduced with it. As a result, the scale spread rapidly throughout citrus orchards, many crops were lost, and the orchards depreciated in value. In 1888, both enemies were introduced, and they soon became established in citrus orchards. However, the vedalia beetle was found to be the more effective in the controlling of the scale. Within a year, orchards in which the beetles were first released were practically free of the scale, and within two years the cottony-cushion scale was no longer a serious problem in California.

The tomato hornworm eats the leaves of tomato plants. Healthy, rapidly growing worms reduce the photosynthetic surface in a short time, and accordingly they reduce the yield and quality of the fruit. In the southeastern United States these worms rarely do serious damage. In a short time after they appear, many of them become heavily parasitized. The female parasitic wasp lays large quantities of eggs in the body of the caterpillar, and the numerous larvae rapidly consume the flesh and vital organs of the worm. As a result, the worm dies, or at least it is rendered inactive quickly, and the application of an appropriate stomach poison is generally unnecessary.

In general, a biological balance exists between certain insect pests and their enemies. With many horticultural industries the maintenance of this balance assumes great practical significance. In fact, it may entirely eliminate the need for other methods of control. For example, the use of chemicals is seldom necessary for the control of insects and mites in avocado orchards of southern California. The natural and imported predators and parasites keep the potentially serious insects and mites under control, e.g., the looper, the long-tailed mealybug, the black scale, the soft brown scale, the six-spotted mite, and the avocado brown mite. Numerous experiments have shown that when the predators and parasites are excluded from the trees these insects and mites multiply rapidly and reduce the photosynthetic capacity of the leaves and the vigor and yield of the trees. Thus, the main advantage in using natural enemies— the so-called biological method—is that the use of chemical compounds and other methods are unnecessary. However, the main disadvantage is that the pests are not entirely eliminated.

USING CHEMICAL COMPOUNDS

A large number and a wide variety of chemical compounds are used in the control of pests. These compounds are classified according to their principal use as follows: (1) stomach and contact poisons, (2) contact poisons, (3) systemics, (4) fumigants, (5) seed and seed-stock treatment materials, (6) fungicides and bactericides, and (7) antibiotics.

Stomach and Contact Poisons. Stomach and contact poisons are used for the control of insects with either biting or sucking or rasping mouth parts. For insects with biting mouth parts applications should be made just before the insect begins to feed, and the poison should remain on or adhere to the tissues until the insect has fed. For many insects with sucking or rasping mouth parts applications should be made just as the insect begins to feed, and the poison should adhere to the body of the insect until the insect has been killed, e.g., rotenone, pyrethrum derivatives, DDT, chlordane, dieldrin, lindane, malathion, methoxychlor, and parathion. A particular advantage of the pyrethrum products is that they are nonpoisonous to man. However, their high price has limited their use.

Contact Poisons. As previously stated, contact poisons are used to control insects with sucking or rasping mouth parts. In general, the contact insecticides are specific in action, e.g., oil emulsions for the control of scale and mealybugs, nicotine sulfate for the control of many kinds of aphids, and Aramite for the control of phosphate-resistant red spider mites.

Systemics. Systemics are chemical compounds which enter the conducting systems of plants. They may be applied as a foliage spray or to the soil. In the first case, they enter the plant through the openings of the leaves at the end of large veins, and, in the second case, they enter through the region of water absorption. On a theoretical basis these compounds should be equally effective for the control of insects with either biting or sucking or rasping mouth parts. However, experiments have shown that they are more effective against insects with sucking or rasping mouth parts. Further, since the systemics are highly poisonous to man, their use is limited to crops the products of which are not used for human consumption, as for example cotton and crops grown for their flowers. Examples of systemics are Demeton and OMPA or Pestox-3.

Fumigants. Fumigants are chemical compounds which change from either the solid or liquid form to the vapor or gaseous form. These gases stop the respiration of insects and nematodes and enter the cells of fungi and bacteria. In general, they may be placed in two groups: (1) compounds applied to soil and (2) compounds applied to crops growing in greenhouses or similar structures. Compounds applied to soil are used mainly for the control of injurious nematodes and for the control of the peach tree borer. Examples of nematocides are chloropicrin, methyl bromide, Nemagon, Vapam, and VC-13. Compounds used for the control of the peach tree borer are paradichlorobenzine and ethylene dichloride. Compounds applied to crops growing in greenhouses or similar structures are used mainly for the control of insects with sucking mouth parts and the red spider mite, e.g., the aerosols of dithio compounds, parathion, malathion, and TEPP.

Seed and Seed-stock Treatment Materials. Seed treatment materials are chemical compounds which are applied to the surface of seeds, tubers, bulbs, and fleshy roots. In general, they are used to protect the young plants against certain types of fungi or bacteria which would otherwise damage or destroy them. They are applied in carefully measured doses which kill the cells of the bacterium or fungus and at the same time do no damage to the seedling plants, e.g., mercuric chloride, Captan, Chloronil, Diclone, and thiram.

Fungicides and/or Bactericides. In general, these compounds are used to prevent or inhibit the growth of germinating spores or mycelium of fungi or the cells of certain bacteria on the surface of plants. In other words, these compounds prevent any given fungus or bacterium from invading the tissues and getting inside the plant. Once these organisms have successfully invaded the tissues the use of these compounds is ineffectual. Consequently, correct timing of applications is essential. In general, these compounds should be applied just before rather than after a rain for crops outdoors, since they will have better opportunity to kill germinating spores. Examples of fungicides and bactericides are copper sulfate and fresh hydrated lime in a suspension with water, com-

Fig. 15.9. Spraying an apple orchard.

Fig. 15.10. Spraying a tomato field.

monly called Bordeaux mixture; quick lime and sulfur in solution with water; colloidal, or wettable, sulfur; sulfur dust; and the dithiocarbamates —Dithane, Fermate, Manate, Parzate, Captan, Mildex, and Cyprex.

Antibiotics. Antibiotics are definite chemical compounds which are made by a given organism for its protection against disease-producing organisms. For example, the fungus *Penicillium notatum* makes and secretes the antibiotic penicillin for protection against its bacterial enemies. In other words, the penicillin kills the invading bacteria. For this reason, plant scientists believed that antibiotics may be effective in the control of certain bacterial diseases of plants. Experiments have shown that this is the case, and in some instances the antibiotics are effective against certain diseases caused by fungi also. In general, antibiotics are systemic in action; that is, when they are applied in solution with water, they are absorbed and become part of the sap of the plant. In this way they are not washed off by irrigation water or rain, and they protect the internal tissues and destroy the disease-producing organism which may be present. Examples of antibiotics used to control certain plant diseases are streptomycin, Streptomycin-Terramycin, and Actidione. Figures 15.9 and 15.10 show two types of sprayers in operation: one for trees in the orchard and the other for large areas of herbaceous crops.

Precautions in Using Pesticides. Since many pesticides are highly poisonous to man, they should be handled with care and should be used only for the purpose for which they are recommended. Thus, the grower would do well to (1) read and follow the directions on the label or container to the letter; (2) keep pesticides in their original containers, preferably in a room for their storage only, and under lock and key; (3) destroy the containers as soon as they are empty; (4) avoid breathing the gas of volatile chemicals and use a mask if necessary; and (5) become familiar with the tolerance requirements of each pesticide.

Tolerance Requirements. As previously stated, certain compounds are nonpoisonous to man. Thus, the amount of residue of these compounds on the product for human consumption is of no consequence. However, other compounds are poisonous to man even in small quantities. Thus, the amount of residue of the compounds on the product is of considerable consequence. Naturally, the amount which has no injurious effect on the consumer must be determined, and this amount is called the tolerance requirement. In other words, it is the maximum amount of pesticide as determined by scientists that may remain as a residue on the product with no injurious effect on the consumer. In general, the amount is expressed in parts per million (ppm), and the amount varies with the poisonous nature of the pesticide. For example, the tolerance requirement expressed as ppm for each of the following pesticides is dieldrin, 0.25; chlordane, 0.3; DDT, 7; malathion, 8; lindane, 10; methoxychlor, 14; and Captan, 20.

Disadvantages in Using Pesticides. Disadvantages in using pesticides are as follows: (1) Insecticides are likely to kill beneficial insects, for example, the honeybee and predators and parasites of certain pests. The killing of honeybees may result in inadequate pollination of the crop, and the killing of predators and parasites may upset the biological balance between the insect and its natural enemies. This is likely to result in a rapid infestation of the pest against which the insecticide is used or a rapid infestation of insects which are rare and of no economic importance before the insecticide is applied. (2) All pesticides add to the cost of production. (3) Many pesticides have unfavorable effects on the fundamental processes, particularly on photosynthesis and transpiration. For example, tests have shown that Bordeaux mixture, lime sulfur, and certain oil emulsions markedly reduce the rate of photosynthesis of apple leaves and that Bordeaux mixture markedly increases the rate of transpiration of leaves of many herbaceous plants, e.g., tomatoes, cucumbers, cantaloupes, and carrots. All these effects are undesirable and have led to the development of less injurious materials and to an intensification in the breeding of resistant varieties.

GROWING RESISTANT VARIETIES

Growing resistant varieties is a most practical method of pest control. The buying and applying of chemicals are unnecessary, the rate of photosynthesis is not reduced, and the rate of transpiration is not increased. Thus, great economies are effected and high marketable yields are obtained. Within the past 20 years considerable emphasis has been placed on the development of resistant varieties. Examples of horticultural crops are presented in Table 15.2.

Table 15.2.   RESISTANT VARIETIES OF CERTAIN CROPS

Crop	Variety	Resistant to:
Pear	Baldwin, Pontotoc	Fireblight
Peach	Shalil,* Yunan*	Nematode (certain strains)
Potato	Katahdin, Kennebec	Mild mosaic
Onion	White Persian	Thrips
Squash	African	Vine borer
Tomato	Pan-American	Fusarium wilt
China aster	Tilford	Fusarium wilt
Gardenia thunbergii		Nematode
Snapdragon	Outdoor varieties	Rust

Used as stocks.

QUESTIONS

1. State the three conditions necessary for the spread of insects and diseases.
2. What is meant by elimination of the causal organism?
3. Crops in greenhouses are usually markedly free from disease, whereas the same crops grown outdoors frequently show disease infection. Explain.
4. What are certified seed tubers of the potato?
5. In the production of certified seed tubers of the potato, control of insects is essential. Explain.
6. How does crop sanitation control pests?
7. What are the limitations of crop rotation in pest control?
8. How do natural predators and parasites control pests?
9. Give an advantage and a disadvantage of the so-called biological method.
10. Stomach poisons are used for insects with biting mouth parts. Explain.
11. Contact poisons are used for insects with sucking or rasping mouth parts. Explain.
12. What is the main difference in time of application of stomach poisons and contact poisons?
13. What are systemics? What is the chief limitation in their use?
14. How do fumigants kill pests?
15. State the purpose of using seed and seed-stock treatment materials.
16. What is meant by correct timing in the application of fungicides and bactericides?
17. What are antibiotics? How do they protect plants from certain fungi and bacteria?

18. Growers should become familiar with precautions in using pesticides. Explain.
19. What is meant by the tolerance requirements of a given pesticide?
20. Reduction in photosynthesis is a distinct disadvantage in the use of Bordeaux mixture, lime sulfur, and oil emulsions. Explain.
21. In the development of new insecticides and fungicides, attention should be given to their effect on beneficial insects, on photosynthesis, respiration, and transpiration of the crop, and on the bacteria and structure of the soil. Explain.
22. With other factors favorable, pest-resistant varieties should be used whenever they are available. Give three reasons.

16

PRESERVATION

*In the world as a whole
the job of creating abundance
has hardly begun.*
Henry R. Luce

The various methods of preserving plant products are (1) storing, (2) canning, (3) drying, (4) pickling, and (5) freezing. These methods are distinctly beneficial both from the standpoint of the consumer and the producer. In general, products are made available during the entire year and gluts on markets are avoided. As examples consider peaches and sweetpotatoes. Fresh peaches are available on the markets of the continental United States from May to September. There are no fresh peaches available from October to April. The canning, drying, and freezing of peaches during the harvest season make the fruit available not only from October to April, but also during the entire year. The harvest season for sweetpotatoes in the continental United States extends from August to November. If all the fleshy roots were placed on the market immediately after the harvest, gluts would take place. This would result in low prices, and very few roots would be available from November to September.

STORING

The storing of plant products in their natural state is an important practice. Millions of bushels of fruit, millions of bushels of vegetables, and large quantities of flowers are stored annually. The student should remember that horticultural products in storage are alive, that storing consists in maintaining an environment where life processes proceed at a

296

minimum, and that the principal processes concerned are *respiration* and *transpiration*.

RESPIRATION

Since products in storage are alive, their living cells respire to secure energy. The equation for respiration follows:

$$\text{Stored foods} + H_2O \longrightarrow \text{soluble foods} + \text{oxygen} \xrightarrow{\text{(enzymes)}} CO_2 + H_2O + \text{heat and other forms of energy}$$

A comparatively large number of factors influence the rate of respiration of products in storage. These factors are divided into two groups: (1) plant factors and (2) environmental factors.

Plant Factors

Amount of Sugars Available. Scientists have shown that the soluble sugars, particularly glucose, are the chief sugars used in respiration. Hence, with other factors favorable, the greater the concentration of soluble sugars within the living tissues, the greater is the rate of respiration. The effect of storage temperature on potato tubers shows how soluble sugars may become the principal factor affecting respiration. At 32°F, the potato tubers become sweet; that is, comparatively large quantities of sugar are formed at the expense of starch. Because of the relatively greater concentration of sugars in the tubers stored at 32°F than in those stored at 40°F, the tubers stored at 32°F will respire at a greater rate than those stored at 40°F when they are placed in higher temperatures, as is usual in marketing operations.

Number of Living Cells. Because living cells require a constant supply of energy and because respiration liberates the necessary energy, the rate of respiration will be directly proportional to the number of living cells. Thus, 2 bushels of apples will require more energy and will produce more carbon dioxide and liberate more heat than 1 bushel. For the same reason, a cabbage or lettuce head will respire more rapidly in the same environment than a potato tuber or sweetpotato root. In fact, the greater the number of living cells in proportion to the dead cells of a product, the greater will be the amount of carbon dioxide and water given off.

Water Content of the Tissues. In general, the rate of respiration varies directly with the water content of the product. For example, at the Oklahoma Experiment Station, various kinds of vegetable products were stored at 3°C for a period of 26 hours. The succulent vegetables lost 10 to 13 per cent of their dry weight, whereas moderately succulent vegetables lost only from 1 to 2 per cent of their dry weight. Obviously, succulent products respire more rapidly, weight for weight, than relatively non-succulent products. Thus, lettuce heads respire more rapidly than potatoes or sweetpotatoes or even peppers. This means that immature fruit respires more rapidly than mature fruit.

Environmental Factors

Temperature.   In general, with other factors in favorable supply and with the temperature from 10 to 35°C, the van't Hoff rule applies; that

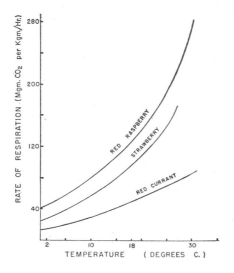

Fig. 16.1. Influence of temperature on rate of respiration of fruits of strawberry, raspberry, and currant.

is, the higher the temperature from 10 to 35°C, the greater the rate of respiration. In storage the respiration rate should proceed at a minimum. Note the effect of temperature on the respiration rate of the red raspberry, strawberry, and red currant as shown in Fig. 16.1. The curves show that the rate of respiration varied directly with the temperature. In other words, the higher the temperature, within 0 and 35°C, the higher was the respiration rate. Numerous investigations have shown that practically the same situation exists with other products. From these studies optimum storage temperatures of many products have been determined. Examples are shown in Table 16.1.

Oxygen–Carbon Dioxide Level.   A study of the equation for respiration shows that oxygen is absorbed and carbon dioxide is given off. Thus, if living products are placed in a gastight room, the oxygen supply of the air will gradually decrease and the carbon dioxide will gradually

Table 16.1.   STORAGE TEMPERATURES
              OF CERTAIN PRODUCTS

31–33°F	30–34°F	40–45°F	33–35°F	55–65°F
Strawberry, raspberry, blackberry, blueberry, celery, onion, root crops	Apple, pear, peach, plum	Potato	Cut flowers (except orchid and gladiolus)	Pepper, squash, pumpkin, sweetpotato

increase. This decrease in concentration of oxygen and increase in concentration of carbon dioxide decreases the rate of respiration in accordance with the law of mass action. As the products of the reaction (carbon dioxide) pile up, the speed of the reaction (respiration) slows down. This principle is now used in the storage of certain varieties of apples, and the practice is known as controlled-atmosphere storage. In general, the apples are stored in gastight rooms maintained at 40 to 42°F; the oxygen and carbon dioxide are kept at 3 and 5 per cent, respectively; and gases given off by the apples, such as ethylene, are removed by means of activated carbon. However, for all products in storage the concentration of oxygen should always be sufficient for the complete combustion of the sugars. If inadequate quantities are available, compounds are formed which are injurious to the tissues and protoplasm. Consider the following equations:

(respiration with adequate oxygen)
$$(1) \quad C_6H_{12}O_6 + 6O_2 \longrightarrow 6CO_2 + 6H_2O$$

(respiration with inadequate oxygen)
$$(2) \quad C_6H_{12}O_6 + O_2 \longrightarrow \underset{\text{alcohol}}{C_2H_5OH} + \underset{\text{acetic acid}}{CH_3COOH} + 2CO_2 + H_2O$$

Note that 6 molecules of oxygen are required for the complete combustion of 1 molecule of glucose and that if only 1 molecule of oxygen is present, alcohol and acetic acid are formed. Alcohol is injurious to the tissues and induces death of the protoplasm. Other intermediate compounds induce death also. For example, with inadequate oxygen potato tubers form tyrosine which is responsible for blackheart, certain varieties of the apple form aldehydes which induce storage scald, and cabbage and celery form compounds which induce speckling and pitting of the petioles and veins. Thus, every storage room should be supplied with sufficient oxygen for normal respiration.

Liberation of Heat.   The equation for respiration shows that heat is liberated. In the storage of certain products the liberation of heat is a vital factor, particularly with products which have a high respiration rate. As an example consider celery. Investigations have shown that the temperature of plants inside the storage crates is always higher than that on the outside. This high temperature is undoubtedly due to the lesser flow of air around the stalks in the center of the crate. Consequently, since relatively large amounts of heat are given off in storage, adequate quantities of air are necessary to carry the heat away. For this reason storage in bulk is generally less satisfactory than storage in various types of containers. This is particularly true for products which have a high respiration rate.

TRANSPIRATION

The student will recall that transpiration is the evaporation of water from living plant tissues and that water is formed in respiration. Consequently, products in storage transpire water and the amount lost may be wholly or partially replaced by the water formed in respiration. For any given unit of time, for example one hour, one day, or one week, the amount lost by transpiration may be equal to, greater, or less than the amount made by respiration. In general, when the amount lost is equal to the amount made, little, if any, shrinkage takes place; and when the amount lost is greater than the amount made, shrinkage takes place and the degree of shrinkage is roughly proportional to the amount of water lost. Since shrinkage is undesirable, a study of the factors which influence the rate of water loss is necessary. These factors are divided into two groups: plant factors and environmental factors.

Plant Factors

Water Content of the Tissues.   Plant products differ in the degree of differentiation of their tissues and hence they differ in the rate of transpiration under the same conditions. In general, nondifferentiated, very succulent tissues contain more water than highly differentiated, nonsucculent tissues. Under the same conditions tissues with a high water content lose water more rapidly than tissues with a low water content. Examples of highly succulent tissues are asparagus spears, young spinach leaves, and young turnip greens. Examples of highly differentiated products are mature cabbage heads, onions, and celery.

Type of Outer Cover.   Two kinds of tissues constitute the outer cover of plant products. These are the epidermis and the periderm. The student will recall that the epidermis consists of a single layer of living cells. On the outer walls a layer of wax may or may not be present. Since a layer of wax on the epidermis retards transpiration, plant products with a cutinized epidermis will shrink less rapidly in storage than those with a noncutinized epidermis. Examples of products which have an epidermis are asparagus spears, spinach, and other vegetables grown for their leaves.

The student will also recall that the periderm consists of several layers of compact, dead, corklike cells. This tissue is admirably adapted to keep the all-important water within the product and disease organisms outside the product. Experiments have shown that plant products with a well-developed and noninjured periderm lose water less rapidly and keep longer in storage than those products with a poorly developed or badly injured or bruised periderm. In fact, long storage life of many products depends on the maintenance of a healthy and intact periderm. Plant products which possess a periderm as the outer cover are apples, pears, citrus fruits, root crop vegetables, sweetpotatoes, potatoes, and gladiolus corms.

Environmental Factors

Temperature. The student will recall how temperature influences the rate of transpiration of a growing plant. Since products in storage transpire, the influence of temperature on their rate of transpiration is much the same as that on growing plants. In other words, the rate of transpiration of products in storage is roughly proportional to the temperature. Thus, a comparatively high storage temperature induces a greater rate of transpiration and greater shrinkage than a comparatively low temperature. Since a high rate of transpiration and excessive shrinkage are undesirable, comparatively low temperatures in storage houses are maintained.

Relative Humidity. The term relative humidity refers to the amount of water vapor in the air compared with the amount of water vapor when the air is fully saturated for any given temperature. Thus, when the relative humidity is 50 per cent the air contains only one-half as much moisture as it would contain if it were saturated for any particular temperature. The student will recall the effect of relative humidity on the rate of transpiration of growing plants. As might be expected, its effect on the transpiration of products in storage is much the same. Thus, with other factors of the storage environment favorable, the rate of transpiration is inversely proportional to the relative humidity. In other words, a low relative humidity induces a high rate of transpiration and a high relative humidity induces a low rate of transpiration. Since a high rate of transpiration induces excessive shrinkage, and since excessive shrinkage is undesirable, a comparatively high relative humidity is maintained in storage houses.

In most crops, experiments have shown that the relative humidity should vary between 70 to 85 per cent. If the humidity is lower than 70 per cent, shrinkage is likely to become excessive. On the other hand, if the humidity is greater than 85 to 90 per cent, environmental conditions become favorable for the condensation of moisture on the surface of the stored products and for the development of storage rots.

Horticultural products classified according to their humidity requirements follow: fruits, 80 to 85 per cent; beets, carrots, parsnips, salsify, turnips, radishes, celery, cabbages, potatoes, and sweetpotatoes, 75 to 85 per cent; onions, beans, squash, and pumpkins, 70 to 75 per cent; cut flowers, 80 per cent; flowering bulbs, 60 to 70 per cent.

TYPES OF STORAGE STRUCTURES

Types of storage houses may be classified according to the degree of temperature control. They are (1) refrigerated and (2) nonrefrigerated. *Refrigerated* storage houses have insulated walls and doors, and the temperature within the house is thermostatically controlled. Substances commonly used to maintain low temperatures are freon, methyl chloride, and ammonia. These gases are compressed and are released through pipes or coils in the storage rooms. On expansion they take up the heat of respiration. The main advantage of this type of storage is that the temperature is thermostatically controlled. Since temperatures are controlled, the relative humidity can be controlled also. In this way ideal storage conditions can be maintained. The stored product has low rates of respiration and transpiration, both of which are conducive to long storage life.

Nonrefrigerated storage structures have temperatures which are not thermostatically controlled, but which are influenced by the outside air temperature. Some of them are specially constructed houses, house cellars, pits, trenches, or mounds. Specially constructed houses have insulated

Fig. 16.2. A modern sweetpotato storage house. (Courtesy, Chesley Hines, Mississippi Agricultural Extension Service.)

walls and doors, properly spaced vents, and false floors. In the operation of these houses ventilation is essential. The function of the lower vents is to bring in cool air and oxygen for respiration, and the function of the upper vents is to carry away the heat of respiration. Large quantities of cabbage, potatoes, and sweetpotatoes are stored in this type of storage house. The storage room in house cellars, pits, and mounds is used mostly for storing products from the home garden. In general, the room in the basement should have outside ventilation, a dirt floor, and shelves. The vents allow cool air to enter and warm air to escape from the storage room. The dirt floor permits a gradual evaporation of water, thus maintaining a high humidity, and the shelves provide room for a large number of products. Figure 16.2 shows a modern sweetpotato storage house located in Mississippi.

CANNING

Essentially, canning consists in subjecting the plant product to high temperatures, usually from 200 to 240°F for 5 to 90 minutes, depending on the kind of product, degree of maturity, and size of can used. The fundamental process concerned is respiration. The high temperature inactivates the enzymes. When the enzymes of respiration are destroyed the process ceases. With the cessation of respiration the sugars, proteins, minerals, and vitamins are conserved. Naturally, the shorter the time between harvesting and processing, the lesser will be the utilization of starches and sugars in respiration.

The canning of fruits and vegetables is an important horticultural industry. In fact, with many crops the acreage given over to canning is greater than that given over to growing the crop for market in the fresh

Fig. 16.3. A modern canning plant located near Griffin, Ga. (Courtesy, H. L. Cochran, Pomona Products Company.)

state. Examples are peaches, tomatoes, sweet corn, and lima beans. Figure 16.3 shows a modern canning plant near Griffin, Georgia.

DRYING

Drying under Natural Conditions. This practice is also called dehydration. As the name suggests drying consists in removing sufficient water from the product to prevent it from spoiling in storage. As with other forms of food preservation the principal process concerned is respiration. Removing most of but not all the water inactivates the enzymes for respiration. In this way the product is conserved. In general, horticultural products are dried in two ways: (1) under natural conditions and (2) artificially. In either case the drying is done by means of warm, relatively dry air. To prevent spoilage of the product the rate of drying is relatively rapid.

Drying under Natural Conditions. This practice is sometimes called sun-drying. Principal environmental factors concerned are (1) degree and amount of sunshine and (2) temperature and dryness of the air. In general, the greater the intensity and duration of sunlight, the higher the temperature; and the drier the air, the greater the rate of drying. Thus, warm-dry climates characterized by abundant sunshine will be more favorable to sun-drying than warm-moist and cold-dry climates. Of the commercial crop-growing regions in the continental United States, the climate of certain intermountain areas of California is particularly favorable for the production and sun-drying of many horticultural crops. In this region large quantities of raisins, prunes, apricots, peaches, figs, and pears are produced. The winters are sufficiently cold to bring the trees out of the rest period; the springs and early summers are sufficiently warm to permit the production of large quantities of high-quality fruits; and the late summers and falls are sufficiently warm and dry to permit rapid drying of the fruit. In these intermountain valleys most of the rains occur during the winter and spring; the summers are practically dry.

Drying Artificially. Drying artificially consists in passing heated air over the product. The principal factors concerned are (1) temperature and dryness of the air and (2) velocity of the air. Heating the air is necessary to increase its drying capacity. For example, within the temperature range for drying, an increase from 20 to 30°F will double the water-holding or drying capacity of the air. Thus, the higher the temperature, without impairing the quality of the product, the greater will be the rate of drying and the lesser will be the reduction in quality. In general, the optimum temperature for drying depends on the type of product and its initial water content. For example, the optimum temperature range for apples and pears varies from 130 to 165°F and for beans and peas from 115 to 140°F. For any one product the lower limit of the temperature range is used when drying begins, and the temperature is gradually increased to the upper limits as drying proceeds.

PICKLING

Essentially, pickling consists in placing the plant product in a salt brine mixture of definite concentration. In general, the salt brine mixture stops or limits the oxidative phase of respiration and allows the fermentative phase to continue. Horticultural crops which are grown for pickling are cucumbers, cabbage, onions, and beets. Special varieties of these crops have been developed for the purpose of pickling. Most of the acreage is located in the northern United States. Michigan is foremost in the production of cucumbers for pickling, and New York and Wisconsin are outstanding in the production of cabbage for sauerkraut manufacture. Numerous pickling and salting stations are located in these states.

FREEZING

Essentially, freezing consists in exposing fruits and vegetables to temperatures ranging from 0 to −50°F. It is generally accomplished by placing the food in a blast of cold air or directly on refrigeration plates. The low temperatures stop enzyme activity and, consequently, the rate of respiration. Vegetables are usually precooked or blanched for a very short time before freezing in order to quickly inactivate the enzymes which are present. Freezing and storing foods at temperatures of 0°F or lower retain the freshness, color, flavor, vitamin content, and nutritive value of fresh fruits and vegetables to a high degree.

An important factor for success in freezing horticultural products is the growing of suitable varieties. Investigations have shown that not all kinds of fruits and vegetables are adaptable to freezing and that certain varieties within a given kind are unsuitable. Examples of products adaptable to freezing are strawberries, raspberries, blueberries, asparagus, green broccoli, and certain varieties of peaches, plums, grapes, snap beans, lima beans, peas, and sweet corn.

Some foods are partially dried before they are frozen. This process is known as dehydrofreezing, and since the water content of the product is greatly reduced, it greatly aids in reducing the weight of food which is shipped. An example of such a product is slices of apple fruits.

In the process of freeze-drying, the food is dehydrated to complete dryness at temperatures below the freezing point of the food. This process retains the original freshness of the product, and, when properly packaged, the food may be stored at room temperatures. Tomatoes and sweetpotatoes are examples of freeze-dried vegetables.

QUESTIONS

1. State two advantages of storing, canning, drying, pickling, and freezing.
2. State the principal processes concerned in storing.
3. Write the equation for respiration.
4. In general, the lower the respiration rate of any given product, the longer the storage life. Explain.
5. Horticultural products in storage always decrease in dry weight. Explain.
6. Two bushels of apples or potatoes in the same storage room will produce more carbon dioxide and require more oxygen than one bushel. Explain.
7. In general, vegetable crops high in moisture respire at a higher rate than those moderately high in moisture. Explain.
8. In general, the storage life of many fruits, vegetables, and flowers is much longer at 35 to 40°F than at higher temperatures. Explain.
9. Given two lots of apples. Lot A was stored in a warm cellar; lot B was stored under refrigeration. In your opinion, which lot would give off the greater quantities of carbon dioxide for a period of 50 days? Give reasons for your answer.
10. Given two lots of garden peas stored for three days. Lot A was stored at 40°F, lot B at 70°F. Lot B became inedible; lot A remained sweet. Explain.
11. Products in storage are usually higher in temperature than the air of the storage room. Explain.
12. How is the law of mass action applied to the controlled-atmosphere storage of certain varieties of apples?
13. The amount of oxygen in storage rooms should always be sufficient for the complete combustion of the sugars. Explain.
14. Show how the accumulation of heat in the storage house increases the respiration rate of horticultural products.
15. In general, products with an intact periderm transpire less and have a longer storage life than those with a broken periderm. Explain.
16. Bruised fruit and vegetables lose more weight over the same period of time than nonbruised fruit and vegetables. Explain.
17. In general, fruits which have a heavy bloom shrink less rapidly in storage than those with a light bloom. Explain.
18. Most horticultural products are stored at a relatively high humidity. Explain.
19. Many products are stored in slatted crates. Explain.
20. The wetting of apple boxes just before they are filled with fruit and placed in storage is advantageous. Explain.
21. State the functions of the top vents and the bottom vents in ventilated storage houses.

22. In average weather with the lower vents open and the top vents closed in sweetpotato storage houses, the temperature of rooms filled with stored products rises. Explain.

23. In average weather and with the temperature in a sweetpotato storage house gradually rising and with the top vents continually open, when should the bottom vents be open and when should they be closed for any given 24-hour period? Explain.

24. If cold storage is not available, will tree fruits keep better for a short period on the tree or off the tree? Give reasons.

25. The warm-dry climate of the Pacific Coast is particularly favorable for the sun-drying of fruit and vegetable products. Explain.

26. What season of the year, if any, is most favorable for sun-drying in your particular community? Give reasons for your answer.

27. In general, vegetable crops are dried to a lower moisture content (5 to 10 per cent) than fruit crops (10 to 20 per cent). Can you think of any reasons for this?

28. Give two prime requirements of packages for dehydrated products.

29. How do canning, drying, pickling, and freezing preserve horticultural products?

17

THE TREE FRUITS

*The finest gift a man can give
to his age and time is the gift
of a constructive and creative life.*

Tree fruits are divided as follows: deciduous and evergreen. In general, deciduous trees shed their leaves in the fall, whereas evergreen trees shed most of their leaves in the spring when the young leaves are expanding. Thus, deciduous trees make foods during limited periods of the year only and evergreen trees make foods the entire year. Principal deciduous-tree fruits are the pomes and drupes, and the principal evergreen-tree fruits are orange, lemon, grapefruit, lime, banana, and olive.

DECIDUOUS–TREE FRUITS

THE POME FRUITS (Apple and Pear)

Plant Characteristics

Root System. The root system usually consists of a relatively short tapering taproot and several large, spreading lateral roots which branch into a network of smaller, threadlike roots. The larger roots are woody and serve mainly for anchorage, transportation, and storage; the smaller roots are nonwoody and serve as the absorbing system. The depth and spread of the roots depend largely on the texture and moisture of the soil. Where the soil is very loose and the soil moisture is deficient, the roots often penetrate many feet into the soil. In general, however, the major portion of the feeding roots is within the upper 15 inches of the soil, and the root spread is several feet beyond the tips of the scaffold branches. Thus, deep plowing or tillage will destroy many of the absorbing roots near the surface.

As discussed in Chapter 8, apples and pears are usually propagated by grafting a piece of twig on the root system of related kinds. Research, particularly at the East Malling Research Station near London, England, has shown that certain related kinds induce a dwarfing effect on the ultimate size of the tree (the cion) but not on the ultimate size or quality of the fruit. These kinds are known as Malling (M) or East Malling (EM) dwarfing rootstocks and are designated by roman numerals. In general, they differ in their dwarfing effect on the tree. For example, Malling IX has the most dwarfing effect, and the trees can be grown as espaliers or cordons on a trellis, wall, or fence. Malling VII has a semidwarfing effect and permits the tree to grow to a height of 10 to 12 feet, and Malling I permits the tree to grow to from one-third to one-half the size of standard trees.

Stems and Leaves.   The woody stem develops from alternate lateral and terminal vegetative buds. These lateral and terminal buds produce the twigs, each with a leaf and vegetative bud at each node. As the top of the tree develops, the twigs become small branches, and finally limb or scaffold branches—the main framework of the tree. The shape of the top of mature trees varies with the species and with the variety. In general, apple trees are more or less globular, and pear trees are shaped like an inverted cone. However, certain apple varieties (Henry Clay and Delicious) have the upright habit of growth, whereas others (Stayman) have the spreading type.

The leaves are simple, alternate, and toothed or lobed. They vary in size, shape, color, thickness, pubescence, and texture. By these differences the several species of apple and pear and certain varieties within a given species can be identified. For example, the leaves of the Baldwin variety are broad and distinctly saucer-shaped; those of the Delicious are moderately broad; and those of the Jonathan are small and narrow at base and apex. In general, the leaves of the pear are usually thicker, greener, less pubescent, more finely toothed, and more ovate than those of the apple.

Flowers and Fruit.   The flowers are perfect, with a five-lobed calyx, five moderately large separate petals, numerous distinct stamens, and a five-celled, five-styled ovary. Five or more blossoms are borne from the mixed flower bud on the end of each spur. The fruit varies in shape, color, texture, size, time of maturity, and other characteristics. In general, apples are spherical, with cavities at the basal (stem) end and apical (blossom) end, and the skin is green, yellow, or red or may develop two or all three of these pigments. The flesh is white or yellow and free of grit cells. On the other hand, the pear is pyriform with less distinct basal and apical cavities, and the color of the skin varies from dull yellow in some varieties to dark reddish-brown in others. The flesh is usually white or creamy white and contains numerous grit cells.

Economic Importance and Distribution

Producing Centers. The commercial production of apples in the continental United States is a major horticultural enterprise. In fact, this country leads all others in the production of the fruit. Principal centers of production are south and east of large bodies of water or east of mountain ranges. These afford protection from severe cold. Important commercial districts are (1) the Shenandoah-Cumberland located between the Blue Ridge and Cumberland Mountains, (2) the western New York on the south shore of Lake Ontario, (3) the Hudson and Champlain Valleys in southern New York, (4) the New England extending from southern Maine to Connecticut, (5) the eastern shore of Delaware and Maryland, (6) the western Michigan on the east shore of Lake Michigan, (7) the Ozark in southwestern Missouri, (8) the Wenatchee and the Yakima Valley in Washington, (9) the Hood River Valley in Oregon, (10) the Watsonville and the Sebastopol in central California, (11) the Payette in Idaho, and (12) the Grand Valley in Colorado.

In the continental United States pears are grown much less extensively than apples. Fireblight, a serious bacterial disease, is one of the chief limiting factors in commercial production. Important commercial districts are located in California, New York, Washington, and Oregon.

Varieties. Although about 2,000 varieties of apples and about 900 varieties of pears exist in the continental United States, not more than 8 or 10 varieties of apples and not more than three varieties of pears make up the greater bulk of total production in any particular apple- or pear-producing district of the country. Varieties are selected not only on the basis of yield, but also on other factors, such as (1) length of the formative period; (2) length of the fruiting period; (3) susceptibility or resistance to certain pests, (4) yield, size, color, quality, and shape of fruit; (5) the market demand; and (6) pollenizing value. In addition varieties vary in their adaptation. For example, certain varieties, such as Anoka and Northern Spy, are more adaptable to the northern half of the apple belt, whereas Early Harvest and Williams Early Red are more adaptable to the southern half. In fact, the selection of varieties is a regional problem. Even within a given region the continuous development of varieties and the appearance of bud sports frequently necessitate a change in recommendations. Thus, students who are interested in varieties for particular areas should consult the horticultural staff of the experiment station or extension division of the state in which they are interested in growing these fruits.

Growth and Development

Climatic Requirements.   The principal climatic factors are temperature, rainfall, and light. Of these, temperature is particularly important. In general, winter temperatures should be sufficiently low and prolonged to break the rest period, and at the same time they should not be so severe as to damage the roots and tops of the trees. As stated in Chapter 5, a certain amount of cold is necessary to break the rest period of many woody plants. Observations of the behavior of apple and pear trees grown in various regions of the country indicate that from 900 to 1,000 hours of temperatures below 40°F is necessary. If the trees are not exposed to sufficient cold the buds will fail to open in the spring. In general, the leaf buds require slightly more cold than the flower buds, and frequently in southern latitudes the flower buds open before the leaf buds begin to grow. Unless the leaf system develops simultaneously with, or shortly after, the opening of the blossoms, the young fruits fail to set owing to a lack of necessary foods—the carbohydrates and proteins. Thus, the amount of cold necessary to break the rest period generally sets the southern geographical limits of successful commercial production of those crops.

Although apples and pears require considerable cold to break the rest period, they cannot withstand prolonged exposure to intense cold. The root system is severely injured at a soil temperature below 20°F; and unless the tops are well hardened, air temperatures from −10 to −30°F frequently injure the collar, crown, crotches, and buds of the trees. Sudden drops in temperature, particularly during the late fall and early winter, usually cause great damage. Thus, the intensity and duration of cold generally set the northern geographical limits for the successful commercial production of these crops.

As with other crops, growing-season temperatures markedly influence the amount, color, and quality of the fruit. As stated in Chapter 5, apples and pears are primarily cold-season crops. For apples the optimum temperature range seems to be from 60 to 85°F. Areas in which the average summer temperature range is above 75°F seem to be poorly adapted to apple production. The best pear districts have a slightly higher summer temperature range than do the best apple districts. With both crops excessively high summer temperatures undoubtedly promote a high respiration rate; this in turn lowers the amount of carbohydrates available for growth, flower-bud formation, fruit development, and yield.

Soils.   The ideal soil texture for apples and pears is a loam. However, loamy sand, sandy loam, silt loam produce profitable crops, providing the subsoil is open, porous, and well drained. In no case should there be bedrock, hardpan, or waterlogged stratum within the rooting zone. Important soils are the Dunkirk of the Ontario district, the Dutchess of the Hudson River Valley of New York, the Frederick, Frankstown, and Murrill of the Shenandoah-Cumberland district, the Miami and Hillsdale soils of western Michigan, the Baxter and Clarksville soils of the Ozarks, the Wind River loam of the Hood River Valley, and the Wenatchee loam of Washington.

Disposition of the Carbohydrates. Three more or less distinct though overlapping periods exist in the growth and development of apple and pear trees. These are (1) formative, (2) transitory, and (3) fruiting. During the formative, or distinctly vegetative, period the top-root ratio is small, vegetative growth is vigorous, and the tree uses most of its carbohydrates in the formation of new growth; thus, utilization of carbohydrates is dominant. Since the development of the stems is quite marked during this period, proper selection and training of the scaffold branches are necessary. During the transitory period the tree gradually comes into bearing. Vegetative processes are less evident, carbohydrates accumulate, flower-forming substances are made, and flower buds are formed. During this period, since utilization and accumulation of carbohydrates are more nearly balanced, excess nitrogen or heavy pruning would promote excessive vegetative growth and delay fruitfulness. Within the bearing or fruiting period there are alternating cycles of vegetative and reproductive processes. Note the diagram.

A Formative period, 1–4 years	B Transitory period, 5–8 years	C Fruiting period, 8–20 years
Utilization dominant	First, utilization dominant Later, utilization and accumulation balanced	Alternating cycles of utilization and accumulation, with accumulation becoming dominant

When a tree begins to bear full crops vegetative growth gradually becomes less vigorous each year, carbohydrates accumulate, and reproductive processes become dominant. During this period the trees require more nitrogen than during the transitory period. In fact, nitrogen deficiency often becomes a limiting factor in fruit production. As the tree grows older additional nitrogen and pruning are required to make utilization processes more dominant.

Principal Cultural Practices. Apple and pear orchards are established according to definite systems or designs. Principal planting systems are (1) rectangular and (2) contour. In the *rectangular* the trees are planted at right angles to each other, with a tree at each corner of the rectangle.

This system favors the effective use of filler varieties, permits two-way cultivation, facilitates spraying and pruning operations, and supplies maximum access of sunlight to the trees. It is principally adapted to level or slightly sloped land. In the *contour* the trees are planted on the contours in one direction and usually are "staggered" at definite distances in the other. Where the contour lines change direction to the extent that it is impossible to line up in parallel all the rows in the opposite direction, a radial system of contour planting is employed. This system requires the use of surveying instruments to establish the contour lines and the building and maintaining of terraces. It has been designed to retard soil erosion and to permit cultivation across the slope and is, therefore, particularly adapted to hilly or sloped land. Note the airview of the apple orchards in Virginia shown in Fig. 17.1.

As stated in Chapter 2, intervarietal pollination is necessary for fruit setting of the apple and pear. Two factors are concerned: (1) the potency of the pollen; that is, the ability of each pollen grain to produce a tube, and (2) the time of pollen shedding in relation to the time of pistil receptivity. Effective pollinators have potent pollen which is shed at the time the pistils of the variety to be pollinated are receptive. With the apple,

Fig. 17.1. Airview of apple orchards in Virginia. Note that the trees were planted on the contour. (Courtesy, National Fruit Company, Winchester, Va.)

varieties differ in these respects. For example, the Winesap group (the Stayman Winesap, Winesap, and Arkansas) have impotent or sterile pollen; and McIntosh and Delicious, two well-known and widely adapted varieties, have potent and effective pollen. Thus, McIntosh and Delicious are more effective pollinators than the members of the Winesap group. In addition, certain varieties shed their pollen before or after the pistils of the main variety are receptive. For example, Rome Beauty sheds its pollen in western South Carolina after early blooming varieties are receptive. Thus, Rome Beauty is useless as a pollinator for early varieties in South Carolina orchards. With the pear, practically all varieties are interfruitful; that is, the pollen of one variety is as effective as another for pollination.

Important practices in the growing of fruit trees involve (1) systems of soil management, (2) water supply, and (3) essential-element supply. In general, trees in the formative stage are grown under the clean cultivation system of soil management, and trees in the fruiting period are grown under either the clean cultivation–cover crop system, the controlled–cover crop system, or the sod system of soil management.

As previously discussed, the water supply may be regulated by drainage, by irrigation, by controlling the growth of the cover crop, and by controlling weeds. As stated in Chapter 13, irrigation is necessary in apple or pear orchards of semiarid regions, and this practice is becoming increasingly common in many producing districts of humid regions.

The use of commercial fertilizers in the orchard has two objectives: (1) to supply the needs of the soil bacteria and the cover crop and (2) to supply the specific needs of the trees. In general, complete fertilizers are necessary to supply the needs of the bacteria and the cover crop, and quickly available nitrogen is usually necessary to supplement the supply of nitrate-nitrogen in the soil for the nitrogen requirements of the trees. The amount of nitrogen required varies with the phase of growth, whether formative or transitory, and with the vegetative vigor of the trees during the fruiting period. For example, $\frac{1}{4}$ pound of sodium nitrate or its equivalent is usually necessary for each year of growth during the formative period, from 5 to 6 pounds per tree may be necessary during the early part of the fruiting period, and from 8 to 12 pounds may be necessary during the latter part.

If apples or pears are grown in your community, what type of soil management is used? How is the water supply controlled? What is the recommended commercial fertilizer program for maintaining fertility of the soil and productivity of the trees?

Use of Growth Regulators. The shedding of leaves, flowers, and fruit is a familiar occurrence in many plants. A good example is the shedding of the leaves of deciduous trees and shrubs in late summer and fall. How does this natural shedding of certain organs take place? What changes take place in the tissues? In general, a layer of cells develops at the point of separation, for example, at the base of the petiole in the shedding of leaves and at the base of the pedicels in the shedding of flowers. This layer of cells is called the abscission layer, and in woody plants it consists of a cork cambium and a layer of corklike cells. As would be expected, this cork-like layer functions as a protective barrier, particularly in preventing the tissue from drying out and preventing the entrance of decay-producing organisms.

With certain varieties of the apple, the abscission layer forms before the fruit is at the proper stage for picking. As a result, the fruit drops from the trees and becomes badly bruised. This lowers their market value and reduces their storage life. Investigations have shown that certain hormone-like chemicals called growth regulators retard the formation of the abscission layer and enable the fruit to remain on the tree. Of the numerous chemicals which have been tried, alpha-naphthaleneacetic acid (NAA) and its metallic salts and alpha-naphthaleneacetamide (NAd) have been found to be particularly effective. In fact, these compounds are now used in many commercial orchards. As would be expected, many factors influence their effectiveness. Some of these factors are the variety, the concentration of the chemical, the time and number of applications, and the temperature of the weather. In general, when preharvest dropping of the fruit is a problem, a single application just before dropping begins provides about all the necessary protection.

Principal marketing operations are picking, brushing, grading, packing, and selling. *Picking* consists in separating individual fruits from the tree, placing the fruit in an appropriate container, transferring the fruit to an orchard box or crate, and transporting the fruit to a packing house or shed; *brushing* consists in using soft brushes to remove residue and to polish the skin; *grading* consists in separating the fruit into market classes or grades on the basis of size, shape, and color according to the variety; and *packing* consists in placing the graded specimens in a definite manner or style in the market container.

QUESTIONS

1. What is the essential difference between deciduous trees and evergreen trees?
2. The depth of root penetration of an apple or pear tree depends largely on the texture and internal drainage of the subsoil. Explain.
3. Most apple-growing districts are in the Northeast, Middle West, and on the upper Pacific Coast. Explain.
4. Why are there no commercial apple districts in (*a*) Florida and along the Gulf Coast? (*b*) North Dakota and South Dakota? Explain.

5.   Apples on a commercial scale are grown on the southeast side of Lake Michigan and not on the northwest side, on the south side of Lake Ontario and not on the north side. Explain.

6.   Name the periods in the growth and development of an apple or pear tree.

7.   The transitory period is considered the most critical period from the standpoint of pruning and fertilizing. Explain.

8.   A fruit spur usually bears in alternate years, whereas the tree as a whole bears annually. Explain.

9.   How do frosts during the blossoming period induce biennial bearing of apple varieties?

10. In general, the rectangular system is adaptable to level or slightly sloped land, and the contour system should be used on hilly land. Explain.

11. What are the requirements of an effective pollinator in apple and pear orchards?

12. A colony of bees and an effective pollinator should be within 1,000 feet of every tree in the orchard, particularly during cold, wet weather. Explain.

13. In general, trees in the formative period require the clean cultivation system of soil management. Explain.

14. The available nitrogen supply regulates to a marked degree the vegetative and reproductive phases of fruit trees. Explain.

15. How do certain growth regulators prevent the preharvest drop of fruit of certain varieties of apple?

16. Sunny days and cool nights during the fruit-ripening period are particularly favorable for the production of highly colored fruit and cloudy days and warm nights are particularly unfavorable. Explain.

THE DRUPE FRUITS (Peach, Nectarine, Plum, Apricot, Cherry, and Almond)

Plant Characteristics

Root System.   Mature trees of the drupe fruits have several large woody roots which branch into many small roots and numerous absorbing roots. In general, the root system is less extensive and less deep than that of the apple and pear. For these reasons the trees suffer more quickly from drought or from weed competition. However, the root spread is roughly proportional to the size of the tree. As with pome trees, the lateral spread of the roots is usually a foot or more beyond the spread of the branches.

Stems and Leaves.   The stem system consists of (1) main or scaffold stems called limbs and (2) smaller branches and twigs from which arise shoots containing leaves, flowers, and fruit. In general, the buds are produced on current-season wood. Buds are (1) lateral or (2) terminal. Lateral buds are (1) vegetative or (2) flower, whereas terminal buds are always vegetative. Both terminal and lateral vegetative buds give rise to

(1) shoot growth (long) or (2) spur growth (short). The peach and almond produce shoots mostly, and apricots, plums, and cherries develop both shoots and spurs. The leaves are alternate, simple, long in proportion to width, short-petioled, and finely toothed. The teeth and petiole often contain glands. As is common with apples and pears, the leaves unfold about the time of blossoming and absciss after growth ceases in the late summer or fall.

Flowers and Fruit. The flowers of the drupe fruit crops have characteristics in common and characteristics in distinction. Characteristics in common are the hermaphroditic sex expression, regular arrangement of flower parts, with a five-lobed, bell-shaped, or tubular calyx, a five-petaled corolla, numerous stamens attached to the rim of the calyx, and a solitary pistil attached at the bottom of the calyx. Characteristics in distinction are the number of flowers per node, the color of the petals, and length of the flower stalk. In the peach and apricot the flowers are in singles or pairs, the petals are white, pink, or red according to the variety, and the flower stalk is very short. In the plum and cherry the flowers occur in groups, the petals are white, and the flower stalk is long.

The fruit develops from ovary tissue only and varies greatly in size, shape, pubescence, color of the skin, and color and texture of the flesh. In general, peach fruits are comparatively large, subglobular, and slightly grooved on one side and have a pubescent skin, firm greenish, white, or yellow flesh which either separates from or clings to the stony endocarp. Varieties which produce fruit in which the fleshy mesocarp and the stony endocarp separate on ripening are called "freestones," and varieties which produce fruit in which the fleshy endocarp and stony exocarp remain attached are called "clingstones." Plum fruits are moderately large, globular, and have a smooth skin and smooth pit. Apricot fruits are similar to peach fruits in size and shape and have a fine pubescence and smooth pit. Cherry fruits are comparatively small, smooth, long-stalked and have flesh which is either sweet or sour to the taste and small, smooth pits. Fruit of the sour cherry is about ½ inch in diameter and pale red or dark red; and fruit of the sweet cherry is about ¾ inch in diameter with light yellow, red, or dark red skin, and firm flesh. Almond fruits are much compressed. The mesocarp, instead of being fleshy as in the other drupe fruits, becomes leathery and tough and at maturity separates from the stone. The kernel or seed of the almond is the edible portion.

Economic Importance and Distribution

In the continental United States, a large number of drupe fruit industries have developed. *Peaches* are produced chiefly on the Pacific Coast and in the Southeast, Northeast, and Middle West. The leading states are California, South Carolina, Georgia, North Carolina, and Pennsylvania. In California yellow-fleshed clingstone varieties are grown mainly for canning, and yellow-fleshed freestones are grown for drying. In states other than California yellow-fleshed freestones are grown for immediate consumption and for canning. *Plums* are grown chiefly on the Pacific Coast. In this region the principal varieties belong to the prune group—a type of plum high in sugar content and adapted to natural dehydration. *Apricots* and nectarines are grown chiefly in California. *Cherries* are produced in two regions: (1) the Pacific Coast and (2) the Great Lakes. Sweet cherries are grown mostly in the former region, and sour cherries are grown mostly in the latter. *Almonds,* like apricots, are grown chiefly in California. The two general types or races of almonds are bitter and sweet. Sweet, edible almonds consist of two groups: (1) hard shell and (2) soft shell. Of these the soft shell is the more important.

Growth and Development

Climatic Requirements. The principal climatic factor in drupe fruit production is temperature. In common with the apple and pear, the drupe fruits have distinct winter and growing-season temperature requirements. Within commercial drupe-growing districts winter temperatures are sufficiently low and of sufficient duration to bring the trees out of the rest period, but are not sufficiently low to damage the root or top system severely. In general, an exposure of 700 to 1,000 hours of temperatures below 45°F is necessary to break the rest period fully, depending on the species and varieties within the species. For example, some American plums require more cold than peaches, and Elberta, an important peach variety, requires more cold than the variety Babcock.

The minimum temperatures which trees withstand vary with the crop. In general, well-hardened trees of American plums and sour cherries withstand temperatures of about —30°F; well-hardened trees of European plums and sweet cherries withstand temperatures of about —20°F; and well-hardened trees of peaches and apricots withstand temperatures of about —10°F. Thus, of the drupe fruits American plums and sour cherries are the most hardy, European plums and sweet cherries are intermediate, and peaches and apricots are the least hardy. This relatively less hardiness of the peach explains why commercial peach belts in the northern regions are located on the leeward side of the large bodies of water. Examples are the peach belts on the southern shore of Lake Ontario and Lake Erie and on the eastern shore of Lake Michigan.

Optimum growing-season temperatures vary also with the crop. The main centers of sour cherry production in the continental United States have a mean summer temperature of about 65°F, and those of the sweet cherry and plum have a mean summer temperature of 70°F. On the other hand, although peaches are grown in regions with summer temperatures as low at 65°F, the highest production and quality are obtained in regions which have a mean summer temperature of 75°F. Thus, the sweet cherry requires somewhat lower growing-season temperatures than the peach or apricot. These different growing-season temperature requirements partially explain why sour cherries are grown in the northern regions and not in the southern, and why peaches produce profitable crops in both regions.

Soils.   As with apples and pears, the ideal soil texture for the drupe fruits is a loam. However, profitable production is secured on many soil types provided the subsoil contains no bedrock, hardpan, or waterlogged stratum in the rooting zone. Sands, gravelly sandy loams, loams, and silt loams are used. In general, peaches are better adapted to sands than are plums and cherries.

Disposition of the Carbohydrates.   As with apples and pears, the life cycle of trees of the drupe fruits may be divided into three more or less distinct but overlapping periods: (1) the formative, (2) the transitory, and (3) the fruiting. During the formative period root and shoot growth is evident only; thus, during this period most of the carbohydrates made are utilized for vegetative processes. During the transitory period the trees continue to produce roots and shoots, and flowering and fruiting begin. During this period the trees are gradually coming into the bearing stage, and carbohydrate utilization is less dominant and accumulation becomes more evident. During the fruiting period within any one season there is a period of shoot, flower, and fruit growth followed by a period of shoot and fruit maturation and flower-bud differentiation. Thus, carbohydrate utilization is dominant during the first part of the growing season, and accumulation is dominant during the latter part.

During the productive life of the tree a close positive relation exists between the length of shoot growth in any one season and the quantity of fruit produced the following year. In general, short shoots, made by weakly vegetative trees, have one and rarely two flower buds in the nodes; moderately long shoots, made by moderately vigorous trees, have two, rarely one, flower buds at each node; and long shoots, made by extremely vigorous trees, have only vegetative buds at the nodes. Clearly, the moderately vigorous tree is the most fruitful.

Principal Cultural Practices.   The same systems are used in planting orchards of the drupe fruits as are used with the pome fruits. The rectangular system is commonly used on fairly level land, and the contour system is necessary on sloped or hilly land. Figure 17.2 shows a contiguous group of peach orchards planted on the contour. Note how the correct distance between the rows is maintained.

Among the drupe fruits there are wide differences in incompatibility

Fig. 17.2. Airview of peach orchards, supply store, and packing shed in South Carolina. (Courtesy, Soil Conservation Service, U.S. Department of Agriculture.)

of the pollen. As stated in Chapter 2, incompatibility is due to the failure of the pollen tube to grow down the style in time to liberate the sperms which unite with the egg and the endosperm nuclei. When union does not take place, the young fruit ceases to grow and dies. Two kinds of incompatible pollen exist: (1) self-incompatible and (2) cross-incompatible. Thus, where self-incompatibility and cross-incompatibility exist, the interplanting of suitable pollinator varieties is necessary.

The situation of the drupe fruits is set forth briefly as follows. In general, in the peach and apricot practically all varieties are self- and cross-compatible; in the plum with the Japanese type most varieties are self-incompatible and a few are cross-incompatible, and with the European type some varieties are self-compatible, others are self-incompatible, and others are cross-incompatible; in the sweet cherry most varieties are self-incompatible and some are cross-incompatible; and in the sour cherry most varieties are self- and cross-compatible. Thus, solid blocks may be given over to the self-compatible sorts, but interplanting of suitable varieties is necessary for the self- and cross-incompatible sorts.

In general, trees of the drupe fruits thrive best under the controlled–cover crop system of soil management. During the spring and summer the cover crop is disked or mowed at regular intervals to reduce competition for water and essential raw materials and to promote the vegetative phase of the trees; and during the early fall the cover crop is established to promote carbohydrate accumulation in the trees, to conserve essential elements, and to reduce soil erosion. In practically all commercial districts the trees require nitrogen, and in some districts in addition to nitrogen they require phosphorus, potassium, magnesium, calcium, and in certain soils trace elements. In general, the amount of nitrogen required varies with the kind of drupe fruit, the vigor and age of the trees, and soil fertility. For peaches sufficient available nitrogen is applied to induce a terminal growth of 16 to 25 inches per year. For example, $\frac{1}{4}$ to $\frac{1}{2}$ pound of nitrogen, usually in the form of ammonium nitrate, is applied to young trees, and $\frac{1}{2}$ to 1 pound or more is applied to old trees.

The principal marketing operations are picking, grading, packing, storing, and selling. In general, peaches for fresh market are packed to reach the consumer when the fruit is in the ripe stage of maturity. Thus, the fruit is picked in the hard-ripe stage of maturity for long distance shipment and in the ripe stage for local markets. Popular market containers are the bushel, $\frac{3}{4}$ and $\frac{1}{2}$ bushel, climax baskets, corrugated or fiberboard cartons, wire-bound boxes or crates, and wooden lugs or flats. In general, certain varieties of plums (prunes) are harvested and sold with the stems unattached, whereas other varieties of this fruit are harvested and sold with the stems attached. Sweet cherries are picked with or without the stems depending on the intended use, and the common container for this fruit is the quart basket.

QUESTIONS

1. How does a peach fruit differ from an apple fruit?
2. In general, drupe fruit trees are less drought resistant than pome fruit trees. Explain.
3. How does the fruit of the peach differ from that of the apricot?
4. How does the fruit of the almond differ from that of the peach?
5. Which is the leading region in peach production? Give reasons for your answer.
6. Set forth briefly the set of environmental conditions which determine the southern geographical limits for commercial peach production.
7. Peaches for commercial production are not grown along the Gulf Coast of Texas, Louisiana, Mississippi, and Florida. Explain.
8. What set of environmental conditions determines the northern limits of commercial peach production? Give reasons for your answer.
9. Peaches thrive satisfactorily in southern Michigan; they do not thrive well in central Iowa. Explain.
10. Where are most of the sweet cherries grown? Most of the sour cherries? Give reasons.

11. Classify the fruiting wood of the peach according to its degree of productivity.
12. The vigor of shoot growth of the peach tree is associated with the number and kind of buds formed. Explain.
13. How can the grower determine the immediate productivity of peach trees?
14. A student goes into a peach orchard and examines two trees, A and B. The shoots of tree A have many fruit buds in twos at the node. Those of tree B are mostly single. Which tree will produce more fruit? Explain.
15. The fruiting spurs of the plum are straighter than those of the apple. Explain.
16. Given two cherry trees, A and B, each 10 years old. On tree A spurs make from 1 to 2 inches of growth each year; on tree B spurs make from 2 to 3 inches of growth each year. Which tree will be the more fruitful? Explain.

EVERGREEN–TREE FRUITS

THE CITRUS FRUITS (Orange, Lemon, Grapefruit, and Lime)

Plant Characteristics

Citrus trees are broad-leaved evergreens. The trees vary in height from 10 to 15 feet (lime), 10 to 20 feet (lemon), 25 to 40 feet (orange), and 30 to 50 feet (grapefruit). They differ little in habit of growth. When young, the trees are upright and spreading; as they grow older they become somewhat pyramidal in shape. In general, citrus trees are long-lived and begin bearing at four to six years of age.

Root System. Citrus trees are propagated by budding. This helps to ensure the production of uniform trees and the development of satisfactory root systems. The principal stocks are (1) sour orange, (2) rough lemon, (3) sweet orange, and (4) trifoliate. Of these the sour orange stock was the most widely used for many years. However, since this stock is susceptible to a disease known as quick decline (tristeza disease), resistant stocks are now used in districts where this disease is prevalent, i.e., trifoliate Troyer citrange stocks in California and rough lemon, sweet orange, and Cleopatra stocks in Florida. Rough lemon stocks are more adaptable to sandy soils, and trifoliate stocks are more adaptable to the well-drained flatwood soils and especially where cold resistance is needed.

Stems and Leaves. The trunks are usually short, and their diameter depends on the kind of crop and age of the tree. In general, most trees are headed "low." At planting, the young trees are headed-back 24 to 30 inches to induce "low" heading. This produces a dense to fairly open head, with the lower branches drooping almost to the ground, thus protecting the trunk from cold weather. The wood is very strong and elastic. For example, heavily loaded orange and grapefruit limbs, though their normal position is from 8 to 12 feet above the ground, often bend at fairly narrow arcs without breaking.

The leaves are rather rough and leathery in texture, light green on the under side, and deep glossy green on the upper. They vary in shape and size according to the kind of fruit. In general, the larger the fruit, the larger the leaf; thus the leaves of the lime are small and ovate, those of the lemon are a little larger than the lime and also ovate in shape, those of the sweet orange are medium, fairly broad, and long ovate, and those of the grapefruit are large, long, and broad. The petioles are broadly winged (grapefruit), narrowly winged (sweet orange and lime), or not winged (lemon), a characteristic which serves as a means of identifying the various kinds.

Flowers and Fruit. The flowers occur singly or in groups consisting of small axillary or terminal cymes. Individual flowers have four or five white or purplish petals (lemon petals are white inside and purple outside), numerous stamens, usually 20 to 40, and a single 7- to 15-celled pistil. Some kinds are extremely fragrant (sweet orange and grapefruit), which can often be detected for a considerable distance from the orchards. The size of the flower varies with the kind of plant. For example, flowers of the grapefruit are large; those of the sweet orange are moderately large; and those of the tangerine (mandarin) are small.

From February to April, depending upon the area in which the orchards are located, the main bloom of the year takes place. In areas that are sufficiently warm, lime and lemon flowers appear each month, but most of the flowers open in late winter or early spring.

The fruit is derived from ovary tissue only and consists essentially of a leathery rind or skin (the outer portion) and of soft juicy flesh (the inner and edible portion). The rind is derived from the outer ovary wall and has numerous oil sacs embedded in its tissue. It varies in depth (thin to thick) and in color (light yellow to deep orange-red), depending on the kind of fruit. The rind serves as a cover and provides protection for the inner ovary wall which is divided into five or more segments by means of thin, radial, grayish membranes. Each segment is packed with club- or spindle-shaped sacs, called vesicles, which contain soluble sugars, various organic acids, and more particularly comparatively large quantities of ascorbic acid or vitamin C. Most varieties of orange and grapefruit are self-fruitful, but citrus flowers are very attractive to several kinds of insects, including honeybees, and when two or more varieties are available these insects cross-pollinate many flowers. A few, the Washington Navel orange and Tahiti lime, for example, produce parthenocarpic fruit.

Economic Importance and Distribution

Citrus fruits are grown in many parts of the world. Important commercial industries are located in Spain, Italy, Palestine, India, China, Australia, and North and South America. The industry is foremost in value and importance in the continental United States and is located in the southern regions of the country. Outstanding industries exist in Orange, Los Angeles, San Bernardino, Tulare, Riverside, Ventura, and San Diego counties of southern California, in the Rio Grande Valley of south Texas, in central and southern Florida, and the Plaquemines district below New Orleans, Louisiana. Most of the oranges are produced in California and Florida; most of the grapefruit in Florida and Texas; most of the lemons in California and limes in southern Florida.

Growth and Development

Climatic Requirements.   Citrus and other subtropical fruits thrive best in regions between the tropics where frost or freezing temperatures never occur, and the temperate zone where freezing temperatures occur for a considerable period during the winter season. This zone is known as the subtropical zone. Within this zone growing-season temperatures are usually sufficiently high for the production of profitable crops and for proper maturation of the fruit. On the other hand, winter-season temperatures frequently cause the grower great concern. Unlike apple and peach trees, citrus trees are nonhardy. They can withstand only a few degrees below 32°F. For example, the critical temperature of the sweet orange is about 24°F and that of the lemon is about 26°F. Even the Satsuma orange, the hardiest of the citrus family, cannot withstand temperatures below 18°F. In citrus-growing districts temperatures below these critical points occur frequently, and orchard or grove heating, a unique practice in citrus culture, has been developed. Oil or gas heaters and to a lesser extent coke and briquet heaters or small piles of wood are placed at definite intervals in the orchard, and while burning they raise the temperature of the air to a maximum of 8°F under favorable conditions. Other methods of protection are mounding the trunks of young trees with soil, using wind machines with or without orchard heaters, and using irrigation water in combination with wind machines and orchard heaters. Since orchard heating is an expensive practice, growers should use all available information when selecting sites and should practice all orchard operations to aid the trees in functioning normally. For example, trees that are affected by mineral deficiencies cannot withstand as low temperatures without injury as can trees supplied with all necessary minerals. Can you think of any reason for this?

Research work indicates that about 35 inches of water is necessary for the annual production of most of the citrus crops. In Florida the rains occur mostly in summer, and they supply most of the water requirements of the trees. However, in February and March when the trees are in blossom and through June irrigation may be necessary. In the lower Rio Grande Valley of Texas, the Salt River Valley of Arizona, and the various citrus districts in California, the mean annual rainfall varies from 5 to 20 inches and the deficits varying from 12 to 30 inches are made up by irrigation.

Soils.   Like other orchard trees, citrus trees require well-drained, well-aerated, and moderately fertile soils. Excellent soil drainage is particularly necessary. Soils extensively used are Norfolk fine sand, Blanton fine sand, and Orlando fine sand in Florida; Hidalgo fine sand and Victoria fine sandy loam in the Rio Grande Valley; and Fallbrooke fine sandy loam, Hanford silt loam, and Placentia silt loam in California.

Disposition of the Carbohydrates.   Like the temperate tree fruits, citrus trees have three more or less distinct but overlapping phases of development: (1) formative, (2) transitory, and (3) fruiting. During the formative period the young trees develop the main branches of the root system and the framework of the tops—the trunk and primary and secondary scaffold branches. Thus, practically all the carbohydrates are used for vegetative growth. During the transitory period the young trees continue their root and top growth, but in addition, flower buds are formed, followed by the initiation of the fruiting period. Thus, not all of the carbohydrates are used for root and stem growth; some are used for flower-bud formation and for fruit development and maturation. During the fruiting period there are alternate cycles of shoot, flower, and fruit development followed by shoot and fruit maturation. In sharp contrast to deciduous trees, citrus trees develop stems and leaves two or three times each year. The period of vegetative growth takes place whenever the temperature, water supply, and essential-element supply are favorable. The behavior of citrus trees in Florida is shown in the following diagram.

February–March	April–May	June	September–April
Blossoming and first cycle of shoot growth	Growth of young fruit	Second cycle of shoot growth and development of fruit	Maturation of fruit

A   B   C   D   E

Principal Cultural Practices.   Common planting systems for establishing citrus orchards are (1) the square and (2) the contour (see Fig. 17.3).

Fig. 17.3. Airview of citrus orchards in southern California. (Courtesy, Los Angeles Chamber of Commerce.)

When the contour system is used, the rows can be made straight in one direction (up and down the slope) unless the contour of the land is quite steep and irregular. For high crop production per acre during the first part of the life of the orchard, double planting, particularly with lemons, is often practiced and the excess trees are removed when crowding occurs. Intercropping with vegetable crops in some areas provides an income until the trees begin bearing. In California citrus trees are planted usually from early spring to early summer, and in Florida they are planted in winter or just after the beginning of the rainy season in the summer.

As with many other tree-fruit enterprises, the controlled–cover crop system is usually necessary for the production of citrus fruits. The time during which cover crops are grown coincides with the period of heaviest rainfall. In California practically all the rain occurs in the winter. Thus, cover crops that grow in cool weather are started in the fall just before the rains occur and are incorporated in the soil in the spring just before the rains cease. Mustards, *Melilotus indica,* malva, and natural or introduced weeds are commonly used. In Florida since most of the rains occur in the summer, cover crops are started in the spring and are cut or incorporated in the soil in the fall—usually just before the harvest season. In this state warm-season crops adapted to acid soils are grown, e.g., beggar weed, velvet bean, crotalaria, and natural weeds.

As with other crops, the use of commercial fertilizers depends on the available essential-element content of the soil and on the age, vigor, and growth characteristics of the plant. In California most soils in the citrus districts contain sufficient quantities of all the essential elements except nitrate-nitrogen and available zinc. Common organic nitrogen carriers used are manure, alfalfa hay, bean, and cereal straw, and the principal inorganic nitrogen carrier used is ammonium sulfate. The common carrier of zinc is zinc sulfate. This compound is needed to avoid or correct mottle leaf due to a lack of available zinc in the soil. Applications are made to the leaves in the form of a dust or spray. In Florida and adjacent districts most soils are deficient in available nitrogen, phosphorus, or potassium; and in addition some soils are deficient in calcium and magnesium, and others in manganese, copper, iron, or zinc, or any combination of these essential elements. Thus, the commercial fertilizer program in the Gulf Coast districts consists in using complete mixtures and carriers of the other essential elements in accordance with the needs of the soil and the trees. For example, until recently iron chlorosis was prevalent in certain citrus districts in central Florida, and as pointed out in Chapter 7, certain organic compounds containing iron—the chelates—were found to correct iron deficiency. Consequently, these compounds are now used, and they may be applied directly to the soil or as a foliage spray.

The marketing of citrus fruits is a highly developed and most efficient system. Many operations are involved, but most important are *picking, transporting* in field boxes to the packing shed, *degreening* to destroy chlorophyll and to unmask the yellow and orange pigments, *washing* to remove spray residue, smudge, and other deposits, *drying* to remove moisture from the rind, *waxing* to reduce transpiration and to polish the skin, *applying* 2, 4-D with or without wax to lemons to prolong keeping quality, *X-raying* to detect frost-damaged or granulated specimens (operators are able to see the internal structure of the fruit as it passes through a fluoroscope), *grading* according to size into three or more market classes, *stamping* individual specimens, *wrapping,* and *packing.* Common containers are boxes, crates, cartons, and open-mesh bags.

QUESTIONS

1. Name the important citrus fruits.
2. How do the size and habit of growth of citrus trees compare with those of apple and peach trees?
3. The various kinds of citrus are not grown on their own roots. Give two reasons.
4. Compare the life of citrus leaves with those of the apple.
5. Some citrus flowers have a strong, sweet scent. Compare this with deciduous fruit flowers.
6. Some citrus fruits are always seedless. Explain.
7. During the days of sailing ships, fresh vegetables and deciduous-tree fruits were not part of the diet of the crews of the ships, but limes, lemons, or oranges usually were found on all ships. Explain.
8. Florida and California grow most of the citrus fruits in the United States. Explain.
9. Oil heaters are extensively used in citrus culture in the United States. Explain.
10. Compare the time of vegetative growth of citrus fruit trees with that of deciduous fruit trees.
11. How is the application of nitrogen carriers to bearing citrus trees the same as that to bearing apple trees? How different?

18

NUT FRUITS, TROPICAL AND SUBTROPICAL FRUITS, TUNG

The life and soul of science
is its practical application.
Lord Kelvin, 1883

NUT FRUITS

The most important nut fruits of the world fall into two groups: (1) the evergreen tropical nonhardy and (2) the deciduous semihardy.

EVERGREEN NONHARDY

Principal evergreen nonhardy crops are coconut, Brazil nut, and cashew. These crops require very warm growing seasons and extremely mild nongrowing, or dormant, seasons. At present coconuts are grown widely in the tropical regions of the world, Brazil nuts are confined largely to the valleys of the Amazon River and its tributaries, and cashew nuts are grown mainly in the tropics of India.

DECIDUOUS SEMIHARDY (Pecan, Walnut, Filbert)

Plant Characteristics

Root System. Although little experimental evidence is available on the nature and extent of the root system, authorities believe that the taproot forms a system of laterals which branch to form the absorbing system. In general, the degree of ramification is proportional to the size of the tops. For example, trees of the Persian walnut produce relatively small tops and a correspondingly sparse root system. On the other hand, trees of the

332

black walnut and pecan develop a large top and a correspondingly well-developed and extensive root system. As with other tree crops, the depth of penetration depends largely on the looseness, drainage, and aeration of the subsoil.

Stems and Leaves. In general, the size and shape of the top vary with the kind of plant. For example, California walnut trees are small and round-headed; Persian walnut trees are medium-sized and round-headed; and pecan trees are tall and globular-headed. As with many other tree crops, the stem system consists of a trunk, primary, secondary, and tertiary scaffold branches, and small branches or shoots. On the twigs and young branches the bark is smooth, and on the large branches and trunk it is rough and shaggy. The leaves are alternate and pinnately compound, and vary in number, size, and shape with the kind of crop. For example, pecan leaves have a large number of small, pointed leaflets, and walnut leaves have a small number of large, oval leaflets.

Flowers and Fruits. The deciduous nut crops are monoecious. In other words, the pistils and stamens are borne in separate flowers and both types of flowers are borne on the same tree. The pistillate inflorescence, called a cluster, develops from terminal buds on the past season's growth, and the staminate inflorescence, called a catkin, develops from buds at the base of one-year-old wood. Individual flowers are small and inconspicuous. The stamens produce large quantities of fine, fluffy pollen and the pistils present a comparatively large stigmatic surface. Air currents, the agent of pollen transfer, carry the pollen from the stamens to the stigmas.

Individual fruits are dry, indehiscent, one-seeded ovaries. According to the kind of plant, they vary in size from $\frac{1}{2}$ to $1\frac{1}{2}$ inches, in diameter and length from 1 to 2 inches, and in shape from round to oblong. The edible kernels are enclosed in a hard pericarp or ovary wall and contain from 65 to 70 per cent fat, from 10 to 16 per cent protein, and about 14 per cent carbohydrates. They are good sources of the B vitamins.

Economic Importance and Distribution

In the United States Persian walnuts are produced mostly in the Pacific Coast region, with California the leading state; and pecans are produced mostly in the southern regions, with Texas the leading state. Other important states are Georgia, Alabama, Florida, and Mississippi.

Growth and Development

Climatic Requirements. The principal climatic factor is temperature. Like other deciduous crops, the nut fruits have rather distinct temperature requirements. In general, pecans require long, warm summers and short, mild winters. The long, warm, frost-free growing season is necessary for the full maturation of the nuts, and the short, mild winter is sufficiently cool to bring the buds out of the rest period. Thus, the crop is adapted to the warm summer, mild winter climates of the Southeast and Southwest rather than to the cool summer, cold winter climates of the Northeast and Middle West.

In contrast to pecans, walnuts and filberts require cool summers and moderately cold winters. Long, cool summers are more favorable for the development of the nuts than long, warm summers, and a rather long exposure to moderate cold is necessary to break the rest period. In fact, certain varieties of walnuts require as much cold as apples, and others require only as much cold as peaches. In addition the trees are susceptible to foliage disease in humid climates. Thus, English walnuts and filberts are better adapted to the summer-dry climate of the Pacific Coast than to climates in the other regions.

Soils. In common with deciduous-tree fruits, deciduous nut crops require well-drained, well-aerated, and moderately fertile and fertile soil. According to observations at the California Experiment Station, adapted soils of the Imperial Valley should be well aerated to the 7- or 9-foot level, and those of the coastal areas should be well aerated to the 5-foot level. Within the pecan belt, highly productive trees are found growing on the well-drained, alluvial soils of the river valleys, particularly those of the Mississippi River and its southwest tributaries, and on the well-drained, fertile soils of the Piedmont and upper Coastal Plain regions. Infertile sands with a low water table and heavy clays with compact subsoils are unadaptable. Filberts seem to be more tolerant of rather compact soils than walnuts or pecans.

Disposition of the Carbohydrates. As with other woody plants, the growth periods of deciduous nut crops are (1) formative, (2) transitory, and (3) fruiting. During the formative period the young trees develop their root and stem systems—the trunk and primary and secondary scaffold branches. Thus, all the carbohydrates which are made are used for vegetative processes. During the transitory period, although the trees continue to develop their root and stem systems, they begin to produce flowers and fruits. Thus, not all the carbohydrates are used for vegetative processes; some are needed for reproductive processes. During the fruiting period for any one year, vegetative processes are dominant during the first part of the growing season and reproductive processes are dominant during the latter part. Carbohydrate utilization is necessary for the development of the flowers, shoots, and young fruits, whereas carbohydrate accumulation is necessary for and is associated with the formation of flower buds and the maturation of the nuts.

Principal Cultural Practices. Principal cultural practices involve (1) planting distances, (2) systems of soil management, (3) application of commercial fertilizers, (4) pollination requirements, (5) pest control, and (6) harvesting.

In general, planting distances vary with the ultimate size of the trees. Pecan trees are set 60×60 feet or 70×70 feet. Walnut trees may be set 30×30 feet, and later, usually when they are from 10 to 14 years old, three-fourths of them are removed so that the remaining trees stand 60×60 feet. Filbert trees are set 20×20 feet or 25×25 feet.

As with other tree fruits, the cultivation–cover crop system or the controlled–cover crop system is used. In the cultivation–cover crop system, cultivation is practiced during the first part of the growing season, and an adapted cover crop is established and maintained during the latter part. In the controlled–cover crop system, the cover crop is kept mowed or heavily grazed during the first part of the growing season and allowed to grow or be grazed lightly during the latter. In either case the vegetative and reproductive phases of the trees are more or less controlled.

The commercial fertilizer program depends largely on the type and fertility of the soil. For example, pecan soils, particularly those of the southeast region, require applications of complete mixtures, and walnut soils of the Pacific Coast contain sufficient quantities of all essential elements except those supplying nitrate-nitrogen and zinc. As with other crops, the U.S. Department of Agriculture and agricultural experiment stations have developed commercial fertilizer programs for local growers. Thus, students who are interested in the commercial fertilizer program for any one of the nut crops in any given district should consult the staff of the horticulture department of the state in which the crop is located.

As with apples, pears, sweet cherries, and other crops, the successful production of nut fruits requires a working knowledge of pollination requirements. With the pecan and walnut, dichogamy—the shedding of pollen of any given variety before or after the pistils of the same variety are receptive—is involved. Some varieties of pecan shed practically all their pollen before their pistils are receptive; others shed most of their pollen after their pistils are receptive; and the same variety may shed pollen too soon in some seasons, about the right time in others, and too late in others. Certain varieties of walnut frequently shed most of their pollen before the pistils are receptive, and other varieties frequently shed most of their pollen after the pistils are receptive. With both of these crops growers plant, at definite intervals, pollinator trees that shed pollen at the time the pistils of the commercial varieties are receptive. In addition, some growers of walnuts gather catkins of related species in mosquito-net bags, distribute the bags throughout the orchard, and strike them with a pole to help spread the pollen into the wind. Most varieties of filberts are partially self-incompatible, but all varieties are

Fig. 18.1. Pecan orchards in south Mississippi. (Courtesy, I. H. Bass, Lumberton, Miss.)

cross-compatible. Thus, growers of filberts interplant at least two varieties in any given orchard. Figure 18.1 shows two contiguous pecan orchards near Lumberton, Mississippi. Note the large size of the trees, the wide spacings, and the cover crop system of soil management.

Harvesting and marketing operations of deciduous nut crops are quite similar. Pecan fruits are knocked from the trees, usually with bamboo poles, or are allowed to fall to the ground or on canvas spread under the trees. The fruits are then carried to the packing shed and "shucked." Walnut trees are shaken to make the fruits drop to the ground or the fruits may be allowed to drop in the natural way. Filberts are allowed to drop to the ground in the natural way, carried to the drying sheds, and husked if necessary. After removing the hulls and washing (walnuts only), the nuts are dried, either naturally or artificially, to induce a dormant condition of the embryo and are graded according to size into several market classes to standardize the community's output. They are then packed in large bags for shipping large quantities or in small bags and paper boxes for retail trade. For long storage life a cool (35 to 40°F), dry, odorproof environment is necessary.

QUESTIONS

1. How do the pecan and Persian walnut differ in the size of the tree?
2. The deciduous nut crops produce enormous quantities of pollen, and the stigmatic surface is quite large. Explain.

3. Although pecan trees grow along the southern boundary of the Middle West, they rarely produce nuts. Explain.
4. Shading of the leaves of nut trees results in the development of poorly filled nuts of low oil content. Explain.
5. On heavily loaded filbert trees nuts in singles or in twos are usually better filled than those in threes or fours. Explain.
6. Water deficits during the period of kernel development are likely to result in poorly filled nuts. Explain.
7. A severe drought during July and August usually results in poorly filled pecan nuts. Explain.
8. Moderately vigorous vegetative growth favors maximum nut crop production. Explain.
9. How do the essential-element requirements of pecan trees grown in the Southeast differ from those of apple trees grown in the Northeast?
10. What is dichogamy?
11. How does the grower overcome dichogamy in the pecan and walnut orchard?
12. How does the grower overcome self-incompatibility of filberts?

TROPICAL AND SUBTROPICAL FRUITS (Date, Avocado, Persimmon, and Fig)

THE DATE

Plant Characteristics. The date is a member of the palm family—monocotyledonous evergreen trees which produce leaves from terminal buds only. The date attains a height of 100 feet. Its wood is fibrous and spongy. The root system is adventitious, arises at the base of the stem, and consists of a large number of lateral roots which give rise to numerous absorbing roots. Roots penetrate to 20 feet or more. The leaves which arise from a terminal bud are large, 9 to 20 feet long, and parallel-veined. The blade consists of 100 to 260 leaflets called pinnae. At the base of each pinna several stiff hairs are borne. The date, like the persimmon, is dioecious. The inflorescence, both male and female, arises in the axils of the leaves, is large, much-branched, and contains thousands of individual flowers. Scientists have found that the pollen has a marked effect on the size, shape, and time of maturity of the fruit. After pollination, two of the three carpels in each female flower drop and the remaining carpel grows to maturity. If pollination does not take place, all three carpels or fruits remain on the tree but do not develop into high-quality fruits. Hence, pollination of all three carpels is necessary for the proper development of the fruit. The fruit is a one-seeded, oblong berry; the skin color varies from yellow to purplish-black; and the flesh is dry, semidry, or moist. The water content varies from 22 to 51 per cent, and the sugar content varies from 71 to 86 per cent. Thus, dates are very nutritious.

Fruiting Habit.   Since the main axis grows like corn, the only pruning necessary is removing old leaves as the terminal bud elongates. Pruning is done by cutting the leaf petiole about 8 to 12 inches from the trunk at the rate of 12 to 20 leaves per year and by removing all suckers from the base of the trees during the early period of growth. In Arizona, growers usually remove the shoots between April 15 and July 1. In general, growers are very careful to avoid wounding of the trunk. Wounds of this type of tree, a monocot, fail to heal. The date is essentially a high-temperature plant. Temperatures as low as 15 to 18°F severely injure the leaves, but apparently fail to harm the terminal bud.

Uses.   The date, believed to be a native of northern Africa or Arabia, has been in cultivation for over 4,000 years. It is grown in arid tropical and subtropical regions where sufficient water is available for the trees. In the United States commercial crops are grown in the Coachella Valley of southern California and Arizona. In this country only the fruit is used, as dessert either in the fresh or dry state. In many other countries (North Africa) both the fruits and trees are used. The fruit constitutes the chief article of diet of the Arabian people; the sap is fermented for the making of alcoholic liquors and vinegar; the trunk is made into fence posts; and the leaves are made into ropes, baskets, and crates.

THE AVOCADO

Plant Characteristics.   The avocado is a dicotyledonous evergreen. Trees attain a height of 60 feet. They differ in habit of growth. Some are low and spreading; others are tall and upright. The roots are shallowly situated and hence occupy the upper portion of the soil. The leaves are thick, leathery, and bright green. They vary in shape and in length—3 to 16 inches. The flowers, which are borne in clusters at the tips of branches, are smooth and possess two series of petal-like structures called perianth lobes. Scientists have discovered a remarkable synchronization in the opening and closing of the flowers and in pollen shedding and pistil receptivity. Certain varieties open their flowers in the morning, at which time the pistil is receptive, close again in midday, and open again the following afternoon, at which time the pollen is shed. Other varieties open their flowers in midafternoon, at which time the pistil is receptive, close again in late afternoon, and open again the following morning or morning of the second day, at which time the pollen is shed. Thus, when the pistils of the one variety are receptive, the pollen of the other variety is shedding; conversely, when the pistils of the other variety are receptive, the pollen of the one is shedding. In this way, the various varieties are successfully pollinated. Within any variety marked changes in the weather will greatly change the normal schedule.

The fruit is a one-seeded, fleshy berry and varies from round to oval to pyriform or necked. Both seed and flesh vary greatly in size. The skin is yellowish-green, purplish-green to purplish-blue, thin and membranous in some varieties and thick and woody in others. The flesh, which separates readily from the skin, is light green to yellow and has a buttery consistency. It contains from 10 to 20 per cent fat and about 80 per cent water and is a good source of vitamin C. Thus, the fruit is very nutritious.

Importance and Uses. The avocado is a native of tropical America. In the United States it is grown in southern Florida and in southern California only. Avocados are used as salads, in ice-cream making, as a base for milk shakes, and in the manufacture of mayonnaise. There are three horticultural races: (1) West Indian, (2) Guatemalan, and (3) Mexican. The West Indian is the least resistant to cold and is grown principally in Florida; the Guatemalan is moderately resistant to cold and is grown mostly in California; and the Mexican is the most resistant to cold and is grown in Florida and California.

THE PERSIMMON

Plant Characteristics. The persimmon is deciduous. There are two kinds: (1) Japanese and (2) native. With the Japanese the tree is upright spreading, has a round, open top, and attains a height of 40 feet. With the native type the tree is upright, has a pointed top, and attains a height of 50 feet. In both types the roots develop a taproot and several laterals which penetrate the soil rather deeply; the leaves are simple, thick, large, leathery, and glossy green on the upper surface and light green on the lower surface; and the sex expression is dioecious. In other words there are male and female trees. Both sexes are borne in the axils of the leaves of the current season's wood. The female flowers are solitary, and the male flowers occur in clusters of three or four. The fruit is a round to oblong conicle, few-seeded and nonseeded, fleshy, juicy ovary. The skin is light orange or bright red. The flesh is yellow to cinnamon brown, soft and pasty in some varieties and stringy in others. A marked characteristic of the flesh is its astringency, which is due to tannin. When the fruits are immature, the walls of the cells which contain tannin are soluble in the mouth; hence, the tannin is released and the mouth puckers. When the fruits are mature, the walls of the cells containing tannin are insoluble; hence, the tannin is not released and the mouth does not pucker. Scientists have found that the astringency of the fruits can be removed by exposing them to ethylene. Ripe persimmons contain about 66 per cent water and 32 per cent sugars and are a good source of vitamin C.

Fruiting Habit. The young trees are usually headed-back to about 36 inches when they are set and trained to four or five scaffold branches in much the same way as for peaches. The fruit is borne on the current season's wood, usually in alternate years. If annual crops are desired, some pruning is necessary. The Japanese prune off all shoots which have borne fruit in any particular year. The Chinese prune off the twigs bearing fruit at the harvest with long poles or sticks.

Importance and Uses. The Japanese persimmon originated in China. It has been grown in both China and Japan for hundreds of years. In the United States the trees thrive well in the Southeast and Southwest and in California. The fruit is used mostly as a dessert.

THE FIG

Plant Characteristics. The fig is a deciduous bush[1] or tree. The root system is extensive. The laterals occupy the upper layer of soil and extend considerable distances, usually 50 feet or more. The branches or trunks are short. The bark is gray, and the twigs have well-developed pith. The leaves are simple, alternate, three- to seven-lobed, thick, leathery, light green, and hairy (pubescent). The flowers are borne on the interior of a pear-shaped peduncle. This peduncle ripens and thus becomes the edible portion. When ripe, the flesh is coarse, pink, red, purple, or violet, and contains about 80 per cent water, 1.5 per cent protein, and 15 per cent sugar.

Fruiting Habit. There are two main types: (1) the Adriatic, or common, which grows in the Southeast, and (2) the Smyrna, which grows in California. The Adriatic fig is parthenocarpic; hence, it is seedless and does not require pollination. The Smyrna fig is nonparthenocarpic and hence requires pollination. The pollen used on Smyrna figs is secured from wild figs called caprifigs. A small wasp called blastophaga carries the pollen.

The fig is prolific. In the United States two crops are usually borne and a third crop is not uncommon. The first main crop is borne on previous season's wood. The second and third crops are borne on current season's wood. As stated previously, figs are trained to the bush or tree form. Of these the bush form is preferred in the Southeast, since the plants are often killed by subfreezing temperatures.

Importance and Uses. The fig is now widely distributed through tropical and subtropical countries. In the United States it is grown in the southeast region and in California. In the Southeast many farm homes have one or two fig bushes growing in the yard. Figs are used in the fresh

[1] The fig is trained to several main branches in the southeastern United States and is called a bush.

state or in various forms of preservation—canned, dried, preserved, candied, and pickled.

TUNG

Tung trees are grown for their seeds, which contain large quantities of oil. This oil has excellent drying properties. Thus, it is used extensively in the making of paints, varnish, linoleum, oilcloth, and printer's ink.

Plant Characteristics. The trees are deciduous and monoecious. They attain a height of 12 to 20 feet and have a tendency to produce whorled branches. The leaves are comparatively large, simple, heart-shaped or three-lobed, and dark green. The inflorescence is a cluster. This cluster arises on the terminals of twigs of the past season's growth and contains from one to three pistillate flowers and a relatively large number of staminate flowers. The individual flowers are showy, open just before the unfolding of the leaves, and are white or tinged with pink in the throat. Since no pollination problems have been reported, dichogamy or incompatibility is apparently not present. The mature fruit is round or globular, 2 to 3 inches in transverse diameter, has a dark brown outer cover, and holds from four to seven of the relatively large, firm, brown seeds which contain the oil. Figure 18.2 is a close-up of a tree in the Wade orchard,

Fig. 18.2. Close-up of tung tree. Note that the fruit is borne on the young wood. (Courtesy, G. F. Potter, U.S. Department of Agriculture.)

Lucedale, Mississippi. Note the leaf and fruit characteristics and the age of wood on which the fruit is borne.

Economic Importance and Distribution.   Tung is a native of central China. The trees were first grown in the United States in 1904. Since that time, ecologic studies and trial plantings in the warm sections of the United States showed that the trees thrive best in a belt from 50 to 100 miles wide extending from northern Florida westward to southern Louisiana and eastern Texas. At present Mississippi leads in commercial plantings with over 10 million trees, followed by Florida, Louisiana, Alabama, and Georgia in the order named.

Growth and Development.   From the standpoint of temperature, tung requires a long, warm, frost-free growing season and a short, comparatively mild nongrowing season. The long, warm growing-season temperature permits maximum photosynthesis, which in turn is manifested by maximum growth of the tree and yields of the fruit. The short, mild nongrowing-season temperature is necessary to bring the trees out of the rest period. From the standpoint of the water supply, the abundant rain during the spring and summer promotes rapid vegetative growth and the relatively light rains during the fall favor carbohydrate accumulation which is necessary for oil formation. From the standpoint of soil, slightly acid sandy loams underlaid with a uniformly brown or reddish sandy clay are considered best. Ruston, Orangeburg, Norfolk sandy loams, and closely related types are well adapted to tung production.

Fig. 18.3. Row view of tung orchard during period of clean cultivation. (Courtesy, G. F. Potter, U.S. Department of Agriculture.)

Principal Cultural Practices. Cultural practices are in accordance with the nature of the climate and needs of the soil in the tung belt and with the essential-element requirement of the trees. In general, satisfactory yields require (1) selecting well-air-drained sites; (2) planting trees of recommended strains on wide-based terraces in January, February, and early March (usually the trees are set 20 feet apart in rows 35 feet apart); (3) training the young tree to the open-center form; (4) applying commercial fertilizers to promote the desirable amount of shoot growth, number of flower buds, and fruits per year; (5) using the controlled–cover crop system of soil management with the land free from the cover crop in March, April, and May; (6) allowing the fruits to drop from the trees and to remain on the ground under the trees from four to six weeks; (7) placing the fruit in burlap sacks and hanging the sacks in the trees for additional drying; and (8) transporting the fruit to the drying shed. Figure 18.3 shows a down-the-row view of a nine-year-old tung orchard near Alford, Florida. The soil is sandy for a depth of 4 to 5 feet, beneath which is a friable sandy clay.

QUESTIONS

1. Describe a date tree.
2. A wound in a date tree does not heal as readily as a wound in an apple tree. Explain.
3. The three races of avocados differ in the degree of low temperature they can withstand. Which race will do best in Florida? In California?
4. Describe the opening and closing of avocado flowers.
5. Immature fruit of the Japanese persimmon is astringent; mature fruit is not astringent. Explain.
6. Compare pruning the Japanese persimmon with pruning the peach.
7. The fig is difficult to graft, and pruning wounds often fail to heal. Explain.
8. The Adriatic fig is not propagated by seed. Explain.
9. How are Smyrna figs pollinated?
10. Although tung is monoecious, considerable self-pollination takes place. Explain.
11. Transplanting tung trees in late March and April usually results in poor stands and unsatisfactory growth. Explain.
12. Tung trees require clean cultivation during March, April, and May. Give two reasons.
13. In your opinion would summer or winter cover crops be the more satisfactory for tung production?
14. Given two growing seasons. Season A has a dry April and May and a wet September and October; season B has a wet April and May and a comparatively dry September and October. In your opinion which season would produce fruits with the highest percentage of oil? Give reasons.

19

GRAPES AND SMALL FRUITS

To look up and not down,
to look forward and not backward,
to look out and not in,
and to lend a hand.
Edward Everett Hale

GRAPES

The three most important species of grapes are (1) vinifera, (2) labrusca, and (3) rotundifolia. Vinifera, or European, grapes are native to southwestern Asia and have been cultivated for more than 4,000 years. In the United States they are grown mainly in the Pacific Coast region, notably in Fresno, Tulare, and San Joaquin counties of California. On the other hand, labrusca and rotundifolia grapes are natives of North America and were undoubtedly cultivated before America was discovered. In the United States labrusca grapes are grown in the Northeast and Great Lakes region, mostly in New York and Michigan, and rotundifolia grapes are grown in the southeast and southwest regions, mostly in the Gulf Coast states.

PLANT CHARACTERISTICS

Root System.   The root system of mature vines is relatively extensive. In most well-aerated soils the roots extend from 8 to 12 feet in the horizontal direction and from 5 to 6 feet in the downward direction. Like the pomes and drupes, the primary and secondary roots are woody and are used mainly for support, transportation, and storage of carbohydrates.

Stems and Leaves.   The stems are climbing, woody vines which possess tendrils, enlarged nodes, well-developed conducting tissue, and a large

344

pith. The buds are (1) terminal and (2) lateral. The terminal buds are always vegetative, and the lateral buds are either mixed or vegetative. The mixed buds give rise to flower-bearing canes, and the vegetative buds give rise to nonflowering canes. The leaves are simple. They vary in size, shape, color, and number of lobes according to the species and variety.

Flowers and Fruit. The flowers are borne in clusters called panicles. These clusters arise on the basal nodes of the flower-bearing shoots opposite a leaf or tendril. In labrusca grapes each flower-bearing shoot contains from two to six flower clusters, and in other species each shoot has two clusters. Individual flowers are hypogynous and perfect with five united, greenish-white petals, five reflexed or upright stamens, and a single rudimentary, or functional, pistil. The upright or reflexed position of the stamens and the functional condition of the pistil are important horticultural characteristics. Varieties with upright stamens produce functional pollen, and varieties with reflexed stamens produce abnormal, impotent pollen. This nonfunctional, impotent pollen cannot germinate and is, therefore, useless in fruit production. The mature fruit is a moderately large, juicy, round to elongated ovary which contains relatively large quantities of soluble sugars, notably glucose or grape sugar. With labrusca grapes the skin of the fruit (epicarp) readily separates from the pulp (mesocarp), and in vinifera grapes the skin and pulp remain attached.

GROWTH AND DEVELOPMENT

Climatic Requirements. The three species differ in growing-season requirements, relative susceptibility to fungus diseases, and hardiness. In general, vinifera varieties require warm, dry weather for the development, maturation, and drying of the fruit, are susceptible to foliage diseases, and are relatively tender; labrusca varieties require moderately cool weather, are moderately resistant to foliage diseases, and are hardy; and rotundifolia varieties require a long, warm growing season, are resistant to foliage diseases, and are relatively tender. These differences explain, partially at least, why the vinifera varieties are grown in the San Joaquin Valley of California; why the labrusca varieties are grown in the Northeast and Great Lakes region, particularly on the south shore of Lake Erie, in the Finger Lakes region of New York, and in southwestern Michigan; and why the rotundifolia varieties are grown in the Southeast and Gulf Coast region. The vegetative and mixed buds of the three species have a rest period. Thus, a period of exposure to cold is required to break the rest.

Soils. Ideal soils for grapes are deep, well-drained, well-aerated, and moderately acid to slightly alkaline loams. In many important grape-growing districts the subsoil contains considerable quantities of gravel and shaley rock fragments. Typical soils of important districts are Dutchess gravelly silt loam of the Hudson Valley, New York; Dunkirk gravelly loam on the Lake Erie shore of New York and Pennsylvania; Chenango gravelly loam of western New York; Baxter silt loam of the Ozarks; and Aiken gravelly loam, Pleasanton gravelly silt loam, and Placentia silt loam of California. In general, very heavy soils are avoided since they retard maturity of the fruit and have poor internal drainage.

Disposition of the Carbohydrates.   As discussed in Chapter 14 and illustrated in Fig. 14.6, the grape bears its fruit on stems of the current season's growth. These stems are called shoots. Thus, for bearing vines during the first part of the growing season, there is a rapid extension of the shoots concomitant with the opening of the flowers and the enlargement of the fruit, and during the latter part there is a cessation of extension and thickening of the shoots concomitant with the ripening and maturation of the fruit, storage of carbohydrates in the roots and stems, and the laying down of mixed buds for the next year's crop. Consequently, carbohydrate utilization is dominant during the first part of the growing season. As shoot growth subsides and ripening of the fruit begins, carbohydrate utilization is less dominant and accumulation is more evident. Finally, during the latter part of the growing season carbohydrate accumulation is dominant over utilization.

Principal Cultural Practices.   Principal cultural practices involve (1) establishing the vineyard, (2) providing for adequate pollination, and (3) using a recommended soil management, commercial fertilizer, and pest-control program.

Both level and sloped sites are used in commercial production. For example, in the interior valleys of California level sites are common and in the northeast region sloped sites are preferred. In general, straight rows are used on level land, preferably in the north and south direction, and plantings on the contour lines are required on sloped or hilly land. About three years are necessary to bring a vineyard into profitable production. Principal operations are as follows for the first year: (1) preparing the land, (2) plowing out the rows, (3) heading back both the roots and the tops of the young plants, (4) setting the plants, and (5) establishing a trellis. For the second year, the vines are headed-back at the beginning of the growing season; and for the third year, heading back and thinning out the canes are done according to the training system desired. Figure 19.1 is a general view of the Delaware vineyard at State College, Mississippi. The Dog-Ridge stock on which the cions were grafted promotes vigor and productivity under southern conditions.

From the standpoint of the functional ability of the sex organs three groups of varieties exist: group 1—varieties with functional stamens and functional pistils; group 2—varieties with nonfunctional stamens

Fig. 19.1. The Delaware vineyard at State College, Mississippi. The cions were grafted on Dog-Ridge stock. (Courtesy, J. P. Overcash, Mississippi Agricultural Experiment Station.)

and functional pistils; and group 3—varieties with functional stamens and nonfunctional pistils and with nonfunctional stamens and functional pistils, i.e., the dioecious varieties. Thus, from the standpoint of pollination, varieties of group 1 may be planted in solid blocks; those of group 2 require interplanting with a variety of group 1; and those of group 3 require interplanting pollen-producing vines with fruit-producing vines. The majority of grape varieties belong to group 1. Thus, they are self-fertile and present no pollination problem. However, certain varieties of group 2 belong to the labrusca species and require interplanting with plants which have functional stamens and functional pistils, and certain varieties of group 3 belong to the rotundifolia species and require interplanting with plants that have functional stamens, or the so-called male plants.

In practically all grape-growing districts, the clean cultivation–cover crop system of soil management with certain modifications is practiced. Clean cultivation is necessary during the period of shoot growth to reduce competition for water and essential raw materials, and cover cropping is necessary during the latter part of the growing season and during the winter. The cover crop promotes the ripening of the fruit and the maturation of the wood, holds snow in cold climates, and reduces erosion and leaching of nitrate-nitrogen and other essential ions in all climates.

As with other crops, the commercial fertilizer requirements of grapes depend largely on the natural fertility of the soil and the system of soil management. As previously explained, the shoots develop during the first part of the growing season, and the fruit ripens and the wood matures during the latter part. Thus, unless the soil is very fertile, applications of available essential elements, particularly available nitrogen, are necessary at the beginning of shoot growth; and applications, usually complete mixtures, are necessary to establish and supply the needs of the cover crop.

Grapes are raised for raisins, for wines, for juice, and for the table. Grapes for raisins are dried, either naturally or artificially, and are marketed in boxes lined with wax paper and in paper cartons. Grape wine is marketed in bottles of various shapes and sizes, and grape juice is marketed in jars, bottles, and cans. Grapes for the table are picked in the cluster. The individual clusters are handled carefully to preserve the bloom of the individual berries and are placed in relatively small containers. The climax basket is commonly used in the Northeast and the Middle West.

SMALL FRUITS

Small fruits include the brambleberries, strawberries, currants, gooseberries, blueberries, and cranberries.

BRAMBLEBERRIES

The brambleberries include red raspberry, purple raspberry, black raspberry, blackberry, dewberry, loganberry, and boysenberry.

Plant Characteristics.   The root system of the brambleberries is moderately extensive. As with grapes, the primary and secondary roots are woody and are used for support, transportation, and storage. The stems possess numerous terminally curved spines called "prickles." Stems are erect (for example, the red and black raspberry) or decumbent (the dewberry). As a rule these stems, called canes, have a life cycle of two years. During the first year they attain their growth and differentiate their flower buds, and during the second year these flower buds develop into fruit-bearing shoots.[1] When the fruit has matured, the canes die and are removed by pruning. The leaves are alternate and contain from three to five leaflets. The flowers

[1] However, the everbearing varieties produce terminal clusters of flowers and fruit the first season.

are borne in clusters. Individual flowers are comparatively large and perfect in all kinds of varieties, except the Pacific Coast dewberry, which develops both hermaphroditic and pistillate plants. The receptacle is convex and bears numerous stamens and pistils; and each pistil develops into a small drupe or drupelet. In the raspberry the cluster of drupelets of each fruit separates from the receptacle at maturity, forming the familiar thimble-like mass of fruit. In the blackberry, dewberry, and loganberry the drupelets remain attached to the receptacle at maturity.

Economic Importance and Distribution. The bramble fruits are grown commercially in many regions of the United States. Important districts are (1) red raspberry—the Pacific Coast, western Washington and Oregon, the Great Lakes, southern Michigan, western New York, and eastern Minnesota; (2) black raspberry—the Great Lakes, southwestern Michigan, western New York, northeastern Ohio, and northwestern Pennsylvania; (3) blackberry and dewberry—the Southwest and Middle West, Texas, Oklahoma, and Kentucky; and (4) loganberry—the Pacific Coast, western Oregon, and Washington.

Growth and Development. Although definite chilling requirements of these crops have not been determined, brambles require a certain amount of exposure to cold to break the rest period. However, they vary in relative hardiness and in growing-season requirements. In general, raspberries are the most hardy and require relatively cool summers to produce satisfactory crops, whereas blackberries and dewberries are the least hardy and thrive best in the warm summer climate of the Southeast and Southwest. Thus, the raspberry industry is located in the upper Pacific Coast and the Middle West, and the blackberry and dewberry industries are located in the lower Middle West and Southwest.

In general, the brambleberries are grown on well-drained, well-aerated, moderately to slightly acid sandy loams, loams, and silt loams. Representative soils are Napanee silt loam of Michigan, Baxter silt loam of the Ozarks, Norfolk fine sandy loam of Texas, and the Everett-Alderwood-Kittsap association of soils in the Puyallup Valley of Washington. Good air drainage is essential.

Essentially, the growth and development of the brambles consist in the development of flowers and fruit of the second-year canes and in the development of new canes for the next year's crop. Thus, carbohydrate utilization is dominant during the first part of the growing season in order to develop the flowers, young fruits, and young canes. As the fruits attain maturity and young canes acquire their growth, carbohydrate utilization becomes less dominant. Thus, accumulation takes place with the formation of flower-forming hormones, the laying down of flower buds, and the maturity of the cane's tissues.

Fig. 19.2. Washington red raspberries at State College, Mississippi, trained to the hedgerow system. (Courtesy, J. P. Overcash, Mississippi Agricultural Experiment Station.)

Culture.   In general, two systems are used to establish and to maintain bramble fruit plantations: (1) the hedgerow and (2) the hill. In the hedgerow system, the plants are set 2½, 3, 4, or 5 feet apart in rows 7, 8, 9, and 10 feet apart. As growth proceeds, the plants form solid rows from 2 to 4 feet wide. In the hill system, the plants are set 5 × 5 feet, 6 × 6 feet, or wider spacings with one or two plants per hill, depending on the kind of crop and fertility of the soil. In both systems the clean cultivation–cover crop system of soil management is used; and commercial fertilizers, if required, are applied at the beginning of the growing season to stimulate growth of the canes and the fruit, and just before the cover crop is established to promote the rapid production of organic matter. A close positive association exists between the size of the cane and the size of the crop. In general, vigorous canes produce the most abundant crops. Note the three-wire vertical trellis used in the hedgerow system shown in Fig. 19.2.

Mature brambleberry fruits are highly perishable and easily bruised. In general, they are picked in the early morning directly into pint and quart boxes—the containers in which they are sold. Crates holding 16, 24, 32, or larger quantities of these pint or quart boxes are used to ship the different types of berries to the market.

STRAWBERRIES

Plant Characteristics

Root System.   The root system of the strawberry is relatively shallow and moderately extensive. Studies at the Nebraska Experiment Station have shown that most of the roots extend horizontally and vertically for a distance of about 12 inches. A few roots were found between the 1- and 2-foot levels. Since the range of the root system is limited and shallow, strawberry plants are mulched in regions of comparatively high transpiration.

Stems and Leaves.   The stems are short and thick and are called crowns. They bear three kinds of buds: (1) those which develop into short, thick stems called crowns, (2) those which develop into long, slender stems called runners, and (3) those which develop into flowers. New plants are formed from runners. They have long internodes and form a new plant at the second node and every other node thereafter. Gardeners take advantage of this method of asexual reproduction in the establishment of new plantations. The leaves arise in rosettes around the short crownlike stem and are long-petioled and trifoliate.

Flowers and Fruit.   The flowers occur in groups or clusters. Mature individual flowers are relatively large with five or more green sepals, five or more white petals, and numerous stamens and numerous pistils distributed over a fleshy receptacle. The mature fruit is the fleshy receptacle to which is attached a large number of small "seedlike" fruits called achenes.

Economic Importance and Distribution

The strawberry is the most widely adapted of the small fruits. Strawberries are grown throughout Europe, in every state of the United States, as well as in Canada and South America. The principal producing centers of the United States are located in the regions east of the Mississippi River and on the Pacific Coast. The wide variation in climates within these regions and the wide adaptation of the strawberry plant permit harvesting and marketing the fruit during the greater portion of the year. Commercial centers in southeastern Texas, southern Louisiana, central Florida, and in south, central, and northern Alabama supply markets from December to April. Producing districts in Tennessee, western, eastern, and central Arkansas, southwestern North Carolina, and the Norfolk and Eastern Shore district of Virginia supply markets from April to June. Producing districts in Kentucky, Missouri, Maryland, and central California, Illinois, Michigan, and New Jersey supply markets from June to July, and districts in New York, Oregon, and Washington supply markets from July to September. Varieties adapted to the many producing districts have been developed. For example, the variety Klondike has a short rest period, is relatively nonhardy, can produce large quantities of fruit during cool weather, and endure relatively hot summers. Thus, the Klondike is adapted to the warm-humid summers and mild winters of the southeast region. On the other hand, the variety Premier has a long rest period, can withstand mild subfreezing temperatures, and cannot endure hot summers. Thus, Premier is better adapted to the northeast and middle west regions.

Growth and Development

Climatic Requirements.   The principal factors are temperature, length of the light period, and moisture supply. From the standpoint of temperature some varieties are tender and others are hardy. However, even with the hardy varieties the crown of the plants is injured when the temperatures fall below 20°F. Since temperatures at the ground level are usually several degrees lower than those a few feet above the ground, winter protection in cold climates is necessary.

From the standpoint of response to length of the light period, strawberries are placed in two groups: (1) varieties that develop flower buds during both long and short light periods, the everbearing varieties, and (2) varieties that develop flower buds during the short light periods only, most commercial varieties. In the northern half of the country these commercial varieties form flower buds in September and October only, and in the southern half they form flower buds both in the fall and in the spring. Thus, the southern regions provide for a longer fruiting period than the northern regions.

From the standpoint of the water supply, since strawberries are relatively shallow-rooted, they are susceptible to conditions of drought. Thus, if hot, dry weather occurs during the period of fruit maturation and if plants are not irrigated, the size of the individual fruit is small and yields are low. If it occurs during the period of flower-bud formation, yields of the following season's crop are likely to be curtailed.

Disposition of the Carbohydrates.   The life of modern commercial varieties is divided into (1) the vegetative period (usually one year or less) and (2) the fruiting period (one to three or more years). During the vegetative period the young plants develop their short, thick stems and the root system. During the production period the adult plants in any one season develop, in sequence, leaves, flowers, fruit, runners, and flower buds. Thus, utilization of carbohydrates is dominant during the first part of the growing season and accumulation is dominant during the latter part.

Principal Cultural Practices

Establishing the Plantation. In the United States a variety of planting or training systems are used, but the principal systems are (1) the hill and (2) the matted row. In the hill system the plants are set in single, double, or triple rows and all runners as they appear are removed. In the matted-row system the plants are set in a single row and the runners are allowed to root and produce additional plants. A modification of the matted row is the hedgerow, in which a definite number of runners are set by hand until the desired stand is obtained, after which all surplus runners are removed. Each system has advantages and disadvantages. In many strawberry-growing districts of the Southeast, the plants are grown on raised beds to facilitate drainage and aeration.

Soil Management and Fertilizers. In strawberry production the clean cultivation–mulching system of soil management is used. In general, cultivation is necessary during the seedling stage of growth to control weeds and to promote the rapid development of stems and leaves, and mulching is necessary during the fruiting period. The mulch keeps the fruits free from soil, reduces decay of the fruit, conserves moisture, lowers soil temperature in hot weather, protects flowers from frost in mild climates, and protects plants from freezing injury in cold climates. In the Southeast the mulch is usually applied just before flowering begins, and in the Northeast and Middle West it is applied just before freezing weather begins. Mulching materials used are pine needles, hay, straw, and sawdust.

In many commercial districts throughout the United States, strawberries require the application of commercial fertilizer. However, on fertile soils high in organic matter, when planted in rotation with other crops which have been heavily fertilized, strawberries make less response to fertilizer than most other cultivated crops. Since the analysis and rate of application required depend largely on the composition of the soil, this problem should be solved by each grower according to his own conditions. In general, plants which are mulched with sawdust or similar material require more nitrogen fertilizer than unmulched plants.

When applications of fertilizer are needed, they are applied (1) at the time of soil preparation to promote the growth of stems and leaves, (2) in the late summer after new plants have formed on the runners in order to develop the new plant growth, and (3) prior to blossoming in the spring—a light application, if needed. The use of excessive nitrogen fertilizer in the spring of the fruiting year may result in delayed maturity,

Fig. 19.3. Strawberry harvesting scene near Hammond, La. Note that needles of the longleaf pine are used as a mulch. (Courtesy, J. A. Cox, Louisiana Agricultural Extension Service.)

softer berries, and an increased amount of rotted fruits. Fertilizer applied when not needed may reduce yields. Agricultural experiment stations have developed fertilizer and pest-control programs for the many strawberry-producing districts, just as they have for many other crops. Figure 19.3 shows a harvesting scene in a field in the Hammond, Louisiana, commercial district. Note the type of picking container, the single-row system of culture, the absence of weeds, and the longleaf pine needle mulch.

Marketing

Like the bramble fruits, strawberries are highly perishable. Usually the fruit is picked in the early morning and sent to the market in the afternoon of the same day or is picked in the late afternoon, stored overnight in a cool place, and sent to market the following morning. A common market container is the 1-quart basket. Ordinary shipping crates contain 24 of these baskets, and pony refrigerator crates contain 32, 64, or 80. Ventilator and refrigerator cars are used to transport this highly perishable fruit from the various regions of production to the many centers of consumption.[2]

[2] In many producing districts near large cities, consumers pick the fruits they buy.

CURRANTS AND GOOSEBERRIES

Plant Characteristics. Currants and gooseberries form many stems which arise from many points of the root system. In gooseberries the stems possess spines or prickles, and in currants they are smooth. In fruit-bearing plants the crops are borne on one-year wood or on one-year-old spurs borne on two- or three-year-old wood. When the stems become four or five years old, they cease to bear fruit. Thus, productivity is maintained by removing the old stems. The leaves are alternate and palmately lobed. The inflorescence is a raceme. Individual flowers are perfect and epigynous with four or five calyx lobes, four or five petals, four or five stamens, and a single, inferior pistil. Cross-pollination, chiefly by insects, is the rule and, with rare exceptions, all varieties are self-fertile. As with pomes, the mature fruit consists of ovary wall and receptacle tissue. In currants ripe fruit is black, red, or white, according to the variety.

Economic Importance and Distribution. Throughout the United States the production of currants and gooseberries is a minor horticultural crop industry. The acreage is between 4,000 and 4,500, and the annual production of fruit approximates 5,000,000 quarts. The principal producing districts are located in southern New York and in the Great Lakes and Pacific Coast regions.

Growth and Development. The principal climatic factors are temperature and water supply. Currants and gooseberries thrive best in regions characterized by cool weather with abundant rain or irrigation. These crops are very resistant to low winter temperatures. Hence, they are best adapted to the northern regions of the country. In the Southeast the growing-season temperatures are generally above the optimum for high production, and in the Southwest the weather is exceedingly hot and dry. Currants and gooseberries require deep, fertile loams, silt loams, and clay loams, since these soils are less susceptible to drought than sands and sandy loams. In bearing plants the flowers appear first in the spring followed by the production of leaves, the development and maturation of fruit, and the production of new canes. Since the open flowers are susceptible to frost injury, growers use sites which are adequately protected and air drained.

Culture. In commercial plantings the plants are set 4 or 5 feet apart in rows 7, 8, or 9 feet apart. They require the clean cultivation–cover crop system of soil management, and in some cases applications of complete fertilizers are necessary to maintain growth and vigor. The fruit is picked in clusters and marketed in relatively small containers. Quart baskets in crates are standard market containers and 6- to 8-pound grape baskets are used for the cannery. Because the fungus which produces blister rust on five-needle pines spends part of its life cycle on currants and gooseberries.

this pest has practically precluded the planting of these fruits in locations where white pines are commercially important.

BLUEBERRIES[3]

Plant Characteristics.   There are many kinds of blueberries. Six important commercial kinds or species are listed in Table 19.1. Note the

Table 19.1.   **IMPORTANT SPECIES OF *VACCINIUM* (BLUEBERRIES)**

Species	Common name	Plant height, ft	Habitat	Regional adaptation
V. australe	Highbush	10–15	Moist places	Atlantic Coast Plain; Middle West
V. ashei	Rabbiteye	4–8	Well drained	Southeast
V. pallidum	Dryland	1–3	Dry, well drained	Appalachian Mts.; northwest Arkansas
V. angustifolium	Lowbush	½–1½	Dry, well drained	Northeast; Canada
V. ovatum	Evergreen	20	Dry, well drained	Northwest
V. membranaceum	Mountain	3	Dry, well drained	Northwest

differences in plant height, habitat, and regional adaptation. In general, the root system of blueberries is shallowly or deeply situated, according to the species and habitat, finely divided, and devoid of root hairs; the woody stems develop from underground rootstocks forming suckers; the flowers are relatively small, perfect, sympetalous, and usually occur in clusters; and the fruit is a relatively small, juicy ovary which, when ripe, varies from black to light blue.

Climatic Requirements and Culture.   Until recently, most blueberries were harvested from wild plants. However, as a result of research,

---

[3] The material on blueberries is contributed by Prof. W. T. Brightwell, The Coastal Plain Experiment Station, Tifton, Ga.

Fig. 19.4. The original plant of Calloway, a variety of blueberry released in 1949. (Courtesy, W. T. Brightwell, The Coastal Plain Experiment Station, Georgia.)

plants of excellent varieties are now available for commercial plantings of both highbush and rabbiteye types.

In general, the highbush blueberry has a comparatively high chilling requirement (about the same as that of the peach) and requires a continuously moist soil, whereas the rabbiteye blueberry has a comparatively short chilling requirement and thrives well in dry, relatively infertile soil. For both types very acid soils, usually from pH 4.3 to 4.8, are most favorable. Figure 19.4 shows the original plant of Calloway, a new variety adapted to the southeastern United States.

CRANBERRIES

There are two types of cranberries: (1) the highbush and (2) the lowbush.[4] The highbush is used as an ornamental plant and is not grown commercially to any great extent. The lowbush is the large fruited cranberry which is grown commercially—chiefly in Massachusetts, New Jersey, Wisconsin, Washington, and Oregon.

Plant Characteristics. The lowbush cranberry is a vinelike evergreen with a mass of fine, fibrous roots which possess no root hairs and with upright stems that vary from ½ to over 1 foot in height. Uprights, about 6 inches in height, are most desirable, since they produce large crops and

[4] The highbush cranberry is of the *Viburnum* genus, and the lowbush cranberry belongs to the genus *Vaccinium*.

facilitate picking of the fruit. The stems possess the ability to form roots wherever they come in contact with moist soil.

Culture.   In the United States major producing districts exist in Massachusetts, New Jersey, and Wisconsin. Minor producing districts exist in Washington and Oregon.

The growing of cranberries is a highly specialized industry, and the crop requires rather unique cultural practices. Suitable bogs are sandy, relatively level, and close to a body of fresh water. The bogs are first cleared, graded, and ditched. The ditches have several purposes: to ensure adequate drainage during the growing season, to float off fallen berries by flooding, to protect the plants against low temperatures, and to help control insects. The bog is established by planting cuttings in hills, and the plants are ready for their first harvest in four years. Principal cultural practices for established bogs are (1) draining the bogs in the spring, (2) controlling insects by using dusts and by flooding, (3) harvesting the attached berries by using wooden, round-toothed scoops, (4) harvesting the fallen berries by flooding and floating off to the sides of the bog, (5) flooding at the beginning of winter to protect the plants against low temperatures, (6) resanding if necessary (this is usually done every three or four years), and (7) draining the bog the following spring.

Processed products are cranberry sauce, cranberry juice, cranberry cocktail, and dehydrated cranberries. Figure 19.5 shows a general view of

Fig. 19.5. A three-year-old cranberry bog in the northeastern United States. (Courtesy, C. M. Chaney, American Cranberry Exchange.)

Fig. 19.6. Six kinds of small fruits. How many can you identify?

a three-year-old cranberry bog in the northeastern United States, and Fig. 19.6 shows six kinds of small fruits—raspberry, blackberry, dewberry, strawberry, currant, and gooseberry. How many can you identify?

QUESTIONS

1. Differentiate between the root system of the strawberry and that of the grape.
2. What is the function of tendrils?
3. Male muscadine vines are nonproductive yet essential for fruit production. Explain.
4. How does the stem of a grape differ externally from that of a raspberry?
5. How does a flower and fruit of the grape differ from those of the raspberry?

6. The principal centers of commercial production of strawberries are located in the Southeast and Pacific Coast regions. Give two reasons.

7. Although the strawberry is grown in all states of the United States, most commercial varieties have only narrow adaptation. Explain.

8. Currants and gooseberries are grown in the region of the Great Lakes and on the upper Pacific Coast. Give two reasons.

9. How do the roots of blueberry plants differ from roots of apple and peach trees?

10. What is the optimum soil pH range for blueberries?

11. How are cranberries harvested?

20

VEGETABLE CROPS GROWN FOR THEIR STEMS OR LEAVES

When tillage begins, other arts follow.
The farmers, therefore,
are the founders of civilization.
Daniel Webster

THE PERENNIALS

ASPARAGUS

Plant Characteristics

Root System. Asparagus has two kinds of roots: (1) fleshy (storage) and (2) absorbing. The fleshy roots are about the size of an ordinary lead pencil. In general, they grow in a lateral direction from 8 to 14 inches per year for about three to four years. Their principal storage constituent is sucrose. The absorbing roots arise from the young portions of the storage roots. Thus, the roots of mature asparagus plants have a spread of 3 to 5 feet or more.

Stems and Leaves. Asparagus has two kinds of stems also: (1) underground (rhizomes) and (2) aerial (spears and stalks). The rhizomes are short, thick, and stubby. They grow upward at the rate of about 2 inches per year and form buds which develop into the aerial stems.

The stems which are cut for market are called spears, and those which grow after the cutting season are called stalks. In general, spears are cut when they are 6 to 8 inches long for a period of six to eight weeks. The leaves are small, triangular, scalelike, vestigial structures. They do not manufacture food. The stems which contain chlorophyll are the real food-

361

manufacturing organs. Thus, asparagus stems have been modified for the manufacture of the carbohydrates.

Flowers, Fruit, and Seed.   Asparagus is dioecious. Investigations have shown that male and female plants differ in earliness, yield, and size of spears. In general, male plants produce spears smaller in size, greater in quantity, and earlier in the spring than female plants. The flowers of both sexes are small, numerous, and axillary. Various species of bees carry the pollen.

The fruit is a small, spherical berry, green when immature and red when ripe. The seed are relatively large, black-coated, and angular. The principal reserve carbohydrate is hemicellulose. Investigations have shown that germination is facilitated by soaking the seed in warm water at 84°F for 84 hours. The water is changed frequently to supply the necessary oxygen.

Economic Importance

Asparagus is used fresh, frozen, and canned. It is grown in many home gardens, particularly in the northern sections of the continental United States. Since extremely hot summers and mild winters do not favor the development of a large number of spears, asparagus is not grown in the Gulf Coast region. The commercial asparagus industries in this country have developed since 1900. The principal districts are located in the Sacramento and Imperial Valleys of California, in the upper coastal plain section of New Jersey, South Carolina, and in Illinois. Figure 20.1 shows a field of asparagus in full fern in the Sacramento district of California.

Growth and Development

Climatic Requirements.   The principal climatic factors are temperature and moisture. As stated previously, asparagus thrives well in all regions of the country except along the Gulf Coast. In this area there is a continual development of stalks throughout the latter part of the growing

Fig. 20.1. A large field of asparagus in full fern in the Delta-Sacramento district of California. (Courtesy, G. C. Hanna, University of California.)

season. This excessive stalk production utilizes sucrose which in turn limits the amount for storage and subsequent spear growth. As a result, the spears are small in size and few in number and yields are low. However, high growing-season temperatures alone do not inhibit profitable spear production. In the Imperial Valley of California the excessive heat of summer inhibits stalk growth, but applications of irrigation water keep the tops green. In late summer irrigation is discontinued. This stops stalk growth and facilitates the storage of sucrose in the roots.

Soils. Ideal soils for asparagus are deep, well drained, friable, fertile, and slightly acid. In general, soils of a peat-sediment mixture, mucks, and loams are used. These soils, being loose and friable, allow the point of the spear to remain straight. Clay soils do not drain readily and produce a large percentage of crooked spears.

Disposition of the Carbohydrates. As previously stated, spears are harvested at the beginning of the season, and stalks are allowed to grow after the harvest. Thus, carbohydrate depletion, utilization, and accumulation occur in succession.

spear production	stalk growth	manufacture of sucrose
A depletion	B utilization C	accumulation D

In general, the growing season for asparagus varies from 24 to 32 weeks depending on the region of the country. Thus, line AD can be used to represent the length of the growing season; line AB the length of the harvesting season; and line BC the period of stalk growth and development. The periods represented by lines AB and BC shows that carbohydrate depletion is taking place, since from AB spears are removed and in BC most of the stalks are produced; and the period represented by line CD shows that carbohydrate accumulation is taking place, since stalk growth has practically ceased at point C.

Culture. The life of asparagus plants may be divided into three stages: (1) seedling, (2) preproductive, and (3) productive. The seedling stage involves the growth of the plants, usually from seed, in the nursery and lasts for one or two years; the preproductive stage consists of the plants' first two years in their permanent bed; and the productive stage consists of the plants' development of spears and stalks. In the productive stage for any one season, the plants produce spears for a period of from six to eight weeks, after which the spears are not cut but are allowed to grow and develop into stalks. The principal practices in consecutive order are (1) applying a complete fertilizer and disking the rows just before the cutting season begins; (2) cutting, grading, and marketing the spears; (3) applying fertilizer and furrowing the rows at the end of the cutting season; (4) allowing the stalks to grow; and (5) controlling weeds and insects.

For long distance markets the spears are packed in bunches, placed in pyramidal crates, and shipped under refrigeration.

QUESTIONS

1. One-year-old asparagus roots recover more rapidly from the check in growth incident to transplanting than two-year-old roots. Explain.
2. The crowns are set from 8 to 10 inches deep. Explain.
3. Before asparagus is cut the plant is allowed to grow two to three years. Explain.
4. The cutting of the spears usually extends for six to eight weeks. Why is cutting stopped at the end of this period?
5. In which region of the country should cutting the spears extend the longer—in the northern region or in the upper part of the southern region? Give reasons for your answer.
6. What do you suppose is the relation of size of spear to the carbohydrate content of the storage roots? Give reasons for your answer.
7. Would you expect the spears to maintain their diameter with each successive cutting or to decrease in diameter? Explain.
8. The sugars in asparagus roots gradually decrease throughout the cutting season. They rapidly decrease during the period of stalk growth. Explain.
9. What are the indications that an asparagus plant has been cut too long in any given season? Give reasons for your answer.
10. The sugars in asparagus roots markedly increase after most of the stalks have fully developed. Explain.
11. When would you apply nitrogen to asparagus: (a) at the beginning of the cutting season, (b) at the end of the cutting season, or (c) at both periods? Give reasons.
12. A severe infestation of asparagus beetles during the latter part of the growing season will result in low yields the following year; infestation at the beginning will not. Explain.
13. Given two asparagus plantations at the end of the growing season. In plantation A the stalks are cut while they are still green. In plantation B the stalks are cut after they become dry. Which plantation has the greater carbohydrate supply? Give reasons.
14. The life of the average commercial planting is about 15 years, yet some home-garden plantings remain productive for 20 to 30 years. Can you think of any reasons for this?

RHUBARB

Plant Characteristics.   The root system of rhubarb consists of absorbing roots and is extensive. The stems are of two kinds: (1) rhizomes and (2) aerial. The rhizomes are fleshy and woody and bear buds at the crown. The aerial stems attain a height of 3 to 4 feet and produce a spike with large numbers of small, greenish-white, perfect flowers. The leaves arise in the form of a rosette from the buds on the crown. The blade is simple and large. The petiole, or leafstalk, is the edible portion and is long, fleshy, and well developed. The color of the petiole varies from green, due to chlorophyll, to dark red, due to anthocyanin.

Economic Importance. Rhubarb is grown in home gardens, commercial gardens, and for forcing. Home-garden and market-garden production are quite popular in the northern United States, Canada, and the British Isles and forcing for winter market takes place in the vicinity of Detroit, Michigan; Boston, Massachusetts; and Chicago, Illinois.

Rhubarb is adapted to comparatively cold regions. It thrives well in regions north of the Potomac and Ohio Rivers and in the mountains of Virginia and North Carolina. Well-drained, moderately to slightly acid, fertile sandy loams and silt loams, and slightly acid, highly decomposed mucks are better than poorly drained and infertile soils.

As with asparagus the harvesting period of rhubarb usually lasts from six to eight weeks only, and the leaves are allowed to grow during the remainder of the growing season. Hence, as with asparagus, carbohydrate depletion, utilization, and storage occur in succession.

Culture. In home and commercial gardens rhubarb is propagated by division of the rhizomes. The rhizomes of comparatively large plants are divided into several pieces in such a way that each piece has at least one vigorous bud. Between the planting of these pieces and the first harvest of the petioles, a period of one to two years is necessary for the development of a large storage structure.

In the commercial forcing of rhubarb, two-year-old crowns are plowed out in the fall, exposed to temperatures between 20 and 25°F for four to six weeks, and placed side by side with a light covering of moist soil in opaque, windowless structures maintained between 55 and 65°F. Since the crowns are in the dark most of the time, the leaf blades are small, the petioles are long and juicy, and they develop anthocyanin with little or no chlorophyll.

Marketing operations consist in (1) pulling the petioles when they are from 15 to 18 inches long, (2) grading the petioles according to their diameter, (3) packing the petioles in 5-pound lots in paper cartons, and (4) packing the cartons in groups of 10 in pasteboard boxes. Special varieties for forcing have been developed.

GLOBE ARTICHOKE

Plant Characteristics. The root system is extensive. The stem consists of two kinds: (1) rhizome and (2) aerial. The aerial stems are relatively long and bear long, deeply lobed, thistle-like leaves. The flower head, the edible part, terminates the stem and consists of a mass of fleshy, imbricated bracts which when young are tender and edible. They contain inulin—a form of starch.

Climatic Requirements.   The Globe artichoke is adapted to regions characterized by mild temperatures. Low temperatures, those below freezing, injure the leaves and stems, and high temperatures, those above the optimum, induce opening of the flower buds and reduce tenderness and quality. For commercial markets the crop is grown along the coast in Monterey, Santa Cruz, and San Mateo counties of California.

Growing the Crop.   The Globe artichoke is propagated by offshoots from the rhizome. In California the rows are usually 8 feet apart, and the plants are 6 feet apart in the row. Clean cultivation is given as needed.

As with asparagus and rhubarb the harvesting period is from six to eight weeks, and the tops are allowed to grow during the remainder of the growing season. Consequently, carbohydrate depletion, utilization, and storage proceed successively.

QUESTIONS

1. In the northern United States harvesting of rhubarb does not take place until the plants are two years old. Explain.
2. The disposition of the carbohydrates in rhubarb is quite similar to that in asparagus. Explain.
3. Harvesting longer than six to eight weeks is likely to exhaust thoroughly the carbohydrate supply in the rhizomes and thus excessively devitalize the plant. Explain.
4. In your opinion, when should available nitrogen be applied—at the beginning or at the end of the cutting season, or both? Give reasons.
5. In commercial plantations seedstalks are usually cut off when they begin to develop. Explain.
6. In what ways is the growing of rhubarb similar to the growing of asparagus? In what ways different?
7. Rhubarb grows satisfactorily in the mountains of Virginia and North Carolina; it does not thrive in the Gulf Coast section of the United States. Explain.
8. In what respects is the growing of the Globe artichoke similar to that of asparagus and rhubarb? In what respects different?

THE BIENNIALS

THE CABBAGE CROPS

The cabbage crops, sometimes called the cole crops, consist of cabbage, Brussels sprouts, cauliflower, green broccoli, collards, kale, and kohlrabi.

During the first year the plants develop the edible part, a distinct storage organ, and during the second year they develop flowering stems, flowers, fruit, and seed. Plants of the cabbage crops are closely related and have characteristics in common and characteristics in distinction.

Common Plant Characteristics

Root System. The plants develop a much-branched, highly ramified root system. For example, investigations have shown that the roots of half-grown cabbage plants extended laterally for a distance of from 2 to 4 feet. These roots were much-branched especially in the upper 4 inches of soil. Consequently, deep cultivation of the cabbage crops during the late stages of growth is likely to cut the feeding roots just beneath the surface.

Stems and Leaves. The vegetative stems are comparatively short, and the leaves are simple, large, well developed, and fleshy. Those that consist of the storage organ contain large quantities of starch which gradually change to sugar. The flowering stems arise from the axils of the leaves of the storage organ and are from 2 to 4 feet high.

Flowers, Fruits, and Seed. The inflorescence is a terminal raceme. Individual flowers are perfect and regular with four sepals, four white or light-yellow petals, six stamens, and a two-celled pistil. The flowers are mostly insect-pollinated and varieties within each group cross readily. The fruit is a long, slender pod called a silique. The seed are quite similar in appearance and germinate readily under favorable conditions.

CABBAGE

Cabbage develops a short stem and a *large terminal bud called the head*. The head is the storage structure and the part used for human consumption. It varies greatly in size, shape, texture, and color according to the variety.

Growth and Development

Climatic Requirements. The principal climatic factor is temperature. Cabbage is primarily a cool-season crop. In general, the crop thrives best and produces the best heads at temperatures from 50 to 70°F. Thus, profitable crops can be grown in the Southeast and Southwest during the winter and early spring, and in the Northeast and Middle West during the summer. Climates influenced by large bodies of water are particularly favorable for the growing of cabbage. In both the southern and northern regions of the United States, many commercial districts are located near large bodies of water. In the South, the Atlantic Ocean and the Gulf of Mexico help keep the temperatures from becoming dangerously low in the fall and winter; and in the North, the Great Lakes help keep the temperatures from becoming excessively high in the summer.

Soils.   Cabbage is grown on a wide variety of soils. In general, the crop for early market and long distance shipment is grown on well-drained sandy loams; and the crop for storage, sauerkraut manufacture, or pickling is grown on well-drained silt loams and clay loams. In southern Wisconsin and upstate New York, most of the storage crop is grown on dairy farms in a general crop rotation. In both the early and late crop industries adapted soils are moderately to slightly acid, and if fusarium wilt, a serious fungus disease, is present, resistant varieties are grown.

Disposition of the Carbohydrates.   As stated previously, cabbage is grown for the enlarged bud. As with other crop plants in which storage is required, the first period of growth is given over to the development of roots, leaves, and stems, and the latter period is given over to the development of the storage organ. During the early period of growth cabbage develops a large number of green leaves, and sometime later the young leaves form a compact mass which develops from the inside and contains no chlorophyll. These leaves are fleshy and are full of starches and sugars.[1] Hence, utilization is dominant over accumulation during the early stages of growth. As the plant produces its required number of food-manufacturing leaves, accumulation gradually becomes dominant, thus permitting carbohydrate storage. Growing conditions, therefore, during the first period should be such as to favor the production of stems and leaves, and during the latter period they should be such as to favor the development of the storage organ and the accumulation of carbohydrates. Line AB, which represents a growing period of 70 to 125 days, depending on the variety and the season, illustrates the period of utilization and accumulation.

A   growth of stem,   ————————→   development of   B
     leaves, and roots   storage organ

          utilization   ————————→   accumulation
          dominant   dominant

Economic Importance and Distribution

Of the cabbage tribe, cabbage is the most widely grown and the most commonly known. This crop was grown extensively in ancient times and at present is an important crop in the temperate regions of the earth. In the United States cabbage is grown in home gardens both for immediate use and for storage; in many winter-garden areas of the Southeast and Southwest for long distance shipment in early spring; in many market-

[1] Carbohydrates are stored primarily for the development of flowers, fruit, and seed, and man adapts this behavior for his own use.

garden areas for local markets; and in the Middle West and Northeast for storage, sauerkraut manufacture, and pickling. Shipments from the winter-garden areas of the Southeast and the Southwest usually begin in December and end in July, and shipments from the Middle West and Northeast usually begin in August and continue to December and January. The student will note that the southern regions ship cabbage north in the spring and early summer, and that the northern regions ship cabbage south in the fall and winter. In this way every city and town in the country is supplied throughout the year with this important vegetable.

Types. Distinct types of cabbage have been developed to meet the many present-day requirements: for immediate consumption in local and long distance markets, for immediate consumption and/or sauerkraut manufacture, and for storage. Thus, three varietal groups are recognized: (1) the small-headed, early; (2) the large-headed, midseason; and (3) the large-headed, late and storage. For example, varieties of the first group are grown in the winter-garden areas of the Southeast and Southwest, since they must successfully withstand long periods of cool weather and produce small, quick-maturing heads. On the other hand, varieties of the third group are grown in the Northeast and Middle West, since they must produce large heads which keep well in storage.

Culture. In the United States there are three distinct methods used for starting cabbage crops: (1) planting seed directly in the field, (2) planting seed in open field beds, and (3) planting seed in greenhouses, hotbeds, or cold frames. Planting seed directly in the field is practiced in northern regions and in South Carolina, Louisiana, and Texas; planting seed in

Fig. 20.2. A field of cabbage in the eastern United States. (Courtesy, V. R. Boswell, U.S. Department of Agriculture.)

open beds is the usual method in many winter-garden areas along the Atlantic and the Gulf Coast; and planting seed in plant-growing structures is practiced in certain producing districts in Mississippi and in the northern United States for starting the early crop.

The transplants are set by hand or by machine; complete fertilizer mixtures are required; cultivation is practiced only when the plants are small or when the soil forms a crust after a rain; and the heads are harvested as soon as they are firm and have attained the right size. Figure 20.2 shows a field of half-grown cabbage. Note that the land is free from weeds.

BRUSSELS SPROUTS

Brussels sprouts develop an elongated, unbranched erect stem, and *a large number of small lateral vegetative buds*. In reality these buds are small heads and comprise the storage structures. The food-manufacturing leaves are comparatively large and about as broad as they are long.

Culture. Market gardeners and home gardeners raise Brussels sprouts quite extensively in northern France, Belgium, Holland, and the British Isles. In the United States it is not widely grown in home gardens, and commercial areas are confined to specialized districts. These districts indicate the temperature requirements for Brussels sprouts. They are located in Long Island, New York, and in the Moon Bay region just below San Francisco, California. Note that those areas are adjacent to large bodies of water.

CAULIFLOWER

Cauliflower produces *an undeveloped flower head,*[2] *or curd.* When the head is ready to cut, the flower primordia are not yet present. The leaves of cauliflower are generally longer than those of cabbage.

Culture. Of the members of the cabbage crops, cauliflower is the most sensitive to temperatures below and above its optimum range. In fact, uniformly cool temperatures are required for successful cauliflower production. In general, temperatures below the optimum range during the early stages of growth induce premature heading, and extremely high temperatures during the period of curd formation induce a "riced" condition and leafiness of the heads. Low humidity and high winds are injurious also. In other words, cauliflower requires cool, moist conditions. For this reason cauliflower, like Brussels sprouts, is grown in specialized regions. Chief producing areas are located on Long Island, New York, in certain districts in upstate New York, and in California and Oregon. In general, the plants are grown, transplanted, fertilized, cultivated, and harvested in much the same way as cabbage.

---

[2] Horticulturists are not fully agreed on the nature of the cauliflower head.

GREEN BROCCOLI

Green broccoli develops *a comparatively large number of small, green, undeveloped flower heads*. Individual heads are formed both terminally and laterally, and an individual plant produces shoots for several weeks. The climatic, soil, and cultural requirements are similar to those for cauliflower. Commercial areas exist near Norfolk, Virginia, in California, and in many other market-garden areas.

COLLARDS

Collards develop *large fleshy leaves which are used for greens*. The plants are very hardy to cool temperatures and resistant to high temperatures. Hence, collards are better adapted to the high summer temperatures of the

Fig. 20.3. A field of collards in eastern Virginia. (Courtesy, M. M. Parker, Virginia Truck Experiment Station.)

southern regions than are other members of the cabbage crops. Figure 20.3 shows a field of collards in eastern Virginia.

KALE

Like collards, kale develops *large, green leaves which are used as greens*. Kale varieties vary in plant height (dwarf and tall), shade of green of the foliage (grass green and gray green), and indentation of the leaves (indented and smooth). In general, kale plants can withstand fairly low temperatures but are sensitive to high temperatures. Thus, kale thrives best in comparatively cool weather. Note the fine indentation of the leaves in Fig. 20.4.

Fig. 20.4. A field of kale in eastern Virginia. (Courtesy, M. M. Parker, Virginia Truck Experiment Station.)

KOHLRABI

Kohlrabi develops a short, fleshy, turniplike stem. The enlarged stem is the storage structure and contains starches and sugars. The leaves are comparatively small and oval. In general, the plants thrive best in relatively cool weather and in continuously moist soil, and the fleshy stems are

Fig. 20.5. A plant of kohlrabi. Note that the carbohydrates are stored in the stem. (Courtesy, Associated Seed Growers, New Haven, Conn.)

harvested when they are 2 to 3 inches thick. Note the storage stem and the position of the leaves of the kohlrabi plant in Fig. 20.5.

LAND CRESS

Land cress is a hardy biennial mustard. The plants develop a rosette of edible leaves during the first season, and flowers, fruit, and seed during the second. As with cabbage, a period of exposure to cold—temperatures at or slightly below 40°F—is necessary to induce flower-bud formation.

Commercial districts exist in Virginia, Tennessee, North Carolina, and Georgia. In these districts the small, slowly germinating seeds are planted

Fig. 20.6. Land cress growing in Roanoke County, Va.

in moist, friable soil about 60 days before the first killing frost in the fall; and the plants are harvested during late fall, winter, and early spring. At the harvest the entire plants are cut just below the crown and shipped to the fresh market in bushel baskets or to the cannery in bags. Yields vary from 2 to 20 tons per acre. Figure 20.6 shows typical plants growing in Roanoke County, Virginia.

QUESTIONS

1.   Distinguish between cabbage, cauliflower, green broccoli, Brussels sprouts, collards, kale, kohlrabi, and land cress.

2. Cabbage is grown in late fall, winter, and early spring in the southern regions, in summer and fall in the northern regions. Explain.
3. In the South quick-maturing, small-headed varieties are raised. Explain.
4. In the South well-drained sandy loams and heavy applications of commercial fertilizers are used. In the North well-drained silt and clay loams and moderate applications of commercial fertilizers are used. Explain.
5. In the South young plants are frequently exposed to long periods of low temperatures. Frequently many plants go to seed without forming a head. Explain.
6. Is the biennial habit in cabbage a fixed hereditary characteristic? Cite instances where cabbage is grown commercially and frequently becomes an annual.
7. List those members of the cabbage crops which can be most easily grown; those which are not easily grown.
8. Brussels sprouts are grown extensively in the British Isles and not extensively in the United States. Explain.
9. In the South the collard is quite popular in home gardens. Explain.

CELERY

Plant Characteristics

Root System.   The root system of celery is nonextensive. The taproot is destroyed by necessary transplanting and, as a result, a moderate number of laterals develop. Studies of the root system show that the lateral roots of full-grown plants extend for a comparatively short distance only. For example, at Cornell University most of the roots of plants growing in sandy loam were found within a radius of 6 inches from the base of the plants, and most of these roots were within 2 to 3 inches from the surface. The comparatively sparse root system explains why the plants can be set close together—from 6 to 8 inches; why celery cannot readily compete with weeds; and why the topsoil should be abundantly supplied with water and essential elements.

Stems and Leaves.   During the first year the plants produce a short, stubby stem usually from 3 to 6 inches long and a large number of thick-petioled, pinnately compound leaves. The petioles are conspicuously ribbed, very broad at the base, and contain comparatively large quantities of starch and related substances. During the second year the much-branched flowering stem arises from the axils of the fleshy petioles and on maturity attains a height of 2 to 3 feet.

Flowers and Fruit.   The inflorescence is an umbel. Individual flowers are small, perfect, and are mostly self-pollinated. Mature fruit, called "seed," are small and dry and have corky ribs. For satisfactory germination the seed require shallow planting and a uniform supply of moisture.

Economic Importance and Distribution

Prior to World War I, the fleshy petioles of celery were considered a luxury; now they are considered a necessity. Important commercial districts are the Delta and Los Angeles in California, the Kalamazoo and Muskegon in the Lower Peninsula of Michigan, the Williamson of New York, and the Sanford and Lake Okeechobee of Florida. Modern varieties possess dark green petioles which when blanched become golden yellow.

Growth and Development

Climatic Requirements.   The principal environmental factors are temperature and water supply. Celery is primarily a cool-season crop. It is grown, therefore, as a summer crop in northern regions, as a winter crop in southern regions, and as a spring crop in the intermediate region. California, because of its many climates, grows the crop throughout the entire year—in the Imperial Valley in the winter and in the more northern sections of the state in the spring and summer. In Florida the crop is grown in late winter and early spring, and in New York and Michigan it is grown in late spring, summer, and fall. Thus, the many towns and cities of the United States are supplied with celery throughout the year.

Soils.   Celery grows best on deep, slightly acid mucks and on slightly acid, fertile mineral soils high in organic matter. In California, New York, and Michigan it is grown mostly on well-drained, slightly acid mucks; and in New Jersey and Florida on deep, fertile, slightly acid loams and mucks. Note the large muckland field and the 12-row transplanter in Fig. 20.7.

Because of its nonextensive root system, celery requires a continuous supply of water. For this reason mucks which have a controlled water table are adapted to celery. On mineral soils irrigation is usually necessary.

Disposition of the Carbohydrates.   As stated previously, celery develops a group of leaves with fleshy petioles the first year. Thus, the growth of the plant during the first year may be divided into two stages: (1) the seedling stage and (2) the petiole-thickening stage. Therefore, utilization of the carbohydrates is dominant over accumulation during the seedling stage. As the plants attain their size, utilization becomes less dominant, and with the thickening of the petioles, accumulation becomes more evident. Assuming a period of 90 to 120 days for the development of the petioles, the disposition of the carbohydrates is illustrated as follows:

A	seedling stage	B	development of petioles	C
	utilization dominant		accumulation dominant	

Fig. 20.7. The establishment of a celery field in central Florida. Note the 12-row transplanter. (Courtesy, J. C. Hoffman, U.S. Department of Agriculture.)

Culture.   Celery is always transplanted. In general, the seedlings are grown in continuously moist soil and at night temperatures between 65 and 70°F to prevent subsequent "bolting." The transplants are grown in irrigated, highly fertile loams and mucks to maintain steady growth, and the soil is kept free from weeds to avoid competition for water and

Fig. 20.8. A field of mature celery in south Florida. (Courtesy, J. C. Hoffman, U.S. Department of Agriculture.)

essential raw materials. The plants are harvested as soon as they have attained the proper size, and the petioles are blanched to destroy the chlorophyll and to promote crispness and high quality. They are sent to market in two ways: (1) in the rough and (2) fully trimmed. Plants shipped in the rough are cut, partially trimmed—removing damaged and diseased leaves only—packed in crates in the field, and shipped to market. Plants shipped fully trimmed are cut, transported to the packing shed, fully trimmed, washed in a cool water, graded, packed, and sent to market. The principal shipping container is the crate. Various sizes are used. Note the field of mature celery in the Lake Okeechobee district of south Florida.

CHARD

Chard is a beet developed *for its fleshy petioles and leaves.* During the first year the plants develop a fleshy taproot, a short stem, and a large number of well-developed, simple leaves. During the second year they develop the flowering stems which support the fruit and seed. The outer leaves mature first. As they are harvested, new leaves develop. In this way the plant produces leaves throughout a relatively long growing season. A rich, moist soil is the principal cultural requirement. The plant grows satisfactorily during moderately warm and cool weather. The leaves are prepared for the table in much the same way as other greens.

QUESTIONS

1. On mineral soils, celery responds to continuous cultivation throughout the growing period. Explain.
2. Celery is grown in late fall, winter, and early spring in Florida; in summer and fall in New York and Michigan; and the entire year in Los Angeles county of California. Explain.
3. Celery thrives best and the petioles attain their highest quality in cool weather. Explain.
4. Celery grown on upland soil in the humid East usually requires irrigation. Explain.
5. Celery thrives well on well-drained, slightly acid mucks with a controlled water table. Explain.
6. The climate of Great Britain is adaptable to the raising of high-quality celery. Explain.
7. Celery cannot readily compete with weeds. Explain.
8. What is the purpose of blanching celery?
9. If commercial celery is grown in your state, describe briefly the type of soil used, the system of soil management, the variety, method of plant production, disease-control program, and growing and shipping season.

10. In the South celery is rarely grown in home gardens. Can you think of any reasons for this?

THE ANNUALS

LETTUCE

Plant Characteristics

Root System.   The root system of mature plants is moderately extensive. In upland soil the taproot extends to the 4- or 5-foot level. Branches of the first order extend laterally to a distance of 6 to 8 inches and then turn downward. Branches of the second order are most numerous. They usually fill the upper layer of soil. A direct relation exists between the density of the root system and compactness of the soil. In compact soils the root system is more dense and more shallow than in loose soil.

Stem and Leaves.   During the vegetative stage the stem is short, usually from 4 to 6 inches long. Around it the leaves arise in a rosette. They vary in size (large and small), shape (spatular and circular), color (light green to dark green), and crispness. During the reproductive stage the stems elongate and branch, and each of the various branches forms a terminal inflorescence.

Flowers, Fruit, and Seed.   The inflorescence is a panicle. Individual flowers are perfect, with five stamens and a one-celled ovary. They are usually self-pollinated. The fruit called "seed" are very small; each contains a single embryo and is planted shallowly. Investigations have shown that abundant oxygen is necessary for rapid germination. With other conditions favorable, good germination can be obtained from 40 to 70°F.

Economic Importance and Distribution

From 1917 to the present, consumption of lettuce has increased enormously. In 1917 the average per capita consumption was one head; in 1925 it was five heads. In 1929 only 17,000 acres were grown, in 1958 approximately 209,000 acres were grown. This great increase in consumption has been due largely to the education of the public in the health-giving properties of lettuce. Principal producing districts are the Imperial Valley and Salinas-Watsonville in California, the Oswego in New York, the Wilmington in North Carolina, and the Lake Okeechobee in Florida.

Types. In general, there are two types: (1) heading and (2) non-heading. The heading type may be divided into the crisp and the butter. The nonheading type may be divided into the crisp and the cos. Within recent years varieties adapted to specific regions have been developed.

Growth and Development

Climatic Requirements. The principal environmental factor in the growth of lettuce is temperature. For the development of firm, solid heads, uniformly cool night temperatures, 45 to 50°F, combined with uniformly cool, sunny day temperatures, 55 to 80°F, are necessary. In humid sections growers very often have difficulty in securing firm, solid heads. High night temperatures, particularly during the heading stage, seem to be the main environmental factor responsible for lack of firmness.

Soils. Lettuce is grown on a wide range of soil types. In California the commercial crop is grown on silty clay loams, in New York and Florida on muck, and in North Carolina on sandy loams. The optimum pH range is from 6.0 to 6.8.

Disposition of the Carbohydrates. The phases of growth to the heading stage may be divided into two more or less distinct but overlapping periods: (1) leaf growth and (2) leaf maturation. During the first period the plants are developing their leaves, and utilization of the carbohydrates is dominant over accumulation. As extensive leaf growth subsides and heading begins, utilization processes become less dominant and accumulation processes become more evident. Finally, as the heads become mature accumulation processes become quite marked. Line AB represents a growing period varying from 85 to 100 days, depending on the variety and the season.

leaf growth ⟶	leaf and head maturation

| A | utilization dominant ⟶ | accumulation dominant | B |

Culture. In general, lettuce crops may be established by planting the "seed" directly in the garden or field or by transplanting young plants which have been previously grown in plant-growing structures. Each method has advantages and disadvantages. The first method requires the thinning out of excess seedlings, and the second requires the growing of the seedling plants from 4 to 6 weeks before they are set in the garden or field.

Lettuce may be grown on level land or on ridges. Where spray irrigation

Fig. 20.9. A field of head lettuce in the Salinas-Watsonville district of California. (Courtesy, Chamber of Commerce and Agriculture of the Pajaro Valley, Watsonville, Calif.)

is practiced, either level or ridged land may be used; however, where furrow irrigation is practiced, ridges are necessary to allow the water to run in the furrows. For example, in the Salinas-Watsonville district of California the width of the beds varies from 18 to 20 inches or more and the height from 4 to 10 inches. Two rows 12 to 16 inches apart are planted on the beds. The furrows between the beds carry the irrigation water. Study these features in Fig. 20.9.

Harvesting. Head lettuce grown for market is allowed to develop solid heads before harvest. When grown in the home garden the heads are frequently harvested before they attain full size. Leaf lettuce is harvested at any time after the plants are large enough for use. The plants are cut usually with a large knife. The heads or plants are trimmed and packed in various types of containers—hampers, crates, or baskets. In packing, the stem ends are placed together to avoid injury to the heads in transit.

CHINESE CABBAGE

Chinese cabbage is closely related to and resembles the members of the cabbage crops. The leaves are the edible portion, and during the later stages of growth they form rather loose heads (see Fig. 20.10). They are used for salads or as greens and are fine in texture, succulent, and crisp. In general, the crop thrives best on fertile, moderately to slightly acid sandy loams, loams, and mucks. A continuous supply of essential elements, particularly nitrogen, is essential for steady growth. The heads are harvested when they are well developed. They are cut, trimmed, and packed in baskets, boxes, or crates.

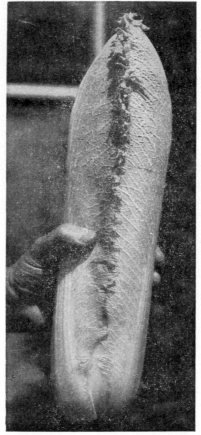

Fig. 20.10. A head of Chinese cabbage. (Courtesy, Associated Seed Growers, New Haven, Conn.)

QUESTIONS

1. In Florida lettuce is grown during the late fall, winter, and early spring. Explain.
2. In New York lettuce is grown in the summer, and in the Imperial Valley of California it is grown in the winter and early spring. Explain.
3. In general, growth should be rapid during the early stages of plant development and moderately rapid during the later stages. Explain.
4. Comparatively cool, sunny days and cool, crisp nights favor the formation of firm heads. Explain.
5. Lettuce heads stored in the refrigerator remain more sweet and crisp than those stored in a warm room. Explain.
6. Name the two types of lettuce.

7. Within the past 30 years consumption of head lettuce has increased rapidly. Explain.

SPINACH

Plant Characteristics

Root System. Spinach has a distinct, well-developed taproot. The laterals are relatively few and short. Most of the absorbing roots arise directly from the taproot.

Stems and Leaves. The stem is short and platelike and bears a rosette of well-petioled, simple, moderately large leaves. The leaves vary in shape (spear-shaped to round) and character of the surface (smooth, slightly undulated or savoyed). The savoyed surface is due to extensive growth of the parenchyma tissue between the veins. The leaves are exceedingly dark green. They are an excellent source of carotene (provitamin A), ascorbic acid, and minerals, as well as being a good source of thiamin and riboflavin.

Flowers, Fruit, and Seed. Spinach is dioecious or monoecious according to the variety. In dioecious varieties the males are of two types: (1) extreme and (2) vegetative. The extreme males have few, if any, well-developed leaves toward the tip of the seedstalk, and the vegetative males have well-developed leaves toward the tip. Since spinach is grown for its leaves in home and commercial gardens, vegetative males are more desirable as breeding parents than extreme males. Female plants are always vegetative. Thus, highly vegetative strains of the dioecious varieties have been developed by roguing out the extreme males in seed-producing fields. In monoecious varieties the plants are highly vegetative.

The flowers are without petals, small, and relatively inconspicuous. Pollen grains are small, produced in abundant quantities, and are carried from one plant to another by the wind. The fruit called "seed" have the ability to germinate at rather low temperatures and require a continuous supply of water. Poor germination frequently occurs in dry soil in the summer.

Economic Importance and Distribution

Spinach is the most important vegetable crop grown as greens. Principal commercial areas are in the vicinity of Baltimore, Maryland; Norfolk, Virginia; Crystal Springs, Texas; and in central New Jersey and southern California. The Virginia and New Jersey districts supply markets during the fall and spring; the Texas district supplies markets in the winter and early spring; and the California district supplies the Pacific Coast markets during the winter. The principal districts which are given over to the raising of spinach for canning are located in California and in south Texas.

Growth and Development

Climatic Requirements. The principal environmental factors affecting the growth of spinach are temperature and length of day. Spinach is primarily a cool-season, long day plant. From the standpoint of temperature, it thrives best in regions characterized by cool nights (40 to 50°F) and clear, sunny days (60 to 80°F). From the standpoint of photoperiod, it produces leaves and stems during the short days, and flowers and fruit during the long days. For this reason spinach is grown in home and commercial gardens in the short days of late fall, winter, and early spring and for seed production during the long days of summer.

Soils. Spinach is grown on a wide variety of soil types. The greatest yields are secured from silt and clay loams and mucks. However, sandy loams are used to grow winter crops. In any case soils for spinach should be slightly acid, well drained, and fertile.

Disposition of the Carbohydrates. As stated previously, in home and commercial gardens spinach is grown primarily for its leaves. Thus, during the seedling stage most of the carbohydrates that are made are used for cell division and enlargement. As the plants attain their size, leaf growth becomes less rapid, carbohydrate utilization in turn becomes less rapid, and accumulation becomes more evident. Line AC, representing a growing period of 45 to 80 days, roughly indicates the period of leaf growth and leaf maturation.

A	period of leaf growth	B	period of leaf maturation	C
	utilization dominant	$\longrightarrow$	accumulation dominant	

Culture. In general, spinach is raised on level land without beds in northern regions and on broad, low beds varying from 8 to 12 feet in width in southern irrigated regions. The "seeds" are usually drilled in rows; spacing of the plants is regulated as far as possible by adjusting the rate of seeding; and complete fertilizer mixtures high in available nitrogen are required. In fact, the cool weather during the winter in southern districts and the growing of the crop on well-drained, sandy loams necessitate frequent top dressings of readily available nitrogen. Note the close spacings within and between the rows in Fig. 20.11.

Preparation for market consists in cutting the taproot just below the

Fig. 20.11. A field of spinach in the eastern United States. (Courtesy, V. R. Boswell, U.S. Department of Agriculture.)

surface of the land and trimming off the dead leaves. For long distance shipment, spinach is usually packed in bushel hampers or crates. When shipped in warm weather, crushed ice is placed in the upper part of the containers.

QUESTIONS

1. Spinach in home and commercial gardens is grown during the fall, winter, and early spring. Give two reasons.
2. Spinach grows poorly on soil greater than pH 7.0 and less than pH 6.0. Explain.
3. Investigations have shown that spinach requires abundant moisture and essential elements, particularly nitrate-nitrogen. Explain.
4. Spinach maturing in the late fall is sweeter than that maturing in late spring. Explain.
5. Since 1910 spinach has become very popular in the United States. Can you think of any reasons for this?

21

VEGETABLE CROPS GROWN FOR THEIR FLESHY STORAGE STRUCTURES

Whether the task be great or small,
do it well or not at all.
Lord Chesterfield

THE ONION CROPS

Common Characteristics. The onion crops consist of onion, shallot, leek, garlic, and chive. These crops have at least four characteristics in common: They possess a characteristic odor and flavor, store carbohydrates in the basal portion of the leaves, develop a nonextensive root system, and produce perfect, insect-pollinated flowers. The characteristic odor and flavor vary with the crop and with the variety within the crop. For example, garlic is more pungent than onions, and the American varieties of onions are more pungent than the European varieties. The basal portion of the leaf is thick and fleshy and constitutes the edible portion. These basal leaves with the short, platelike stem are called bulbs and contain comparatively large quantities of inulin (a type of starch), moderate amounts of sugars, and moderate amounts of ascorbic acid or vitamin C. The nonextensiveness of the root system, with the major portion of the absorbing system of mature plants within a radius of 6 inches from the stem, requires the absolute control of weeds and the selection of soils with high water-holding capacity. The leaves are simple and present a rather small photosynthetic surface. The inflorescence is an umbel; individual flowers possess six stamens and a simple pistil; and they are chiefly pollinated by various species of bees.

ONION

Distinguishing Characteristics. The onion develops *distinct bulbs*. According to the variety, these bulbs vary in size (small, medium, and large), color (white, yellow, or red), shape (flattened, round, or globular), texture (fine or coarse), and pungency. The plant is normally a biennial. The fleshy bulbs develop during the first season, and seedstalks develop during the following season. The leaves develop from a short, flattened stem at the base of the bulb. They consist of two parts: (1) sheath and (2) blade. The sheaths are fleshy and surround the younger leaves within. The blades are green, pointed, and hollow.

Economic Importance and Distribution. Of the onion group, the onion is the most widely grown and the most commonly known. In the United States extensive commercial districts are located in south Texas and Louisiana, in the Pacific Coast region and Rocky Mountain area, and in the northeast and middle west regions.

Types. Onions are classified according to the degree of mildness of the bulb. Three distinct types are recognized: (1) mild, (2) semimild, and (3) pungent, or strong. In general, the mild type develops larger, finer-textured bulbs than the pungent, or strong, type. The commercial varieties of onions are rather specific in their optimum growing requirements. For example, the long-storage, pungent varieties grown in the Middle West and Northeast do poorly in the Southwest and Pacific Coast, and the nonstorage, mild varieties grown in the Southwest are ill-suited to the Middle West and Northeast.

Growth and Development

Climatic Requirements. Onions require a cool temperature range during the seedling stage and a moderately high temperature range during the bulbing stage. The moderately high temperature, particularly if combined with a dry atmosphere, facilitates harvesting and curing of the bulbs. Thus, the crop is grown in winter and early spring in southern regions and during the spring and summer in northern regions. The late summer of the northeast and middle west regions is sufficiently warm to permit normal curing of the varieties adapted to those regions.

The principal factors influencing the formation of the bulb are (1) the supply of available nitrogen and (2) the length of day. If excessive quantities of available nitrogen are present, with other factors favorable, vegetative growth will be excessive and undesirable bulbs will be formed. These undesirable bulbs are known as "thick-necked onions," or scallions. They lack quality, have low market value, and possess poor keeping ability. If the length of day is unfavorable for bulb formation of any given variety, no bulbs will be formed. Varieties differ in their length-of-day requirements. Some require a long period (15 to 17 hours), whereas others require a relatively short period (12 to 14 hours). Thus, varieties adapted to the northern half of the country are unadaptable to the southern half and vice versa.

Soils. Onions thrive best on highly fertile, slightly acid, well-drained sandy loams, silt loams, and mucks. For example, in the winter-garden area of Texas, the crop is raised on sandy loams, and in New York, Ohio, and Michigan highly decomposed mucks are employed. These soils are loose, thus permitting normal development of the bulb, and have a high water-holding capacity.

Disposition of the Carbohydrates. As previously stated, the bulb is produced during the first season and seedstalks are produced during the second. During the first part of the first season the plants develop their leaves and roots, and during the latter part they develop their bulbs. Consequently, environmental conditions should permit extensive foliage and root growth before bulbing begins. Since foliage and root growth precede bulb formation, carbohydrate utilization will be dominant during the first part of the growing season, and carbohydrate accumulation will be dominant during the latter part.

A	growth of roots and leaves ⟶ B	development of bulbs	C
	utilization dominant　　⟶	accumulation dominant	

Line AC represents a growing period of 100 to 120 days of the first year. Line AB represents the period of root and foliage growth, and line BC represents the period of bulb formation.

Culture. Throughout the United States the three distinct methods used to start onions are (1) planting seed directly in the field, (2) planting seed in prepared seedbeds and transplanting the seedlings to the field, and (3) planting dry sets where the crop is to mature. The first method is practiced largely in the Middle West and Northeast; the second method is used principally in Louisiana and south Texas; and the third method is used in certain market-garden districts.

As previously stated, onions are grown on mineral soils and on muck. Satisfactory mineral soils are well drained, slightly acid, and contain moderate quantities of decomposed organic matter; and they generally require complete mixtures high in phosphorus. On the other hand, satisfactory muck soils are deep, well drained, highly decomposed, and slightly acid; and they generally require complete mixtures high in potassium. To develop deep color and thick scales of the bulbs, applications of powdered copper sulfate are necessary in many districts.

Fig. 21.1. A field of onions in Nebraska, stacked in crates for curing. (Courtesy, H. A. Jones, U.S. Department of Agriculture.)

The mature bulbs are lifted by machine or pulled by hand and placed in windrows to cure. Later they are topped, graded according to size, and placed in crates if they are to be stored (see Fig. 21.1) or in 50-pound open mesh bags if they are to be shipped. Onions are shipped to the markets of the country throughout the year. California ships during every month of the year; Texas ships from May to August; and the northern states ship from September to April and May.

SHALLOT, LEEK, GARLIC, AND CHIVE

The shallot develops *several small bulblets, or cloves, held together at the base;* the leek develops *thick, mild, fleshy leaf sheaths;* the garlic develops *a group of small bulbs, or cloves, enclosed in a membrane-like skin;* and chive develops *small, distinct bulbs.* Commercial districts of shallots exist in southern Louisiana, and commercial districts of garlic are located in central California. The climate and cultural requirements are similar to those of the onion.

QUESTIONS

1. In general, the onion group of crops requires continuous cultivation, cannot compete readily with weeds, and can be planted at close distances. Explain.

2. In ancient times masters of sailing vessels frequently took on a supply of onions before making long voyages. Explain.
3. Distinguish the three main types of onions.
4. In the southern regions onions are grown in the winter and early spring; in northern regions they are grown in the summer. Explain.
5. Onions are particularly adapted to loose, friable loams and to slightly acid mucks. Explain.
6. In general, the larger the plants grow before they begin to form bulbs, the larger will be the yield. Explain.
7. In what regions of the United States are most of the pungent varieties of onions grown? In what region are most of the mild types grown? Give reasons for your answers.
8. Name and distinguish the members of the onion group.

THE TUBER CROPS

POTATO[1]

Root System. The root system of asexually propagated crops is fibrous and adventitious. In other words, the roots arise from the nodes of the stem situated in the soil. In adult plants the root system is moderately extensive. Although a few roots extend from 3 to 4 feet, both vertically and laterally, most of the roots are from 6 inches to 2 feet long. These roots are situated in the topsoil, with the greater density in the upper 3 to 4 inches. Hence, if cultivation is necessary during the later stages of growth, it should be shallow to avoid cutting the absorbing roots just beneath the surface.

Stems and Leaves. The stems are of two types: (1) aerial and (2) underground. The aerial stems are angular, green or greenish-purple, depending on the variety, and bear in a spiral arrangement pinnately compound leaves. Under humid conditions the leaves are broad and flat, and under arid conditions they are narrow and cupped.

The underground stems consist of stolens and tubers. The stolens are about the size of a lead pencil and extend laterally for a distance of 1 to 4 inches. The tubers arise at the end of the stolens and are short, thick, and fleshy. They develop scalelike leaves called "eyebrows" which subtend buds called "eyes." These buds are undeveloped branches. Each eye contains both terminal and lateral branches, and each potato has both terminal and lateral eyes. The terminal eyes develop sprouts before the lateral eyes, and the terminal sprouts in each eye develop before the lateral sprouts. However, cutting of the tubers, an important practice, destroys

[1] In the southern United States the term "potato" usually refers to the sweetpotato, and the potato is called the Irish potato.

the dominance of the terminal eyes, and removing the first sprouts destroys the terminal dominance within each eye.

The anatomy of immature and mature tubers differs considerably. The immature tubers consist of an epidermis, a wide band of cortex, pericycle, vascular bundles, and pith. As the tuber develops, the epidermis is replaced by a periderm—the layer of corklike cells. The cortex becomes a narrow band just beneath the periderm, and the vascular bundles extend to the eyes. The pith becomes greatly enlarged and constitutes the major portion of the tuber. The function of the periderm is to keep the all-important water within the tuber and to resist the attacks of rot-producing organisms. The lenticels permit exchange of carbon dioxide and oxygen, and the cortex and pith are abundantly filled with grains of starch. In fact, most of the dry matter of the tuber consists of starch.

Flowers, Fruit, and Seed. The flowers are borne in clusters terminating the stem. Individual flowers are perfect and either white, yellow, purple, or striped, according to the variety. Flowering is usually more profuse in regions characterized by low summer temperatures than in regions characterized by high summer temperatures. The fruit, or seedball, is round, small—$\frac{1}{2}$ to 1 inch in diameter—and contains from 100 to 300 seeds. Seed are used to develop new types and varieties.

Economic Importance and Distribution

The potato is the most important, most valuable, and most widely known horticultural crop. The annual world production is between 6 and 7 billion bushels and is exceeded only by that of wheat. The leading countries are Russia ($1\frac{1}{2}$ billion), Germany ($1\frac{1}{2}$ billion), Poland (1 billion), and France and the United States ($\frac{1}{2}$ billion each). In the United States two rather distinct commercial industries exist: (1) the main crop and (2) the early crop. Important main-crop producing districts are Aroostook County, Maine; western New York; eastern Pennsylvania; northern Ohio; central Michigan; Red River Valley of Minnesota and North Dakota; high-altitude areas of Idaho; and eastern Nebraska. The potatoes are harvested when they are fully mature and are placed in storage to supply the markets in the winter and early spring. Important early-crop producing districts are Mobile Bay, Alabama; Hastings and Homestead, Florida; south Texas; south Louisiana; Charleston-Beaufort, South Carolina; Norfolk, Virginia; Long Island, New York; and Sacramento Delta, California. The potatoes are harvested when immature and are prepared and shipped immediately to the markets. Thus, the many regions of the country supply the consuming public with this important vegetable throughout the year.

Varieties grown in the United States are placed in two groups: (1)

early maturing and (2) late maturing. Early maturing varieties develop tubers in a relatively short time, and late maturing varieties require a relatively long time. In general, the early market varieties are adapted to the southern regions of the country, and the main-crop varieties are adapted to the northern regions. Because of extensive breeding programs, particularly in the U.S. Department of Agriculture in cooperation with many state experiment stations, new varieties are constantly being developed. For the most part, these new varieties combine disease resistance of the plants with high yields of high-quality tubers.

Growth and Development

Climatic Requirements. The principal climatic factor influencing growth and yield is temperature. The potato plant thrives best in uniformly cool weather. In general, the optimum temperature range is considered to be between 45 and 65°F, with a mean of about 60°F. In other words, the highest yields are secured within this temperature range. As explained in Chapter 4, if the temperature is above this range, particularly during the period of tuber formation, yields are low. The high yields secured in Maine, in the British Isles, and in northern Germany are due largely to the comparatively low temperatures in these regions during the period of tuber formation and development.

Soils. In general, the potato is grown on fertile sandy loams and mucks. On mineral soils the addition of decayed organic matter is usually beneficial. Organic matter improves texture and aeration and thus makes the soil more favorable for the development of the tubers. The Wooster and the Washburn series of loams are used in Aroostook County, Maine, the most important potato-growing county in the United States. Well-drained sandy loams are used in New Jersey, New York, Virginia, and in many of the southern states. Both muck and mineral soils are used in Florida, Michigan, and Wisconsin.

Disposition of the Carbohydrates. Since the tuber is the place where carbohydrates accumulate, the yield of the tubers is an expression of carbohydrate accumulation. Before tuber formation can take place, stems and leaves (food-manufacturing structures) and roots (water- and element-absorbing structures) must be formed. Hence, when the plant is developing its root and top systems, it is making numerous new cells and large quantities of carbohydrates are necessary for their formation. Consequently, during the early stages of growth the utilization of carbohydrates is dominant over accumulation. On the other hand, when the plant begins to develop its tubers, root and top growth practically ceases and the carbohydrates become available for tuber formation. Consequently, during the period of tuber formation and development, carbohydrate accumulation is dominant over utilization. Line AB, representing a growing period of from 120 to 200 days, shows the periods within which utilization and accumulation are taking place. The student should remember that there is a gradual transition from the development of roots and tops to the development of the tubers.

growth of tops and roots	formation of tubers	development of tubers
A utilization dominant	$\longrightarrow$	accumulation dominant B

Culture. As previously stated, in home and commercial gardens potatoes are propagated by means of the tubers. Since the tubers are storage stems, they contain terminal and lateral buds and large quantities of starch. Under conditions favorable for development of the buds, the starch changes to sugars which are used to make new cells and to supply energy for the growth of the young plants.

The raising of tubers for starting new crops is a highly specialized industry. At present many varieties are suspectible to many virus diseases. These virus diseases are carried from one crop to the next in the tubers and from infected plants to healthy plants by certain insects. If virus diseases are present in any plant, they impair the development of chlorophyll, reduce the photosynthetic process, and markedly decrease the yield. Consequently, tubers grown for starting other crops should be practically free from these diseases. In general, plants for "seed" are grown under certain rules and regulations in regions characterized by cool weather. The cool weather favors the development of virus-disease symptoms of infected plants. The rules require the inspection of plants and the removal of specimens infected with the virus diseases, the control of insect vectors, and the inspection of tubers in storage. Crops which have passed the requirements of inspection are given a certificate and can be sold as certified seed. Principal certified seed–producing districts are located in Maine, the Maritime Provinces of Canada, New York, Wisconsin, Michigan, Minnesota, North Dakota, Nebraska, and the mountain sections of Maryland, North Carolina, Georgia, and Tennessee.

In general, the tubers are cut into two, three, four, five, or six pieces just before they are planted. These pieces are planted by hand or by machine, and complete fertilizers are required. For the most part, 1-1-1 ratios are used in the Atlantic Coastal Plain, and 1-2-1, 1-3-1, and 1-4-1 ratios are used in the Middle West. For many years, scientists have tested various methods of applying the commercial fertilizer. Many of these tests show that applying the fertilizer to the side of the seed piece produces greater yields than applying the fertilizer under the seed piece.

According to the marketing purpose involved, the growing of potatoes may be divided into two industries: (1) for marketing immediately

Fig. 21.2. Harvesting potatoes in the Mobile Bay district of south Alabama. (Courtesy, The Mobile Press Register, Mobile, Ala.)

after the harvest and (2) for storage or deferred shipment. In general, potatoes grown in the commercial areas of southern regions are marketed immediately after harvest. The tubers are dug when they are immature, washed, and packed in burlap bags and immediately shipped to market. On the other hand, tubers grown in northern regions are marketed after a period of storage. The tubers are dug when mature, placed in storage (temperatures 40 to 42°F with moderate humidity), and later shipped to the market. For the retail trade in large cities potatoes are attractively packed in 15-, 20-, or 25-pound lots in paper boxes and in cotton or burlap sacks. Note the harvest scene in Fig. 21.2.

JERUSALEM ARTICHOKE

The Jerusalem artichoke is a tuber-forming sunflower. The root system is undoubtedly extensive. The stems consist of two types: (1) underground (tubers) and (2) aerial. The tuber stores a type of starch called inulin and develops in much the same way as that of the potato. In the United States experiments have shown that the crop is better adapted to the northern two-thirds of the country than it is to the southern one-third.

QUESTIONS

1. In general, the potato requires shallow cultivation particularly during the period of tuber formation. Explain.

2. Potatoes harvested in the immature state skin easily. Explain.
3. Investigations have shown that potatoes with a well-developed periderm shrink less and rot less in storage than those with a poorly developed periderm. Explain.
4. The climate of northern Maine, the Delta district of California, Great Britain, and Ireland is particularly favorable for the production of high yields of potatoes. Explain.
5. Potatoes are grown in late winter and early spring in southern regions; in the summer in northern regions. Explain.
6. If soil and air temperatures are above the optimum range, particularly during the later stages of growth, yields will be extremely low. Explain.
7. In the southern regions, with due consideration to the date of the last killing frost, the earlier the planting the greater is likely to be the yield. Explain.
8. In Colorado potatoes are grown in the mountains and yields are satisfactory. Explain.
9. What is certified "seed" of the potato?
10. Carefully handled tubers have longer storage life than carelessly handled tubers. Explain.
11. In general, the Jerusalem artichoke produces higher yields in the northern two-thirds of the United States than in the southern one-third. Can you think of any reason for this?

THE ROOT CROPS

The vegetable crops called the root crops include carrot, parsnip, salsify, beet, radish, turnip, rutabaga, and horseradish. These crops develop enlarged storage structures called roots. They contain fairly large quantities of starch, and the size, shape, color of skin, and flesh vary greatly with the crop.

Common Characteristics. The root crops are herbaceous biennials except the radish, which is either annual or biennial. They develop an extensive absorbing system, long-petioled leaves, and they thrive best in cool weather and have similar cultural requirements.

Growth and Development. The growth and development of root crops may be divided into two distinct periods: (1) the production of the enlarged storage structure and (2) the production of flowers, fruits, and seed. In home and commercial gardens these crops are grown for the enlarged structure only. Hence, the disposition of the carbohydrates during the first period of growth only will be considered. As previously stated, the plants develop most of their absorbing roots and most of their leaves before they develop the enlarged storage structure. Thus, carbohydrate utilization should be dominant during the seedling stage, carbohydrate accumulation should be dominant during the growth and maturation of the storage structure, and a gradual transition from dominance of utilization to dominance of accumulation should take place during the intermediate stage. The disposition of the carbohydrates is shown as follows: Line AB represents a growing period varying from 35 to 90 days, depending on the kind of crop.

growth of roots and leaves	development of fleshy structure	
A utilization dominant	accumulation dominant	B

CARROT

A transverse section of the fleshy root shows two distinct regions: (1) the outer and (2) the inner. The outer tissues consist of a thin periderm and a relatively wide band of storage tissue. The periderm reduces transpiration to a minimum and resists the attacks of invading organisms, and the storage tissue of mature roots stores relatively large quantities of starch and carotene (the precursor of vitamin A) and moderate quantities of sugar, thiamin, and riboflavin. The inner core consists of xylem and pith. High-quality carrots contain a relatively small inner core. Scientists have shown that the outer tissues contain more carotene than the inner.

Stems, Leaves, Flowers, and Fruit.   The stem is short and platelike during the first growing season and long and erect during the second. The leaves are decompound and the inflorescence is a conspicuous compound umbel. Individual flowers are small, hermaphroditic, and white and are largely insect-pollinated. The fruits are called "seed" and are small, dry, and indehiscent. Each individual fruit contains one seed. The embryo geminates slowly and requires a fine friable seedbed and uniform supplies of moisture.

Economic Importance and Distribution.   From the standpoint of human nutrition the carrot is most important. Because the enlarged root contains large quantities of carotene, it is an excellent source of vitamin A. Within recent years the demand for carrots has been quite marked. Principal producing states are California, Texas, New York, New Jersey, Arizona, Louisiana, and Florida. California and the southern states supply the markets with carrots during the winter and spring. New York and other northern states supply the market with carrots during the fall and winter.

Culture.   Principal factors concerned are (1) growing-season temperatures; (2) type of soil with particular reference to its water content, drainage, acidity, and friability; and (3) the available nitrogen supply. The optimum temperature range for the growth of the tops seems to be from 65 to 75°F and that for the growth of the roots seems to be from 60 to 70°F. Since size and carotene content of the fleshy root depend on the size and health of the foliage, comparatively high temperatures (65 to 85°F) during the seedling stage permit the development of a large top and somewhat lower temperatures (60 to 70°) after the tops are fully grown permit the development of large, highly colored roots. In general, well-drained, moderate to slightly acid non-self-crusting sandy loams in good tilth are preferred. These soils are advantageous from at least three standpoints: (1) They permit the emergence of the delicate plumule during germination; (2) they promote rapid growth of the plants; and (3) they favor the development of smooth, highly colored roots.

The amount of available nitrogen is particularly important during the early stages of growth. As previously stated, a comparatively large top is necessary for the development of a large root. Hence, the supply of available nitrogen should be sufficient to promote a rapid development of the top and to maintain health and vigor of the top during the period of root formation.

Varieties are classified according to shape and length of the root. Shape refers to the tip of the root, whether blunt or pointed, and length is considered with reference to the diameter. Principal classes are moderately long and blunt; long and blunt; long and pointed; and very long and pointed. Within recent years scientists have developed highly colored strains of certain varieties which are adapted to specific producing districts in the country.

PARSNIP AND SALSIFY

Parsnip and salsify develop enlarged roots which have white flesh without distinct zones. For full growth and development both crops require a relatively long growing season, and the cultural requirements are practically the same as those for carrots. With parsnips the freezing of the roots is unnecessary to improve the quality. At College Park, Maryland, parsnips stored for two weeks at 34°F became just as sweet as roots left in the soil for two months in the late fall. At 34°F the change of starch to sugars was quite rapid. In the United States the crop is grown in many home gardens and in limited quantities in market gardens.

BEET

The enlarged root of the garden beet is quite distinct from that of the other root crops. A cross section shows alternate circular bands of storage and conducting tissues. The broad bands are storage tissues, and the narrow bands are conducting tissues. Frequently, the wide bands are darker than the narrow bands. The contrast in color between these alternate bands is known as "zoning." Zoning varies greatly between varieties, within varieties, and with the environment. Distinct zoning is undesirable.

Many strains of the principal varieties have been developed which are fairly uniform in color.

The leaves are simple and are arranged on a short stem called the crown. They vary from dark purple to light green. The fruit called the "seedball" usually consists of several ovaries, each of which contains a single seed. Since most seedballs contain more than one seed, thinning of beet seedlings is necessary.

Beets are grown in home gardens, in commercial gardens, and for canning. The winter-garden areas of the South and California supply the markets with beets during the winter and spring, and producing districts in the North supply the markets in the summer and fall and grow crops for canning.

RADISH

The enlarged roots of the many varieties and types of radish vary greatly in color, shape, size, season of maturity, and texture of the flesh. Varieties are generally classified according to the time the roots require to attain maturity. Three groups exist: (1) spring, (2) summer, and (3) winter. In general, spring varieties grow quickly and their roots mature in a relatively short time (25 to 30 days); summer varieties grow less quickly and their roots mature in a relatively long time (45 to 50 days); and winter varieties grow slowly and produce large roots which have a long storage life under favorable conditions. The leaves are simple and are arranged in the form of a rosette on a short stem. Later the stem elongates and produces flowers, fruit, and seed.

Radishes are grown in most home gardens, particularly in early spring. The crop has minor importance commercially. Most market gardeners and greenhouse growers produce small quantities to supply local markets, and truck-crop growers in a few localities in the South produce radishes for long distance shipment.

TURNIP AND RUTABAGA

Turnips and rutabagas are closely related and have characteristics in common and characteristics in distinction. In general, the characteristics in common are the necessity for cool weather, moist, moderately fertile, slightly acid soil, and similar cultural requirements. Characteristics in distinction are, for the turnip, green, hairy leaves, an indistinct crown, and a relatively small root; and for the rutabaga, gray-green, nonhairy leaves, a distinct crown, and relatively large roots. With turnips two groups exist: (1) white and (2) yellow. Of these the white-fleshed group is the more widely grown. Within this group certain varieties are grown primarily for their tops for use as greens and other varieties are grown primarily for their fleshy roots. Turnip greens are excellent sources of carotene, thiamin, riboflavin, ascorbic acid, and minerals.

HORSERADISH

Horseradish is grown for thick, fleshy white roots which have a pungent flavor. The fleshy roots are ground, preserved in vinegar, and used as a condiment. The pungent compounds are soluble in water but are volatile; hence, ground horseradish root is kept in sealed containers. The plants form a rosette of long-petioled, narrow, dark green leaves.

The fleshy roots attain their best development in well-drained deep loess and sandy loams. In shallow or "hard" soils the roots become branched, sprangly, and rough. The crop is propagated asexually. Lateral roots $\frac{1}{4}$ to $\frac{1}{2}$ inch thick and from 8 to 12 inches long are saved at the time the main roots are prepared for market, stored during the winter, and planted in the spring about 12 inches apart in rows 36 inches apart in deep friable soil. Since the lateral roots are distinctly polar—producing shoots at the stem end and roots at the root end—the stem end is cut obliquely and the root end is cut square. In this way the planter knows which end to plant uppermost. To obtain smooth, large roots many growers cut away the fleshy laterals from the main root. The principal commercial district is located near St. Louis, Missouri. The deep loess in this vicinity is particularly favorable to the development of large, smooth roots. Other commercial areas exist in New York and New Jersey.

QUESTIONS

1. Name three common characteristics of the vegetable root crops.
2. Young carrots contain less carotene than old carrots. Explain.
3. The development of a large top during the early stages of carrot growth is necessary for the development of highly colored roots. Explain.
4. In Louisiana two crops of carrots are grown each year. The fall crop matures in December and January, and the spring crop matures in May and June. Usually the roots of the fall crop are more highly colored than those of the spring crop. Explain.
5. In general, beets harvested in the summer have poorer color than those harvested in the fall. Explain fully.
6. Usually, the spring varieties of radishes maturing in hot, dry weather tend to become pithy. Explain.
7. Parsnip roots become sweet after exposure to subfreezing temperatures. Explain.
8. Distinguish between turnips and rutabagas.
9. Turnip greens are more widely adapted to growing in southern home gardens than is spinach. Give two reasons.

10. In general, mature root crop vegetables possess a well-developed periderm. They keep satisfactorily in storage pits and banks. Explain.

SWEETPOTATO

Plant Characteristics

Root System. The root system consists of (1) an extensive absorbing system and (2) fleshy roots. The fleshy roots are small at first; later the base of most of them becomes thickened. A few become much thickened and form the edible roots. These enlarged roots have a typical root structure. The young root has an epidermis, a relatively thick cortex, a pericycle, endodermis, and radial bundles. As the root enlarges and matures, a periderm with lenticels takes the place of the epidermis. Cambium arises between the phloem and secondary xylem and phloem is produced in scattered strands.

The function of the periderm, as in the case of the potato, is to keep the all-important water within the fleshy root and to resist the attack of rot-producing organisms. Its formation is influenced by temperature and relative humidity. Investigations have shown that high temperatures, 80 to 85°F, combined with high humidity, 80 to 85 per cent, greatly facilitate periderm formation. Since, at the harvest, the periderm is not fully developed and is easily bruised by handling, the primary purpose of curing is to heal the bruised surfaces and to thicken the skin.

The fleshy root is primarily a storage organ. It contains large quantities of starch which gradually change to sugar. According to the variety, color of the skin varies from creamy white to dark red, and color of the flesh varies from white to salmon pink. Thus, some varieties possess the ability to make carotene, whereas others do not.

Stems and Leaves. The sweetpotato produces a relatively large top which consists of a main axis and primary laterals. The stems vary in length, depending on the variety and the environment. For example, the so-called "vineless" sorts produce stems from 2 to 4 feet in length, and the so-called "viny" sorts produce stems from 6 to 20 feet in length. For the same variety soils with abundant essential elements, particularly nitrogen, combined with optimum moisture and favorable temperature, produce plants with longer stems than soils with moderately abundant nitrogen and low water.

The leaves are long-petioled, simple, cordate, and slightly or deeply lobed depending on the variety. The veins are prominent on the lower surface and usually show the same degree of pigmentation as the stems.

Flowers, Fruit, and Seed. The flowers are perfect, axillary, and resemble those of the morning glory. They occur singly or in clusters on stout peduncles. Color of the corolla varies from white to light purple. In general, there are five stamens clustered around a single superior pistil. The fruit is a round, hairy or nonhairy pod which contains from one to five seeds. The mature seed are black, angular, and have a hard coat. This coat greatly delays germination of the seedling. Recent tests have shown that soaking the seed in concentrated sulfuric acid followed by washing scarifies the seed coat and ensures prompt germination.

Economic Importance and Distribution

The sweetpotato is a major horticultural crop in the southern regions of the United States. Important commercial districts are the San Joaquin and Coachella of California, the Gilmer of east Texas, the Sunset and Oak Ridge of Louisiana, the Edwards of Mississippi, the Mobile Bay of Alabama, the Orangeburg of South Carolina, and the Norfolk-Eastern Shore of Virginia.

Varieties are placed in two groups: (1) varieties grown for table stock and (2) varieties grown for starch and/or feed. Varieties grown for the table are in turn divided into two groups: (1) dry-fleshed and (2) moist-fleshed. Dryness or moistness of the flesh after cooking is due primarily to the type of starch stored in the roots. The dry-fleshed types make a kind of starch which is less sticky and less hydrophilic than the kind of starch made by the moist-fleshed types. The dry-fleshed types are grown principally in the northern part of the sweetpotato belt, and the moist-fleshed types are grown mostly in the southern part. Both types store carotene in the roots; hence, color of the flesh is important.

Growth and Development

Climatic Requirements. The principal climatic factor is temperature. The sweetpotato is primarily a high-temperature crop. In fact, authorities state that no other vegetable crop will stand more heat and few crops require as much. On the other hand, all parts of the plant are particularly sensitive to low temperatures. Below 48°F the leaves turn yellow and the plant dies. At 48°F the leaves remain green, but the plant does not grow. Even a slight touch of frost kills the vines, and exposing the fleshy roots to temperatures at or below 40°F, even for a short time, greatly lowers their keeping quality and plant-producing capacity. Surveys have shown that present-day varieties grow best in regions where the mean summer temperature is from 70 to 75°F, and the frost-free growing period is 150 days or more. Thus, these high temperature requirements and sensitivity to low temperatures explain why sweetpotatoes are grown in the southern regions of the country.

Soils. Most authorities agree that sweetpotatoes, particularly the varieties grown for table stock, thrive best on relatively infertile, well-drained.

moderately to slightly acid sandy loams underlaid with clay. Heavy or highly fertile soil generally produces roots of poor color and quality and induces excessive vine growth. To control soil rot, a serious disease in some districts, the pH of the soil is maintained between 5.5 and 6.0.

Disposition of the Carbohydrates. Suppose line AB represents a growing period of at least 150 days. During the first part of the period the plant develops its system of absorbing roots and stems and leaves. During the later stages of growth the plant develops its fleshy roots. Between these two periods there is a gradual transition from the development of the absorbing roots and tops to the development of the fleshy roots. Consequently, utilization is dominant during the first stages of growth, accumulation is dominant during the later stages, and a gradual transition from utilization to accumulation takes place during the intermediate stage.

	growth of roots, stems,	**transition**	**development and matura-**	
A	**and leaves**	**period**	**tion of fleshy roots**	B

utilization dominant		$\longrightarrow$	accumulation dominant

Culture. In home and commercial gardens sweetpotatoes are propagated asexually by means of the fleshy roots. These fleshy roots contain numerous adventitious buds and large quantities of starch. Under conditions favorable for the development of the buds, the starch changes to sugars which are used in the formation of new cells and in the liberation of energy in the respiration process.

The production of fleshy roots for starting new crops is an important phase of sweetpotato production. As with the potato, numerous varieties are susceptible to certain viruses, and these diseases are carried from one crop to the next in the fleshy roots and from infected plants to healthy plants by certain insects and by mechanical means. Consequently, the use of virus-free "seed" is essential. For this reason, experiment stations in many commercial districts have developed methods of procedure for the production and maintenance of virus-free seed. In this way, a supply of virus-free seed stock is available to the growers at all times.

In general, the fleshy roots are bedded in warm, moist media, usually sandy loam; the young plants, called sprouts or draws, and vine cuttings are set by hand and by machine; and complete mixtures high in potassium are required. The fleshy roots are harvested when they have attained proper size. They are cured naturally if they are harvested during warm weather and artifically, at 80 to 85°F with 80 to 95 per cent relative humidity, if they are harvested during moderately warm weather. They are stored at 55 to 60°F with 75 to 85 per cent relative humidity, and marketed in bushel baskets or crates. The roots are placed on the various markets every month of the year. The Coachella Valley of California and the Mobile Bay district of Alabama ship during July; Texas,

Fig. 21.3. A sweetpotato harvesting scene in Louisiana. The ventilated crates are also used for storage and shipping. (Courtesy, J. A. Cox, Louisiana Agricultural Extension Service.)

Louisiana, Mississippi, Tennessee, Georgia, South Carolina, North Carolina, and Virginia ship from August to April and May; and Delaware, Maryland, and New Jersey ship from December to May. Figure 21.3 shows a sweetpotato harvest scene in Louisiana in 1949.

QUESTIONS

1. Distinguish between the moist-fleshed and the dry-fleshed types of sweetpotatoes.
2. Highly colored roots are more desirable for human consumption than poorly colored roots. Explain.
3. Only roots from high-producing hills should be saved for "seed." Explain.
4. Soils containing abundant nitrogen make for abundant vine growth and low yields of poorly colored roots. Explain.
5. Abundant rainfall during the later stages of growth is likely to crack sweetpotatoes. Explain from the standpoint of outgo and income of water.
6. During the harvest sweetpotatoes should be handled carefully. Explain.
7. What is the prime purpose of curing? Give reasons for your answer.
8. Sweetpotatoes cure best at temperatures varying from 80 to 85°F with high humidity. Explain.
9. Sweetpotatoes lose moisture in curing. They do not decrease in percentage of moisture content. Explain.
10. Growers who store potatoes in banks frequently say they secure excellent results one year and poor results another. Give reasons.

22

VEGETABLE CROPS GROWN FOR THEIR FRUIT OR SEED

Always do a little bit more
than is expected of you,
and you will never fail.

THE SOLANACEOUS CROPS

The Solanaceous crops are tomatoes, peppers, and eggplants. These plants belong to the nightshade family and have similar climate, soil, and cultural requirements.

TOMATO

Plant Characteristics

Root System. The young seedlings develop a taproot and a subordinate system of lateral branches. When plants are transplanted the taproot is destroyed, the laterals become thick and well developed, and adventitious roots arise from the stem located below the surface of the land. In adult plants, the lateral and adventitious roots extend horizontally from 3 to 5 feet. Thus, the tomato develops an extensive root system.

Stems and Leaves. The plant develops a main stem and a system of lateral branches. In all commercial varieties the main stem is erect for the first 1 to 2 feet of growth when it becomes decumbent. In some varieties the stems extend for a small number of nodes only—the so-called determinate sorts; in others they elongate throughout the growing season—the so-called indeterminate sorts. The leaves are alternate, compound, relatively large, well developed, with rather broad leaflets in some varieties,

403

and rather long, narrow leaflets in others. They possess glandular hairs, which when disrupted liberate the odor and stain characteristic of the tomato plant.

Flowers, Fruit, and Seed.   The flowers are borne in clusters on the main axis and on lateral branches. The number of clusters varies from 4 to 100 or more depending on the type and variety. Individual flowers contain a green calyx, a sulfur yellow corolla, five or more stamens, and a single superior pistil. They are mostly self-pollinated. The ripe fruit is a comparatively large, juicy, and fleshy ovary. According to the variety it varies in size (4 to 12 ounces), shape (oblate, globular, or flattened), color (yellow, pink, or red), cell number (5 to 25), and arrangement of cells (regular or irregular). The juice contains moderate quantities of soluble sugars, several organic acids and mineral salts, and relatively large quantities of vitamin C. The seed are imbedded in a jellylike mass of tissue containing large quantities of phosphorus. They are relatively small and are covered with a mass of fine hairs. Under favorable conditions the seed germinates in a short time, from 5 to 10 days.

Economic Importance and Distribution

The tomato is the third most important vegetable crop. It is ranked only by the potato and sweetpotato. It is grown in most home gardens to supply the needs of the family; in most market gardens and many greenhouse establishments to supply the needs of local markets; in the winter-garden areas of the southern regions for long distance shipment; and in the northeast, southeast, and Pacific Coast regions for canning. Principal market-garden areas are located near large cities, such as New York, Philadelphia, Boston, Detroit, Chicago, and Los Angeles. Principal winter-garden areas are east Florida near Miami, west Florida, the Rio Grande Valley and Jacksonville of Texas, the Imperial Valley and Los Angeles of California, the Crystal Springs of Mississippi, the Humboldt of west Tennessee, and the Swedesboro of New Jersey. Principal canning sections are located in southern Indiana, the Sacramento and Santa Clara Valleys of California, the eastern shore of Maryland, southern New Jersey, eastern Virginia, and southeastern Missouri.

Types.   Modern varieties of tomatoes are descended from plants which produced large, oblate, rough, and ribbed fruit. These varieties lack this roughness and ribbing. In general, they are classified according to the length of time the fruits need to become mature. There are three main groups: (1) early, (2) midseason, and (3) late. Under favorable conditions early varieties mature fruit in 90 to 100 days and produce relatively low yields; midseason varieties mature fruit in 100 to 130 days and produce moderately high yields; and late varieties mature fruit in 140 to 160 days and produce high yields. Special varieties have been developed for greenhouse culture.

Growth and Development

Climatic Requirements. The principal environmental factors are temperature and light intensity. Surveys have shown that present-day varieties produce the highest yields in regions characterized by a mean summer temperature of approximately 73°F, combined with moderate light intensity. In the humid section of the United States this mean temperature occurs in southern Indiana, southern Ohio, eastern Maryland, and New Jersey. In regions south of this section the high summer temperatures, combined with the high light intensity, induce a high transpiration rate. Under these conditions the outgo of water frequently becomes greater than the income, a water deficiency exists within the plant, the blossoms drop off, and, as a result, the yields are low. Furthermore, certain diseases are most prevalent. In regions north of this section the mean summer temperature is lower than 73°F and the frost-free growing season is comparatively short.

Soils. The tomato is grown on many soils. When earliness of fruit maturity is important, well-drained sandy loams are preferred. Conversely, when earliness is not important and large yields are essential, clay loams and silt loams are used. In both cases the soil should be well drained and slightly acid.

Disposition of the Carbohydrates. The life of the tomato plant may be divided into two more or less distinct but overlapping stages: (1) seedling and (2) fruiting. The seedling stage begins with germination and continues until the first blossoms are formed, and the fruiting stage lasts for the remainder of the life of the plant. During the seedling stage the plant develops stems, leaves, and roots only, and during the fruiting stage the plant develops stems, leaves, and roots simultaneously with flowers and fruit. Thus, the utilization of carbohydrates is dominant during the seedling stage and very little dominance of utilization and accumulation takes place during the fruiting stage.

The tomato is very sensitive to the environment in which it grows. For example, abundant nitrogen, plus abundant moisture, plus temperatures on the upper half of the optimum range, plus maximum opportunity for carbohydrate manufacture make for abundant vegetative growth and little fruitfulness. This is another way of saying that vegetation is dominant over reproduction. On the other hand, moderately abundant nitrogen, or moderately abundant water, or a relatively low temperature, plus maximum opportunity for carbohydrate manufacture assure moderate vegetative growth and abundant yields. Consequently, the grower should

Fig. 22.1. A mechanical harvester of tomato fruits. (Courtesy, Stanley K. Ries, Michigan State University.)

maintain a fairly even balance between vegetative and reproductive processes to obtain maximum yields. Suppose line AC represents a growing period of 120 to 150 days.

A growth of roots, stems, and leaves **B** $\longrightarrow$	**growth of roots, stems, leaves, flowers, and fruit**	**C**
utilization dominant	**utilization and accumulation processes proceeding in practically equal magnitudes**	

Line AB represents the production of roots, stems, and leaves during the first period of growth. Line BC represents the fruiting period, during which stems, leaves, flowers, and fruit are being produced simultaneously.

Culture. In general, home gardeners, market gardeners, and in fact truck-crop growers, because they are primarily interested in early fruit production, use transplants which have been raised in plant-growing structures. On the other hand, growers of plants for shipments North plant the seed directly in open fields or beds.

Principal practices are as follows: (1) growing the plants in acid, moderately or slightly acid, well-drained sandy loams, silt loams, and clay loams; (2) transplanting the seedlings after the danger of frost is passed, preferably with water or starter solutions; (3) applying commercial fertilizers to maintain steady and moderately vigorous growth throughout the period of fruit production; and (4) controlling insects and diseases in accordance with the latest recommendations.

The fruits are harvested in various degrees of maturity, as green-mature, turning, pink, hard-ripe, and ripe. They are indicated as follows: green-mature—the fruit has attained its full size, but the development of pigment is not apparent; turning—the red pigment is evident at the blossom end; pink—most of the surface of the fruit is pink; hard-ripe—the entire surface of the fruit is red or pink, and the flesh is firm; ripe—color is fully developed, and the fruit is somewhat soft.

Fruit raised in the winter-garden areas of the South are generally picked in the green-mature, turning, or pink stages and are packed in small, flat containers called lugs. Fruit produced by market gardeners are picked when hard-ripe and are packed in various types of baskets. Fruit raised for the cannery are picked in the ripe stage of maturity. In general, fruit ripened on the vine are higher in sugars, organic acids, and vitamin C than those picked in the green-mature stage. Note the harvesting scene of fruit grown for the cannery in Fig. 22.1.

PEPPER

Plant Characteristics.   In bearing plants the root system is moderately extensive. The main axis is erect, woody at the base, and much-branched. The leaves are flat, shiny, simple, and entire. The flowers occur singly in the axils of the leaves. They are both self- and cross-pollinated and have white or purple petals, five stamens, and a single superior pistil. The

Fig. 22.2. A field of Truhart pimiento peppers in Georgia. The insert shows a near-perfect fruit of this variety. (Courtesy, W. H. Greenleaf, Alabama Agricultural Experiment Station.)

fruit is a moderately large, fleshy ovary, dark green when immature, and red or yellow when mature, according to the variety. The outer wall is fleshy and thick, and the inner walls bear placenta, which in turn bear seeds. Both green-mature and mature fruits are high in carotene, the B vitamins, and in ascorbic acid. The seed are flat and disk-shaped and require a fairly high temperature (70 to 75°F) for prompt germination.

Types and Culture. Two types of peppers are grown: (1) sweet and (2) hot, or pungent. Sweet peppers are relatively large and are eaten fresh or cooked. Commercial areas exist in Florida, New Jersey, and Texas. Hot peppers are moderately small and are used for canning, for the making of paprika, and for chili sauce. Peppers for canning are raised in Georgia, Texas, and California; peppers for paprika are raised in Louisiana; and peppers for chili sauce are raised in Mexico and California. In general, the cultural requirements for peppers are essentially the same as those for tomatoes. Note the field and the shape of the pimiento pepper shown in Fig. 22.2.

EGGPLANT

Plant Characteristics. Eggplants develop a moderately extensive root system. As with peppers the main stem of mature plants is woody at the base and is much-branched. The leaves are simple, alternate, large, somewhat angled or lobed. The flowers occur singly or in clusters opposite the

Fig. 22.3. Black Beauty eggplant. (Courtesy, Associated Seed Growers, New Haven, Conn.)

leaves. They are moderately large, hermaphroditic, violet or purple, and mostly self-pollinated. The fruit is a fleshy ovary varying in size (3 to 6 inches in diameter), shape (long, ovate, or pyriform), and color (dark purple, light purple, yellowish, striped, and white), according to the variety. Figure 22.3 shows fruit of Black Beauty, a widely adapted variety.

Types and Culture.   Two distinct types are grown: (1) varieties which develop large, dark purple fruit and (2) varieties which develop small, light purple fruit. For both types climate, soil, and cultural requirements are essentially the same as those for tomato and pepper.

QUESTIONS

1. Tomatoes growing in old barnyards are frequently overvegetative and begin to fruit late in the season. Explain.
2. Tomatoes started in the greenhouse in February require lesser quantities of nitrogen than those started in August. Explain.
3. Tomatoes growing on sandy loam produce lesser yields than those growing on clay loams. Explain.
4. Important tomato-canning states are Indiana, New Jersey, and Maryland. Give reasons.
5. In the extreme South and the extreme North tomato yields are relatively low. Explain.
6. Pruning tomatoes reduces yield per plant, usually increases fruit size, increases blossom end rot, limits the extension of the root system, and permits close planting. Explain fully.
7. What are the similarities and differences in the stems and leaves of the tomato? The pepper? The eggplant?
8. Given two pepper patches of the same variety growing on the same farm. Patch A is growing on bottom land; patch B is growing on hill land. Plants in A were bushy, big, and fruited late. Plants in B were non-bushy, small, and fruited early. Explain fully.
9. The tomato is more popular than the eggplant or pepper. Give two reasons.

THE VINE CROPS

The vine crops are cantaloupes, cucumbers, pumpkins, squash, and watermelons. These crops belong to the cucumber family, and they have similar climate, soil, essential-element, and cultural requirements and are attacked by the same insects and diseases.

COMMON PLANT CHARACTERISTICS

Root System.   The vine crops develop extensive and moderately deep to deep root systems, and as pointed out in Chapter 13 they deposit suberin in the walls of the region of absorption relatively early. Thus, cultivation when necessary should be shallow to avoid cutting the absorbing roots just below the surface, and if the plants are to be transplanted, they should be grown in containers and handled carefully to reduce injury of the root system to a minimum.

Stems and Leaves.   The stem system consists of a main axis and a series of primary and secondary laterals. In adult plants the branches are long and trailing. Consequently, each plant requires a large area of land and planting distances are quite wide. To supply the plant with large quantities of water, the extensive root system is necessary. In addition, the many leaves present a large transpiring surface. Thus, under conditions of rapid transpiration the amount of water lost is large. The leaves are alternate, simple, long-petioled, and palmately veined. Tendrils are formed opposite the leaves. These tendrils twine around objects and help to anchor the vines to the surface of the land.

Flowers, Fruit, and Seed.   The vine crops are monoecious and andromonoecious. The monoecious crops develop flowers of one sex only. Both male and female flowers occur on the same plant. Andromonoecious crops develop hermaphroditic and staminate flowers on the same plant. In all cases the flowers are axillary and develop a moderately large, yellow corolla. These crops are wholly insect-pollinated, the honeybee being the principal carrier. The student will recall the discussion on the effect of temperature and wet weather on the activity of honeybees in the orchard. In like manner, if bees are inactive in cucumber, cantaloupe, squash, pumpkin, and watermelon fields, yields are likely to be low.

The fruit is an enlarged fleshy structure consisting of ovary, the inner portion, and receptacle, the rind. The seed is relatively large, elliptical, with a hard coat. Under favorable conditions the seed germinates in from two to five days.

Disposition of the Carbohydrates.   The life cycle is divided into two stages: (1) seedling and (2) blossoming and fruiting. As with other crops, the seedling stage begins with germination and ends when the first blossom develops. The fruiting stage begins when the first blossoms are produced and ends when the last fruit has matured. Like the tomato, pepper, and eggplant, during the seedling stage the plants are developing roots, stems, and leaves, and during the fruiting stage they are developing roots, stems, and leaves simultaneously with the development of flowers and fruit. Thus, carbohydrates made during the seedling stage are utilized for root and top growth, and the carbohydrates made during the fruiting stage are used for the development both of root, stems, and leaves and of flowers and fruit.

Suppose line AC represents a growing period of 100 to 180 days. Line AB represents the period of stem and leaf growth only. Line BC represents the period when stems and leaves and flowers and fruit are produced simultaneously.

A	growth of stems, leaves, and roots	B ⟶	growth of stems, leaves and roots, and flowers and fruit	C
	utilization dominant		utilization and accumulation taking place together	

The student should remember that the length of the seedling stage varies with the crop. For example, in average weather cucumber varieties for pickling will begin to produce fruit from 40 to 50 days after the seed are planted, whereas watermelons require from 80 to 100 days to produce the first fruit.

CANTALOUPE

The leaves are simple, alternate, and palmately lobed. The fruit varies in size, shape, degree of ribbing and netting of the rind, color, texture, and sweetness of the flesh.

Economic Importance and Producing Centers. The cantaloupe is the most valuable vegetable crop belonging to the cucumber family. In general, there are two types: (1) the netted and (2) the winter. Netted melons have a netted skin, shallow sutures and ribs, loose-textured flesh, and keep for a short time in storage. On the other hand, winter melons have a smooth or ridged skin, firm-textured flesh, and keep for a long time in storage. Of these types the netted is the more important commercially. Important commercial districts are (1) the early—west coast of Mexico, Imperial Valley of California, and Rio Grande Valley of Texas; (2) the intermediate—Salt River Valley of Arizona, Tulare district of California, winter-garden region of south Texas, and Edisto River Valley of South Carolina; and (3) the late—eastern shore of Maryland, Delaware, southern Indiana, northern Arkansas, and southwestern Michigan.

Culture. In general, home gardens and commercial fields may be established by planting the seed directly in the soil where the crop is to mature or by planting the seed in containers for the growing of transplants in plant-growing structures. Planting seed directly is generally practiced in regions with long, warm, frost-free periods, as for example in the southeastern United States, and planting seed in containers is generally practiced in regions with short, warm, frost-free periods, as for example in the northern United States.

Other pertinent practices are transplanting when the weather is warm and all danger of frost is passed, since the plants cannot be hardened-off to withstand frost; using moderately or slightly acid, well-drained, sandy loams; maintaining the moderately vigorous condition throughout the fruiting period; and controlling insects and diseases in accordance with the latest recommendations.

In general, the fruits are picked when they are mature. At this stage of ripeness they have attained their highest quality, flavor, and edibility. An accurate measure of quality and flavor is the percentage of total solids in the juice of the fruit. Investigations have shown that the percentage of total solids is positively associated with sugar content, flavor, and edibility. In other words, melons with a high total solids content (9 to 10 per cent or more) possess a higher percentage of sugars and are sweeter than melons with a low percentage of total solids. At present, the percentage of total solids in the juice is used as a standard test for determining maturity of cantaloupes in many producing districts.

Promptness in picking, hauling to the packing shed, grading, and placing the fruit under comparatively low temperature is essential, since a high respiration rate will rapidly deplete the sugars in the fruit. To provide necessary ventilation cantaloupes are usually packed in crates with solid ends and slatted sides. Various sizes are used.

CUCUMBER

The leaves are simple, alternate, and angular. The staminate flowers occur in clusters, and the pistillate flowers occur singly or occasionally in groups of two or more. The female flowers may be distinguished from the male flowers by the young ovary located in back of the petals. Under field conditions the male flowers appear one to two weeks before the first female flower and are produced in greater numbers than the female flowers. Since the blossoms and fruits are borne in the leaf axils, continuous growth of the stems and leaves is necessary for high yields. In general, the fruits are elongated or cylindrical. They vary in size (long, moderately long, and short), color of the rind (light to dark green), and color of the spines (white or black).

Economic Importance and Producing Centers. In the United States two separate industries exist: (1) the slicing and (2) the pickling. Distinct adapted varieties of cucumbers have been developed for each industry. Varieties for slicing produce long, cylindrical, dark green fruits with crisp flesh, and varieties for pickling produce small fruits which are adapted for preservation in salt brine.

Cucumbers for slicing are grown from seed to harvest in greenhouses, as for example in forcing establishments; or the plants are started in greenhouses and transplanted to cold frames, as for example in the many market-garden districts in the northern United States; or they are grown entirely in open fields, as for example in the truck-crop districts of the southern United States. Principal producing districts are

Fig. 22.4. A field of cucumbers grown for pickling in south Mississippi. (Courtesy, W. S. Anderson, Mississippi State University.)

central Florida, southern Texas, southeastern South Carolina, eastern North Carolina, and the Norfolk section of Virginia.

Cucumbers for pickling are grown entirely in fields. For the continuous production of fruits, harvesting is thorough and systematic. If a fruit is allowed to mature on any given stem, growth of that stem will cease or slow down, and yields will be accordingly reduced. The fruits are usually graded into two or three sizes and delivered to the salting station for preservation in brine. Principal producing districts are located in the southern peninsula of Michigan, Wisconsin, Indiana, Ohio, and southern Mississippi. Districts producing lesser quantities are located in Virginia, New York, North Carolina, Illinois, and California. Figure 22.4 shows a field of cucumbers grown for pickling near Wiggins, Mississippi.

PUMPKIN

Pumpkins belong to two botanical species: *Cucurbita pepo* and *Cucurbita moschata*. Varieties of *Cucurbita pepo* are divided into two groups: (1) those which develop short, erect stems and mature their fruits in a relatively short time, and (2) those which develop long, 6 to 20 feet, trailing stems and mature their fruits in a relatively long time. Both groups have prickly, harsh-textured, deeply notched leaves and a five-sided longitudinally grooved fruit stem. Varieties of *Cucurbita moschata* develop long, trailing stems, soft-textured leaves, and a five-sided indistinctly grooved fruit stem. In addition, these varieties develop white spots at the junction of the veins of the leaves. Varieties of both types are usually monoecious. The staminate flowers have long, slender stalks, and the pistillate flowers have short, thick stalks. Both are axillary and occur singly. The fruiting habit is like that of the cantaloupe. As with the cantaloupe, there are periods of fruit setting alternated by periods of female flower abortion. As with others of the cucumber family, honeybees are the principal agents of pollination. The fruits are fleshy and vary greatly in size, shape, and color. Carbohydrates are stored in comparatively large quantities, and the yellow-fleshed varieties contain carotene.

Types and Culture. As stated previously, pumpkins are divided into two types: (1) bush and (2) trailing. With the bush type, the fruits are usually harvested when immature, and the cultural requirements are practically the same as for cantaloupes. With the trailing types, the fruits are harvested when fully mature. Mature fruits are high in sugars and keep well in storage. The cultural requirements are the same as for watermelons.

SQUASH

Squash belongs to one botanical species only, *Cucurbita maxima.* The plants have long, trailing stems and smooth, soft-textured leaves. The fruit stalk is round, soft, and spongy. The fruits are large and fleshy and contain large quantities of carbohydrates. Cultural requirements are practically the same as for watermelons.

Pumpkins and squash are grown for fresh consumption, for canning, and for drying. The fresh product is grown in home and market gardens. The product for canning and drying is grown chiefly in California.

WATERMELON

The stems are angular in cross section and the leaves are divided into three or four lobes. The flowers occur singly in the axils of the leaves and usually open at sunrise and close on the afternoon of the same day. As with other members of the cucurbits, the principal agent of pollination is the honeybee. According to the variety, the fruits vary greatly in size (5 to 40 pounds), shape (round, oval, oblong, or cylindrical), color and shipping ability of rind (white, black, mottled, or striped), and in color and sweetness of the flesh.

Economic Importance and Producing Regions. The watermelon has been grown in some parts of the United States since about 1600. To supply the various markets at present, watermelon farmers produce from 70 to 80 million melons per year. The principal commercial districts are located in the Southeast and Southwest—southern Georgia, southeast Texas, northern Florida, southeastern South Carolina, southern Alabama, and eastern North Carolina. Figure 22.5 shows a field of watermelons in south

Fig. 22.5. A Black Diamond watermelon field in south Georgia in July, 1949. (Courtesy, Otis Woodard, The Coastal Plain Experiment Station, Georgia.)

Georgia in 1949. Note that vines have been placed over the fruit to prevent sun scald.

Marketing. Market requirements vary. Some markets require an elongated fruit; others a somewhat round fruit. Some markets demand relatively small melons; and others require relatively large melons. If your section raises watermelons for long distance shipment, study the characteristics of the main variety, particularly from the standpoint of color of flesh and seed, shipping ability of the rind, and texture and quality of the flesh. Does your community ship a standardized product?

QUESTIONS

1. Distinguish between netted melons (cantaloupes) and winter melons.
2. Outline a cultivation program for cantaloupe culture for your region.
3. If the weather is cold and wet during the blossoming season, very little pollination is likely to take place. Explain.
4. Given two cucumber plants. On plant A two fruits are allowed to remain on the vine until they are ripe; on plant B all fruits are picked while immature. Which plant produces the greater number of fruits? Give reasons.
5. Nonsystematic, careless harvesting of pickling and slicing cucumbers will reduce yields. Explain.

6. In general, abundant water and moderate supplies of fertilizers are necessary throughout the fruiting period. Explain.
7. In the British Isles cucumbers and cantaloupes are raised entirely in plant-growing structures; in the northern United States the seedlings are raised in plant-growing structures and transplanted to the field; and in the southern United States they are raised entirely in the field. Explain.
8. Watermelon fruits are not harvested until they are ripe. Explain.
9. In general, fruit should be picked in early morning. Explain.
10. Given two watermelons. Melon A was exposed to sunshine for four hours after picking; melon B was kept in shade. Which watermelon would you prefer? Give your reasons.
11. Ripe melons from healthy vines remain sweet if kept on ice. They lose their sweetness if kept in a warm room. Explain.
12. Differentiate between pumpkins and squashes.

SWEET CORN

Plant Characteristics

Root System.   The root system consists of two parts: (1) the absorbing and (2) the buttress. The absorbing roots are adventitious and very extensive. Investigations have shown that the roots of mature plants have a lateral spread of 4 to 5 feet and a vertical spread of 6 to 8 feet depending on soil conditions. The buttress roots arise from the first or second nodes above the soil in the form of a whorl. They proceed outward and downward and penetrate the soil, thus providing for additional anchorage and wind resistance and additional absorbing roots.

Stems and Leaves.   The stem system consists of primary stems and secondary stems. The secondary stems are frequently called suckers. Under field conditions the primary stem bears the staminate and pistillate inflorescences, and the secondary stems may or may not bear flowers. An individual leaf consists of three distinct parts: (1) sheath, (2) ligule, and (3) blade. The sheath is the basal portion of the leaf which is wrapped around the stem; the ligule is attached to the top of the sheath and fits tightly around the stem; and the blade is comparatively long, parallel-veined, and pointed.

Flowers and Fruit.   Sweet corn is monoecious. The staminate inflorescence contains a large number of small flowers, terminates the primary stem, and is called the tassel. Each staminate flower has three stamens and a rudimentary pistil. The pistillate inflorescence also contains a large number of flowers, terminates a short lateral, and when mature is called the ear. The internodes of each lateral are very short. Thus, the sheaths of the leaves overlap and form the husk of the ear. Each pistillate flower has a single pistil and rudimentary stamens. The ovary is the immature kernel and the style is long and branched near the tip. These styles are called the "silk" and protrude through the top of the husk to catch pollen grains which are carried by gravity or wind. Corn is mostly cross-pollinated.

Growth and Development

Climatic Requirements. The principal climatic factors are temperature and water supply. Like many other crops, sweet corn is greatly affected by temperature. Investigations have shown that the higher the temperature between 50 and 90°F, the greater is the rate of growth and the shorter is the time necessary for the plant to attain a particular stage of maturity. Thus, the higher the temperature, within these limits, the shorter is the time from the seedling stage to tasseling or from the premilk to the canning stage of the kernels.

A uniform moisture supply is necessary for rapid growth and development. If the moisture supply is low and the weather is hot, water deficits take place, the manufacture of food declines, and yields are low.

Soils. Sweet corn is grown in a wide variety of soils. Growers for early market usually plant on well-drained sandy loams. Growers for the late market or for the cannery usually select silt or clay loams or well-drained bottom land.

Disposition of the Carbohydrates. Sweet corn has the determinate type of growth, since the main axis and the lateral branches terminate with an inflorescence—the staminate inflorescence on the main axis and the pistillate inflorescence on the lateral branches. As is the case with other plants which have the determinate type of growth, the vegetative and reproductive phases are more or less distinct. Consequently, the plants should be grown so that a comparatively large, deep green photosynthetic surface develops, which in turn is necessary for the development of the extensive and moderately deep root system and for the growth and maturation of the ears. Suppose line AD indicates a growing period of 70 to 150 days. The first part, AB, indicates the period of stem and leaf growth; line BC indicates the period of flower development, pollen shedding, and fertilization; and line CD indicates the period of ear formation and development.

growth of roots, stems, and leaves		development of flowers	formation and development of ears	
A utilization dominant	B		C accumulation dominant	D

Types. Two types are grown: (1) certain strains and varieties of field corn and (2) true sweet corn. Within the past decade many sweet corn hybrids have been developed. In general, these hybrids are more vigorous and disease resistant and produce higher yields than the non-hybrids. The principal states supplying long distance markets are Tennessee, Alabama, Florida, Georgia, and Mississippi. Principal canning states are Illinois, Minnesota, Indiana, Ohio, and Maryland.

Culture. The "seed" are planted by hand or by hand-operated or power-drawn planters. In general, market gardeners use hand machines, and canners or growers of large quantities of ears use power-drawn machines. The seed is planted in hills or in drills. The rate of seeding depends on (1) the time of planting, (2) the spacing, and (3) the variety. In general, the earlier the seed is planted, or the colder the soil, or the closer the spacing, the greater is the rate of planting. Ordinarily, field corn varieties require lesser rates of seeding than the true sweet corn varieties. This is true particularly if the weather is cold and wet at the time seeding is made. From 8 to 12 pounds of seed are usually required per acre.

A practice in sweet corn culture similar to top pruning is known as suckering. Suckering consists in removing the side shoots or secondary stems which grow from the base of the plant. In the early days of commercial sweet corn production, this practice was very common. Growers believed that suckering produced earlier and greater yields and larger ears than nonsuckering. Recent experiments have shown that suckering decreases the total yield and does not appreciably increase the yield of the first harvest and the size of the ear. In addition, suckering markedly decreases the yield of the stover. How does suckering decrease yield? Suckering removes secondary stems. It therefore removes a certain number of leaves. In other words, suckering reduces the leaf area for carbohydrate manufacture. The reduction in the leaf area reduces the

Fig. 22.6. *A sweet corn field in the Lake Okeechobee district of south Florida in early spring, 1949. The low-flying plane was used to keep birds from eating the corn. (Courtesy, R. V. Allison, Florida Agricultural Experiment Station.)*

amount of carbohydrates made, which in turn reduces the growth and yield. Figure 22.6 shows a field of mature plants of sweet corn in early spring in south Florida.

The ears are harvested when the kernels are in the milk stage. When the kernels are young and small, the juice is clear and watery. As they become larger, more plump, and older, the juice becomes milky, and this is known as the milk stage. Finally, the juice becomes doughy, and this is known as the dough stage. At the premilk stage the kernels are very sweet, but they are small and generally lack plumpness. At the milk stage they are also sweet, but they have attained full size and plumpness. At the dough stage most of the sugars have changed to starch. Many growers have found that when the silks first become brown and the ears feel plump, the ears are ready to be picked. For long distance shipment the ears are packed in ventilated crates or in mesh bags and shipped during warm weather in refrigerated cars.

OKRA

Plant Characteristics.   The root system is extensive, and the stem consists of an erect axis and primary laterals which become woody with age. The leaves are ovate and lobed. The flowers are axillary, large, showy, and contain both stamens and pistils. The fruits are elongated, relatively large pods. They vary in color, degree of ribbing, and pubescence according to the variety and are consumed in the immature state. When mature, the pods are hard and woody. The seed are relatively large and dark in color. The optimum temperature for germination alternates between 75 and 85°F.

Growth and Development.   As with vine crops, the type of growth is indeterminate. Thus, the life of the plant may be divided into two stages: (1) seedling and (2) flowering and fruiting. During the seedling stage the plant is developing roots, stems, and leaves, and during the flowering and fruiting stage the plant is developing roots, stems, and leaves, together with flowers and fruit. There is a marked correlation between the growth of stems and leaves and the production of flowers and fruit. If the pods with their large number of seeds are allowed to mature, growth of stems and leaves is retarded. If they are harvested when immature, vegetative growth proceeds until the plants are killed by frost. Thus, the harvesting of okra should be thorough and systematic. Note the cyclic development of the fruit of the plant in Fig. 22.7.

Culture and Uses.   Okra is grown in the southeastern United States to a greater extent than elsewhere. In this region, because of its adaptation to high temperatures and high light intensities, it is a standard home-garden vegetable. Limited quantities are grown for canning. The pods are used

Fig. 22.7. Two cycles of fruit on Clemson Spineless okra. (Courtesy, R. A. McGinty, Clemson College).

principally in soups and stews. They contain moderate quantities of carotene and thiamin.

The pods are harvested usually when they are from 1 to 5 inches in length. At this stage the pods are young, tender, and crisp.

QUESTIONS

1. From the standpoint of human nutrition the yellow varieties of sweet corn are superior to the white varieties. Explain.
2. On self-mulching loams sweet corn need not be cultivated after it is half grown. Explain.
3. On sandy loams in New York tests have shown that removal of suckers (a type of pruning) has decreased yields. Explain.
4. In the home garden sweet corn should be planted in blocks—not in a single row. Explain.
5. Many true sweet corn varieties have loose husks; hence, they are easily

penetrated by the corn earworm. They are not adapted to the South. Explain.

6. A home gardener wants to know how to harvest sweet corn so that it will remain sweet. Outline two methods.
7. For what is okra grown?
8. Okra is grown chiefly in the South. Explain.
9. For continuous fruit production a uniform fertilizer and water supply is necessary. Explain.
10. Given two lots of okra. Lot A is harvested carelessly; marketable pods are missed by the pickers. Lot B is harvested carefully; marketable pods are not missed by the pickers. Which lot will produce the higher yields? Explain.
11. Given two lots of okra. Lot A was irrigated; lot B was not irrigated. A drought of three weeks occurred during the fruiting period. Which lot produced the greater yields? Explain.
12. Harvesting of the immature pods should be thorough and systematic. Explain.

VEGETABLE LEGUMES

The vegetable crop legumes are snap beans, lima beans, certain varieties of soybean, and cowpea and garden pea. All are warm-season crops with the exception of the garden pea, which is distinctly a cool-season crop.

Common Plant Characteristics

Root System. The root system consists of a taproot and extensively branched laterals. These laterals may extend horizontally from 1 to 5 feet. Thus, the root system is extensive and widespread. Like other members of the legume family, vegetable legumes have roots which support the growth and development of nitrogen-fixing bacteria called *Rhizobium*. These bacteria possess the ability to use nitrogen from the air. This nitrogen is combined with sugars by the bacteria to form amino acids which are used by the bacteria and the bean plant. Unless the soil contains abundant quantities of an adapted strain of these bacteria, inoculation with pure cultures is generally advisable. Tests in Washington and Wisconsin, where large quantities of garden peas are grown, have shown that good strains of bacteria have increased yields growing on land which had previously been planted to peas. Growers often test the effect of inoculation by comparing the yield of treated and untreated strips planted side by side in the same field.

Flowers, Fruit, and Seed. The inflorescence is a raceme in the case of beans and cowpea and consists of single or two flowers in the case of garden pea. Individual flowers are moderately large and showy and possess the characteristics of the legume family. The large upper petal is called the standard, the two lateral petals are called the wings, and the two lower petals are called the keel. The keel encloses 10 stamens and a single pistil.

Both self- and cross-pollination take place. Honeybees and bumblebees possess the ability to enter the flowers and cause cross-pollination. The fruit is a one-celled, elongated pod called a legume.[1] The pod varies in shape (flat or round, straight or curved), length (2 to 8 inches or more), color (yellow, yellowish-green, green, and dark green), and number of seeds (3 to 10 or more, depending on the kind of crop and variety). The seeds are relatively large, consist mostly of two well-developed seed leaves —the cotyledons—and are highly nutritious, since they contain large quantities of starch, proteins, and relatively large quantities of thiamin, riboflavin, calcium, and iron.

Disposition of the Carbohydrates.   From the standpoint of type of growth, the vegetable crop legumes may be divided into two groups: (1) determinate and (2) indeterminate. The determinate types—the so-called dwarf varieties—extend their stems for a short distance only, usually until the first inflorescence appears; and the indeterminate types—the so-called pole varieties—extend their stems for a long distance, usually until growing conditions become unfavorable. Thus, with determinate types vegetative processes are dominant from the time of seedling emergence to the development of the first flower, and reproductive processes are dominant during the remainder of the life of the plant; and with indeterminate types vegetative processes are dominant from the time of seedling emergence to the development of the first blossoms, and neither vegetative nor reproductive processes are dominant during the remainder of the life of the plant. Soil management, fertilization, and cultivation practices are handled accordingly.

SNAP BEAN

Snap beans are of two types: the dwarf and the pole. Dwarf varieties produce short, erect, much-branched, determinate stems, and pole varieties develop long, twined, rarely branched indeterminate stems. The leaves of both types consist of three leaflets. These leaflets are either broad, ovate, or long and narrow, and vary from light green to dark green according to the variety. The pods vary in shape (flat, oval, or round in cross section and straight or curved in longitudinal section) and color (yellow, light green, or dark green), according to the variety.

---

[1] The members of the legume family are called legumes not because their roots support the growth of *Rhizobium,* but because they produce a type of fruit called a legume.

Economic Importance and Producing Centers

Important producing districts for long distance shipment are located in central Florida, March to June (spring crop) and August to November (fall crop), near Charleston, South Carolina, March to June (spring crop) and September to November (fall crop), near Norfolk, Virginia (April to June), central Mississippi (May to June), and southern Louisiana (April to June). Important canning areas exist in New York, Maryland, and California.

Culture

Of the two types the dwarf is the more important commercially. Throughout the United States two crops are grown annually: the spring and the fall. Spring crops are grown in practically all regions of the United States and both spring and fall crops are grown in southern regions. In general, spring crops are planted immediately after the last killing frost in the spring, and fall crops are planted 50 to 60 days before the average date of the first killing frost in the fall. To avoid the spreading of anthracnose and bacterial blight, cultivation, when necessary, is done when the foliage is dry.

Snap beans are harvested by hand. From two to five pickings are sufficient to harvest the dwarf varieties, but several more pickings are necessary for the pole varieties. In any case the pods are picked when they have reached their full size, but when the seeds are only about one-fourth mature. Shipping containers are bushel hampers, bushel crates, and

Fig. 22.8. A snap bean harvesting scene in south Florida. (Courtesy, R. V. Allison, Florida Agricultural Experiment Station.)

½-bushel baskets. For long distance shipment during hot weather, snap beans are always shipped under refrigeration. Figure 22.8 shows a harvest scene of snap beans in south Florida.

LIMA BEAN

As with snap beans, there are dwarf and pole types. However, unlike snap beans, there are two groups within each type: (1) small-seeded and (2) large-seeded. Plants of the small-seeded type have erect stems, glabrous, nonhairy leaves, and small, numerous pods; whereas plants of the large-seeded types have large, thick leaves, and large, relatively few pods.

Economic Importance and Distribution

Lima beans are grown in home gardens, in market gardens for local markets, in certain trucking regions in the Southeast for long distance shipment, in certain areas for canning and freezing, and on the coast of California for dehydration. In this region both the small-seeded and the large-seeded types are raised. About 400,000 hundred-pound bags of the small-seeded type and 800,000 hundred-pound bags of the large-seeded type are produced annually.

Culture

The cultural requirements for lima beans are similar to those for snap beans. For green-shelled bean production the bush types are planted in hills or in drills, and the pole types are usually planted in hills and are supported by stakes, poles, or wire trellis. The fertilizer is applied below or on the side of the seed, and the pods are harvested when they begin to turn yellow. For dry-shell bean production both types are planted in drills, and the pole varieties are allowed to spread on the land without support. In California the crop is grown during the dry season, and the dry soil does not injure the pods.

EDIBLE SOYBEAN

Soybeans are grown primarily for feed, as green-manuring crops, for oil, and for the manufacture of plastics. Within recent years varieties suitable for human consumption have become available. The plant characteristics of soybeans are similar to those of other beans. The root system is extensive and supports the growth of *Rhizobium*. The stems are erect, become woody with age, and the three leaflets are hairy and broad. The pods are small and contain from two to three seeds. Individual flowers are relatively small and white or purple. According to certain authorities, soybeans have the same climatic, soil, and cultural requirements as snap beans. Although soybeans are grown extensively in China for human consumption, at present the crop is not widely grown for this purpose in the United States. Recent investigations have shown marked varietal differences in yield, flavor, and palatability of the seed.

COWPEA [2]

Cowpeas are beans because they possess the flower and trifoliate leaves which are characteristic of beans. Cowpeas are grown for many purposes: for hay, ensilage, pasturage, soil improvement, and human consumption. Cowpeas are primarily warm-season crops. The plants are particularly adapted to the hot summers of the South. In home gardens the seed is planted from 2 to 4 inches apart to rows 3, $3\frac{1}{2}$, or 4 feet apart. Suitable soils are well-drained, moderately to slightly acid sandy loams and loams. Soils containing large quantities of available nitrogen are likely to induce the production of excessive vine growth and low yields. For human consumption the seeds are used either in the fresh or dry state.

GARDEN PEA [2]

Garden peas differ from beans in that the stems are hollow and the leaves are pinnately compound with one, two, or three pairs of leaflets and a branched terminal tendril and large stipules; the flowers are borne singly or in pairs on long stalks; the pods are nonconstricted, and the seed is round and either smooth or wrinkled when dry.

Economic Importance and Producing Centers

Garden peas are grown in home gardens, in market gardens, in winter-garden areas for long distance shipment, and in fields for canning and drying. Principal winter-garden areas are located in California, Arizona, central and southern Mississippi, the coastal plain section of South Carolina and North Carolina, the eastern shore of Virginia, and Long Island, New York. For canning the peas are sown with grain drills, the plants are hauled in bulk to a viner or shelling machine, the peas are collected in crates for immediate transportation to the cannery, and the

[2] In the southern United States garden peas are usually referred to as English peas, and edible varieties of cowpeas are called southern peas.

Fig. 22.9. The shelling of garden peas for the cannery in Indiana. Small crates are used to hold the shelled peas, and the vines are stacked for use as feed.

vines are stacked for use as feed. Figure 22.9 shows a viner or shelling station in the Middle West. Principal producing states are Wisconsin—with nearly one-third of the total acreage—followed by Minnesota, New York, Washington, Montana, Oregon, Maryland, Illinois, and Michigan in the order named.

Culture

The climatic factor which gives the grower the greatest concern and which generally limits the production of peas in any particular part of the country is temperature. This crop is a native of, and particularly adapted to, the temperate regions of the old world. The growing seasons of England and northeastern Europe are particularly favorable and almost ideal for the growth and development of the garden pea plants. In the United States there are very few districts which have a growing season similar to that of these countries. Perhaps the growing season of the Puget Sound district of western Washington most closely approaches the climate of these countries. In this district large quantities of peas are raised for seed. Other regions which are less favorable but produce profitable crops are the New England states and the northern portions of the states bordering Canada. For the remainder of the country periods of favorable temperature are short and uncertain. In the corn belt and in the southern regions, early varieties of peas can be grown in the cool weather of spring, but the late or tall varieties are destroyed by the heat of summer. The cool weather in the fall is again favorable for growing peas, but this period of favorable weather is not sufficiently long for the maturation of the crop before frosts occur. Furthermore, the rainfall in the fall is usually insufficient for the rapid growth of the crop.

Peas for home use and for the fresh market are picked by hand. The pods are picked when the peas are fully developed and when the percentage of sugars in the seeds is the highest. Immediately after the peas are picked the sugars in the seed begin to change to starch. The rapidity of this change is a function of temperature. In other words, the higher the temperature for any given period, the greater is the transformation. In addition, high temperatures induce a greater rate of respiration than low temperatures. To retain quality and sweetness peas are, therefore, harvested during the cool portion of the day, handled quickly in grading and packing, and in hot weather are shipped under refrigeration.

QUESTIONS

1. Botanically speaking, what is the fruit of the bean and garden pea?
2. In general, beans and peas require smaller applications of nitrogen than most other vegetable crops. Explain.
3. State the two types of snap beans.
4. Two crops of dwarf snap beans are raised annually in the South; only one crop is raised in the North. Explain.
5. Beans should be planted shallowly and in loose, friable soil. Explain.
6. Usually beans are extremely vegetative and nonfruitful when grown in highly fertile soil. Explain.
7. In general, the light green–leaved varieties produce lesser yields than the dark green sorts. Explain.
8. Pole varieties of snap beans are grown more extensively in the southern regions than in the northern regions. Explain.
9. In general, the commercial fertilizer bill for growing snap beans is less than for many other vegetable crops. Explain.
10. What types of beans are grown in your community? Are they grown for long distance market, local market, or the cannery? Give reasons.
11. Name the two types of lima beans.
12. During hot, dry weather the Henderson Bush lima develops a deeper root system and produces higher yields than the Fordhook. What is the relation of a deep root system to the yielding ability of the crop under conditions of high transpiration?
13. Gardeners use brush for tall peas and stakes or poles for pole beans. Explain.
14. Peas for early market are raised in the extreme South. Peas for canning are raised in Wisconsin and the eastern shore of Maryland. Explain fully.

15. In general, the earlier the planting of garden peas in the southern United States with due consideration to frost, the greater is the yield. Explain fully.
16. Peas produce higher yields in cool weather than in warm weather. Explain.
17. How would you determine whether pea seed should be inoculated?
18. Your mother wants information on harvesting peas so that they will retain their sweetness. Outline two methods.
19. Ice is placed in the center of packages of peas shipped long distances. Explain.

MISCELLANEOUS CROPS

CULTIVATED MUSHROOMS

Plant Characteristics. Cultivated mushrooms are special varieties of the common meadow mushroom, *Agaricus campestris*. Cultivated mushrooms are saprophytic fungi; that is, they live on dead organic matter. As with higher plants, the plant body of mushrooms may be divided into two distinct parts: (1) the vegetative portion, analogous to the roots, stems, and leaves of green plants, and (2) the reproductive part, analogous to the flowers, fruit, and seed. The vegetative part consists of fine, white threads, each about 0.001 and 0.002 inch in thickness, collectively called mycelia. The reproductive part consists of the edible portion and has three distinct parts: (1) the convex cap, or pileus, (2) the stalk, or stipe, and (3) the annulus. The cap consists largely of radiating plates of spore-bearing tissue called gills. The stalk supports the cap, and the annulus protects the gills when the fruit is small. As the cap grows, the annulus is stretched and finally ruptures, giving the appearance of a collarlike structure around the stipe. The function of the mycelia is to absorb water and food nutrients from the compost in which they grow. The function of the fruiting body is to produce spores which are analogous to the seed of higher plants.

Culture. In the United States most cultivated mushrooms are produced in specially constructed houses by growing the mycelia in composts consisting of horse manure, from grain-fed animals, mixed with wheat straw.

The management of mushroom houses is as exacting as that of greenhouses. The principal factors concerned are temperature, relative humidity, and the moisture supply of the compost. As with higher plants, mushrooms have an optimum temperature range for growth. This range is from 65 to 70°F for the development of the mycelia and from 45 to 55°F for the development of the fruiting bodies. Temperatures above 65°F during the fruiting period cause a serious reduction in yields.

The relative humidity is maintained usually between 70 and 80 per cent. If the humidity drops below 70 per cent, the casing soil dries out rather rapidly and the mushrooms become tough and leathery. However, if the relative humidity is maintained above 80 per cent the "spot" disease is likely to become serious.

A uniformly moist compost and casing soil are necessary at all times for high production. Uniformity is accomplished by frequent sprinkling of the beds and by a slow but gradual loss of water from the beds. Excessive water favors the development of green mold and causes the small mushrooms to turn brown and die. If, however, the compost is dry, few mushrooms will develop and these will form beneath the soil layer.

Mushrooms are gathered about 12 hours before the annulus, or veil, would normally rupture. The stalk is pulled from the mycelia and then removed from the cap. The caps are then graded and packed in 1-pound cartons. Mushrooms are usually sold by weight.

HERBS

Herbs are grown for their flavor and fragrance, particularly for their use in the preparation and serving of cooked foods for the table. They comprise a miscellaneous group. Some are annuals; some are biennials; and others are perennials. Some are grown for their leaves, some for their flower parts, and others for their seed. In general, a few plants of any one kind will supply the needs of an individual family. A list of some of the common herbs follows:

Herbs grown for their leaves
Perennials—balm, catnip, lavender, peppermint, spearmint, rosemary, sage, and thyme
Annuals—summer savory and sweet marjoram

Herb grown for its flower heads
Annual—dill

Herbs grown for their seeds
Biennial—caraway
Annuals—anise and coriander

QUESTIONS

1. In what respects are mushrooms similar to higher plants? In what respects are they different?
2. From your knowledge of the effect of temperature above the optimum range for growth, how do high temperatures lower the yield of mushrooms?
3. In the home garden would you place the annual and perennial herbs in the same location? Give reasons for your answer.

23

COMMERCIAL
FLORICULTURE

Habits and customs differ,
but all people have the love
of flowers in common.
Chinese proverb

Most people like flowers. In general, flowers are used to express human sentiments and to beautify the environment. Since in this age of specialization many people have neither the time nor the facilities nor the "know-how" required for raising flowers, they buy flowers. Most flowers are sold for use at weddings, funerals, social functions, and as gifts.

The initiation and development of commercial production coincided with the growth of cities and the social activities of the people. According to Laurie and Kiplinger, the growing of flowers for sale in the United States began in the vicinity of Philadelphia during the early part of the nineteenth century.[1] At first only outdoor gardens and fields were used. Later, as the demand for "out-of-season" flowers increased, greenhouses were erected. Still later, as happened in the growing fruit and vegetable crop industries, the services of the middleman became necessary. Thus, at present, there are wholesale florists who are primarily production specialists or commission merchants, retail florists who are primarily salesmen, and retail growers who primarily grow and sell their own products.

Principal factors concerned in the growth of commercial floriculture are (1) the formation of the Society of American Florists, (2) the development of the Florists' Telegraph Delivery Association (FTD), and (3) the work of the Land Grant College System and the U.S. Depart-

[1] According to the first official census, taken in 1790, the three largest cities ranked as follows: Philadelphia with 42,444, Boston with 33,131, and New York with 18,038.

430

ment of Agriculture. The Society of American Florists initiated the unique and effective advertising slogan "Say It with Flowers." This slogan appeals to the public; it is catchy and all inclusive. The Florists' Telegraph Delivery Association provides facilities for the buying of flowers in any part of the United States and in many other countries of the world. For example, suppose a student wants to buy a corsage for his friend, and he wants to have the corsage presented to the friend as she starts from home to the campus for a visit. He would go to, or phone, the local florist; the local florist would transmit the order, usually by wire, to a florist in the friend's hometown who would make up and deliver the corsage to her. The service rendered by FTD ensures quick and prompt delivery of fresh, high-quality products. As such, it has been of great benefit both to the producer and to the consumer. The work of the Land Grant College System and the U.S. Department of Agriculture consists in the training of students in floriculture, the solution of problems of the many ornamental industries, and the dissemination of research results to producers and consumers. The training of students in and the solution of problems by the scientific method have assisted greatly in placing the many industries on a comparatively firm foundation.

The growing of ornamental plants for sale is divided into the following distinct industries: (1) the production of cut flowers, (2) the production of potted plants, (3) the growing and forcing of flowering bulbs and corms, and (4) the production of bedding plants. Since these industries have special requirements, facilities, and technical knowledge, they are highly specialized.

PRODUCTION OF CUT FLOWERS

Cut flowers are produced in greenhouses, cloth houses, and outdoors. Greenhouses are used for both warm- and cool-season crops during the entire year. Principal crops are carnation, chrysanthemum, orchid, rose, and snapdragon. In general, the principal environmental factors—water, temperature, light, and essential elements—are either entirely or partially controlled. The water is supplied by many specialized irrigation systems and devices; the night temperature is either thermostatically or manually controlled; the light intensity during the late spring and summer is reduced by the use of shading materials and increased in the late fall and winter by the removal of the shading materials; the length of the light period is reduced by the use of black cloth or increased by the use of electric lights; and the essential elements are supplied in solution for the growing of crops in media other than sand or soil and in solution or in the form of organic matter or commercial fertilizers for the growing of crops in sand or soil.

Cut flowers are grown in either ground beds or in raised 4- or 5-foot-wide benches. Two types of benches are used: (1) level and (2) V-shaped. These in turn may be watertight or nonwatertight. In general, the watertight bench requires the V-shaped bottom and a layer of tile or gravel at the bottom of the V. With this type of bench the crops can be irrigated by maintaining a constant level of water in the bottom of the bench or by running water through the tile lines or through overhead pipes. In general, the nonwatertight bench is either V-shaped or flat and requires a layer of sand or gravel at the bottom. With this type of bench the crops are watered by overhead systems of irrigation. Various systems are used; the hand, Skinner, Revere, and Ohio State are examples. Various types of construction materials are used in the making of benches: aluminum alloy, asbestos rock, concrete, concrete slabs, steel, tile, and wood (cypress and redwood). Of these materials, asbestos rock is the most satisfactory. It is strong and durable; it is not affected by heat and moisture; and it will not corrode, bend, rust, or buckle.

Cloth houses are used whenever outdoor temperatures are favorable for the growth of crops. In general, their use is limited to the frost-free growing period, since, unlike greenhouses, these structures provide no protection against subfreezing temperatures. As discussed in Chapter 12, their use is particularly advantageous during the summer and fall of regions characterized by high temperatures and high light intensity. The covers slightly lower the temperature of the air, but they markedly lower the light intensity. This in turn markedly lowers the temperature of the leaves, which lowers the rate of transpiration and allows the rate of absorption to keep up with it. As a result, the guard cells remain turgid, and the stomates remain open. Thus, with other factors favorable high rates of photosynthesis take place throughout the entire light period. At present the principal crops grown within these structures are chrysanthemums and asters. Note the greenhouse roses growing in the cloth house in Fig. 12.4.

Outdoor culture requires the utilization of temperatures which are favorable for the growth of the crop in question. In other words, the crops are grown at temperatures within their optimum temperature range. The principal crops are chrysanthemum, aster, and gladiolus. Chrysanthemums and asters are grown principally in the vicinity of Los Angeles, California; and gladiolus, in many parts of the country. Producing districts exist in central Florida, southern Alabama, the coastal plain section of North Carolina and South Carolina, northern Indiana, northern Ohio, and southern Michigan. In this way a succession of crops is produced, with Florida, the earliest producing district, supplying the markets from October to May; and Michigan, the latest producing district, supplying the markets from August to September. Thus, the flower spikes are made available in many markets throughout the entire year.

Keeping Quality of Cut Flowers. The fundamental processes concerned are (1) water absorption and transpiration and (2) respiration. With water absorption and transpiration the principal plant factors are (1) the relative area of absorption and (2) the water-holding capacity of the tissues. The principal environmental factors are (1) temperature, (2) relative humidity, and (3) wind velocity. Since cut flowers absorb water only through the stem, the area of absorption is exceedingly small compared with the area of transpiration. Thus, the utilization of environmental factors which reduce the rate of transpiration will accordingly reduce water deficits and prolong the life of the flowers. With respiration the principal plant factor concerned is the amount of sugars available, and the principal environmental factors are (1) temperature

Fig. 23.1. A consumer unit package of roses. Note the droplets of water on the leaves and petals. (Courtesy, Alex Laurie, Whistling Pines Gardens, Eustis, Fla.)

and (2) the use of certain chemicals. Since sugars are used in respiration, the greater the actual and potential sugar supply at the time of cutting and the lower the rate of respiration after cutting, the longer will be the life of the flowers. Thus, high sugar content in the tissues should be promoted and low temperatures utilized whenever feasible. In regard to the use of chemical compounds, certain substances have been found that substantially lower the respiration rate and greatly retard the activity of bacteria and fungi that rot the stems. These substances are placed in the water in which the stems are emerged. Two preparations are (1) a solution consisting of hydrazine sulfate, manganese sulfate, and sugar and (2) a solution consisting of potassium, aluminum sulfate, sodium hypochlorite, ferric oxide, and sugar. Commercial preparations are Floralife and Bloomlife. Retail florists frequently place a tablet of these materials in each pack of flowers sold.

Prepackaging of Cut Flowers. Prepackaging consists in packing an average-sized consumer unit in an appropriate package. The processes concerned are (1) respiration, (2) transpiration, and (3) rate of cell division. Naturally, for long storage life and long keeping quality, the flowers should have a low rate of respiration, a low rate of transpiration, and a low rate of cell division. How does the package maintain a low rate of these processes? To maintain a low rate of these processes the pack-

Fig. 23.2. A self-service cabinet for the selling of prepackaged flowers. (Courtesy, Alex Laurie, Whistling Pines Gardens, Eustis, Fla.)

age should fulfill the following requirements: It should have a small volume, and it should be nonwater absorbent, gasproof, and sufficiently strong to withstand handling.[2] The relatively small volume, combined with "misting" of the flowers and the nonwater-absorbent quality of the material, maintains a high relative humidity. Thus, a low rate of transpiration is maintained. The relatively small volume, combined with the gasproof quality of the cellophane wrap, maintains a certain concentration of carbon dioxide—usually from 5 to 15 per cent. Thus, a low rate of respiration is maintained. The fact that the stems are not placed in water permits a slight water deficit within the tissues. Thus, a low rate of cell division is maintained. Figure 23.1 shows a consumer unit package of roses, and Fig. 23.2 shows a refrigerated self-service cabinet for selling consumer units.

PRODUCTION OF POTTED PLANTS

The growing of plants in pots or similar containers differs from the growing of plants in the greenhouse bed or bench, the garden, field, or orchard. The volume of soil in the container is exceedingly small; the root system is greatly restricted; the natural essential-element supply is limited; and the necessity for frequent watering is conducive to the leaching of nitrates and possibly other essential ions. Thus, soils for growing plants in containers are reinforced with heavy applications of highly decomposed organic matter, either in the form of finely shredded peat or highly decomposed organic matter or a mixture of both of these materials. These finely divided forms of organic matter increase the capacity of the mixture to hold available water and exchangeable essential cations and promote drainage and aeration.

In general, important and necessary practices in the production of potted plants include (1) the reinforcement of the potting mixture with superphosphate, since the addition of nitrogen is likely to induce an excessive concentration of nitrates in the mixture; (2) the transplanting of seedlings to a small pot (1 to 2¼ inches) and finally to a larger, or finish, pot or the transplanting of rooted cuttings directly to the final pot; (3) the application of ammonium nitrate and potash or a complete mixture, usually in the liquid form, when the soil is moist. If the fertilizer is applied when the soil is dry, a high concentration of solutes in the soil solution takes place which is likely to retard plant growth; and (4) care in watering to avoid leaching of nitrate-nitrogen and possibly other essential ions.

Ornamental pot plants grown for sale may be divided into two groups: (1) those grown primarily for the beauty of the flowers and secondarily

[2] The packages also have a cellophane window so that the consumer can see what he is buying.

Fig. 23.3. Some ornamental pot plants. Upper row, left to right: maidenhair fern, orchid, jacobinia, poinsettia, and Boston fern. Lower row, left to right: pothos, begonia, kalanchoe, azalea, chrysanthemum, and Saintpaulia.

for their foliage and (2) those grown for their attractive foliage only. Principal kinds of the first group are African violet, azalea, chrysanthemum, begonia, cineraria, cyclamen, geranium, hydrangea, calceolaria, and poinsettia. Principal kinds of the second group are *Asparagus plumosus, Asparagus sprengerii,* caladium, fern (Boston and maidenhair), philodendron, pothos, rubber plants, sansevieria, cacti, dieffenbachia, and succulents. Millions of excellent plants are produced each year. Some common ornamental plants are shown in Fig. 23.3.

GROWING AND FORCING STORAGE STRUCTURES

BULBS AND CORMS

In general, bulbs and corms are developed from the storage of relatively large quantities of reserve carbohydrates—usually hemicellulose and/or starch. These reserve substances are changed to sugars and other similar compounds for the development of the roots, stems, leaves, and flowers. Naturally, with other factors favorable, the greater the amount of carbohydrates which are stored, the greater will be the production of roots, foliage, and flowers. Major crops are gladiolus and lily; minor crops are iris, narcissus, hyacinth, and tulip. In the commercial production of these crops two more or less distinct industries have developed: (1) the production of the storage structures with the simultaneous development of foliage and flowers and (2) the forcing of the storage structures in greenhouses.

Production of Storage Structures. Although the details of cultivation vary with the crop, the main object for all crops is the rapid development of large storage structures tightly packed with reserve food. Thus, as in the development of onions, potatoes, root crops, and sweetpotatoes, the sequence of events is as follows: the development of absorbing roots and a large photosynthetic surface during the first part of the growing season, and the development of the storage structure during the latter part. Consequently, carbohydrate utilization is dominant during the first part of the growing season, and accumulation is dominant during the latter part. For example, in the production of gladiolus corms in southwestern Michigan cormels (small corms) are planted 4 to 6 inches deep and 3 to 6 inches apart in rows 2, 2½, or 3 feet apart in well-drained, moderately acid sandy loams. At first, the cormel develops the absorbing root system and then it develops one, two, three, or four stems. When these stems are 6 to 8 inches high, their basal portion starts to enlarge, and when the stems are 18 to 24 inches high, the young corms are fully grown. At the same time, cormels arise from adventitious buds between the old and new corms. In this way a comparatively large number of corms are produced. The new crop of corms is harvested when the leaves turn yellow or just before the first frost.

In general, commercial districts may be divided into two groups: (1) the southern district in which flower production is the main consideration and (2) the northern district in which corm production is the chief consideration. Outstanding southern districts are located in central Florida and the Mobile Bay area of Alabama. An important northern district is the Holland-Zeeland area of southwestern Michigan.

Forcing Storage Structures in Greenhouses. The main object is to produce attractive foliage and brilliant flowers for sale at the right time. To obtain this objective certain practices are common to all flowering bulbs and corms, and certain practices are specific. Common practices are (1) the use of large, well-developed, disease-free bulbs or corms, (2) the development of the absorbing system and most of the stems and leaves during the first part of the forcing period, and (3) the development of stems, leaves, and flowers during the latter part. Specific practices are a storage period of four weeks at 32 to 35°F for the Easter lily and a conditioning period of two weeks at 80 to 85°F in moist media for the gladiolus. The specific treatment for the Easter lily is necessary to conserve the carbohydrate supply, which is directly related to the number of flower buds produced; whereas the conditioning period of the gladiolus is necessary to develop a large number of cells within the growing points before production begins.

Of the various kinds of flowering plants that are forced from storage structures, the Easter lily is the most important commercially because of the demand as a potted plant at Easter. Since the Easter lily must look its best on one or two days only, preferably on Easter Sunday, a very precise synchronization of treatments and practices has been worked out from the time the bulbs are harvested to the time Easter occurs.

The storage structures of iris, hydrangea, narcissus, and tulips are also forced. The proper size of the bulbs or corms, the preconditioning treatment before forcing, the type of forcing container and media, and the level of the forcing temperature for Thanksgiving, Christmas, or post-Christmas trade are rather specific and exacting. These specific requirements have been developed by growers and certain experiment stations.

PRODUCTION OF BEDDING PLANTS

Ornamental bedding plants are grown in beds of the home grounds and in public places or in porch boxes, window boxes, or urns. In general, the greatest demand takes place just before or immediately after the last frost in the spring, and operations of the commercial florist in the raising of these plants are timed accordingly. Most bedding plants are herbaceous annuals, and most of these are propagated by seed.

Important practices are (1) germinating seed under optimum conditions of temperature, moisture, and oxygen supply, usually in steam-sterilized soil (a necessity for killing weed seeds and the organisms which produce damping off); (2) preparing the mixture for the container (in general, 1 part of finely shredded peat or well-rotted manure to 3 parts of soil); (3) transplanting the seedlings into the containers; (4) placing the containers on boards or gravel rather than on the soil (to restrict the growth of the root system and to produce a more satisfactory top growth); and (5) watering and fertilizing (to ensure a moderately rapid growth). At present, two types of containers are used: small, flat trays and peat pots. Both types have advantages and disadvantages. The first type requires fewer handling operations, but it does not permit grading for uniformity in the preparation for market. The second type permits grading for uniformity, and, since the pot and plant can be transplanted as a unit, there is little if any disturbance to the root system in the transplanting operation.

In the production of plants on a large scale, mechanization of soil and container handling operations markedly reduces the cost of production and increases profits of the enterprise. Some of these labor-saving devices are conveyer belts to carry peat, manure, and soil to the shredder; conveyer belts to carry the prepared soil mixtures to the containers; and the use of dibble boards to punch holes in the soil mixture where the seedlings are to be placed.

Many kinds of ornamental plants are grown for bedding, e.g., coleus, balsam, geranium, pansy, petunia, marigold, salvia, snapdragon, verbena, and vinca.

QUESTIONS

1. State the three factors which have been responsible for the development of commercial floriculture.
2. What is the FTD?
3. You want to send a gift of flowers to a friend living in another region. How would you go about it?
4. Under what conditions do you consider flowers a luxury? Under what conditions do you consider them a necessity? Explain.
5. Show how the law of mass action applies to the prepackaging of cut flowers.
6. In your opinion which is more important in prolonging the life of cut flowers in a room—a low transpiration rate or a low respiration rate? Explain.
7. How does the production of cut flowers in greenhouses differ from the production of cut flowers in cloth houses?
8. Under conditions of high light intensity and high transpiration, pompon chrysanthemums and asters grown under cloth produce longer stems, larger leaves, and larger flowers than comparable plants grown outdoors. Explain.
9. In your opinion in what region of the country could cloth houses be used for the longer period? Explain.
10. Locating cloth houses near large trees should be avoided. Give two reasons.
11. The exclusion of bees by cloth houses prolongs the life of cut flowers. Explain.
12. What are the differences and similarities in growing plants in a garden and growing plants in pots, hanging baskets, or similar containers?
13. In general, the use of steam-sterilized soil is required for the production of bedding plants. Explain.
14. The containers of plants grown for bedding purposes should be placed on bare boards or on gravel rather than on soil. Explain.
15. Give an advantage and a disadvantage in the use of trays and peat pots for the growing of plants for bedding purposes.
16. What is the difference in morphology of bulbs and corms?
17. The forcing of bulbs and corms is entirely a carbohydrate utilization process. Explain.
18. In the greenhouse production of flowering bulbs and corms, extensive root development is necessary before foliage and flower production. Explain.
19. During the rooting period of bulbs and corms, soils should be low in nitrates. Explain.

20. Lily bulbs 5 to 7 inches in circumference produce from three to five flowers per plant, and bulbs 8 to 10 inches in circumference produce from five to seven flowers per plant. Explain.
21. Under optimum conditions in the greenhouse, large gladiolus corms flower two weeks earlier than relatively small corms. Explain.
22. When field-produced gladiolus spikes are cut, at least four leaves should be left on the remaining stalk. Explain.
23. Given two lots of lily bulbs of equal size for planting in the field. Lot A was planted late and harvested early, and it produced from one to two flowers per plant; lot B was planted early and harvested late, and it produced from five to seven flowers per plant. Explain.

24

NURSERY PLANT
PRODUCTION

The nurserymen's forte:
To make the world more beautiful and fruitful.

In general, nursery plants are young trees, shrubs, or herbaceous plants which are grown on specialized farms and which are transplanted to another location. These plants may be divided into two more or less distinct groups: (1) young trees of the tree fruits and plants of the small fruits

Fig. 24.1. Geographical location of nursery plant districts.

and (2) young ornamental plants. The former are grown to establish the many kinds of orchards and small fruit plantations, and the latter are grown to landscape or beautify homes, public and private buildings, schools, highways, parks, and industrial areas.

Distribution.   The geographic location of outsanding nursery districts is presented in Fig. 24.1. Note the large number of nurseries in the Northeast and Great Lakes region, in the Southeast and Gulf Coast region, and in the Pacific Coast region and the small number of nurseries in the Great Plains and intermountain regions. Can you think of any reason for this?

NATURE OF THE NURSERY BUSINESS

Types of Nurseries.   In general, the nursery business may be divided into three more or less distinct enterprises: (1) the production of plants from seed or by the various methods of vegetative propagation, (2) the growing of young plants to marketable size, and (3) the selling of marketable stock. Some nurseries grow seedling plants only; others sell nursery stock only; and others engage in any two or in all three enterprises.

The Propagation Unit.   The object of the propagation unit is to produce young plants. The layout may include the following divisions: (1) actual propagating structures or beds and (2) service structures. Principal propagating structures are greenhouses, hotbeds, cold frames, specially constructed propagating frames, and outdoor propagating beds. In general, the greenhouses are equipped with benches which contain the appropriate bedding media and are maintained at high relative humidity and low light intensity; and hotbeds are heated by hot water, steam, or electricity. For the successful propagation of certain plants special propagating frames have been developed. An example is the Wardian case. The Wardian case is essentially a tightly constructed cold frame. The tight construction maintains a high relative humidity which is necessary for the successful union of the cambium in the grafting of coniferous evergreens and roses. Observe the nonwood lathhouse used for the starting of azaleas in Fig. 12.5.

Principal service structures are the headhouse, storage house, heating plant, and alley house. The headhouse is essentially the service house for the greenhouses and hotbeds, and contains storage space for pots, flats, fertilizers, spray materials, tools, and workbenches. The storage house contains rooms for the storage of seed and other propagating materials, and the heating plant contains the boiler, fuel, and workbenches. At some nurseries any two or all three of these structures are combined into one house. The alley house connects the greenhouses, hotbeds, and cold frames with the headhouse. Its main function is to provide a passageway for the transportation of plants, propagation media, soil, and fertilizers from the headhouse to the propagation structures and to and from the propagation structures themselves. Alley houses sufficiently wide to permit the use of a truck greatly facilitate the movement of these materials. In the growing of the seedling plants the two modes of plant propagation—propagation by seed and propagation by vegetative means—are used. Important nursery practices in the use of seed are (1) collecting the fruits, (2) extracting and drying the seed, and (3) applying certain storage or pregermination treatments. *Collecting the fruits* consists in gathering mature fruit. Maturity varies with the kind of plant. In general, fleshy fruits become soft (apple, peach, plum); dry, green fruits become dark brown (oak); and winged fruits become light green or yellow (maple). Many types of equipment for harvesting fruit and seed are used, e.g., wire nippers, ladders, bags, cutting hooks, tarpaulin, and seed sheets. *Extracting and drying the seed* consist in separating the seed from the fruit and drying the seed to a low water content. Numerous extracting methods and techniques have been developed. In general, these methods vary according to the kind of fruit and are classified as follows: (1) rubbing fleshy fruits on and seed through a two- or three-mesh screen, (2) running fruits through a macerator with or without water, and (3) heating dry fruits lightly and running the seed through a screen. *Storage or pregermination treatments* consist of two types: (1) scarification of the seed coat and (2) stimulation of the embryo. Scarification is necessary for seed with impervious coats to admit water and/or oxygen for germination. Three methods are used: (1) emersing the seed in concentrated sulfuric acid from 20 minutes to 4 hours, according to the kind of seed, (2) revolving seed in a steel drum at about 20 rpm, and (3) soaking the seed in hot or cold water. Stimulation of the embryo is necessary to shorten its rest period. Numerous investigations have shown that the period of rest or period of afterripening is shortened by placing the seed in moist media held at temperatures varying from 32 to 40°F or by planting the seed in the fall. For example, seeds of the highbush blueberry will complete their period of rest in about three or four weeks if they are stratified and placed in cold storage. On the other hand, the period of rest requires from three to five months if the seeds are stored in a dry place. The method of vegetative propagation varies with the kind of plant. In general, cuttage is used for the propagation of herbaceous ornamentals and most woody plants, and graftage is used for the propagation of certain woody plants, the tree fruits, coniferous evergreens, roses, and so forth.

The Production Unit. The object of the production unit is to grow the nursery stock from the seedling stage to the marketable stage. The land is laid out in blocks and each block is given over to one kind of plant only. In this way the keeping of records is greatly facilitated. Principal practices are (1) lining out, (2) top pruning, (3) root pruning, (4) plant removal, (5) storing, and (6) packing.

LINING OUT. Lining out consists in transplanting the nursery stock from the propagation unit to the production unit. An individual plant is called a "liner," and methods of lining out vary greatly with the kind of plant. In general, the plants are lifted, sorted, root-pruned if necessary, placed in transplanting shelters, and placed in transplanting boards if hand-transplanted and in the transplanting machine if machine-transplanted. Many kinds of transplanting machines have been developed.

TOP PRUNING. Top pruning consists in removing branches or parts of branches in order to develop the proper framework or form of the tree. The type of framework varies with the kind of plant. For example, with deciduous shade trees for street planting the branches on the lower part of the trunk are removed, although with apple and peach trees a specific number of lower branches are allowed to remain.

ROOT PRUNING. Root pruning consists in removing portions of or all the younger root sections. The object of this practice is to develop extensively branched root systems at the base of the tree. In this way recovery from transplanting is facilitated. This practice is particularly necessary for the transplanting of evergreens. Can you think of any reason for this? In general, root pruning is done in the fall, and many types of power-drawn cutting blades have been developed.

PLANT REMOVAL. Plant removal consists in removing the plant with part of its roots from the soil. Thus, water absorption stops or is greatly reduced. However, transpiration continues to take place. As a result, plant removal is done in the fall, winter, or early spring when transpiration is at a minimum. Two rather distinct methods of plant removal are used: (1) lifting and moving without soil around the roots (bare root) for deciduous plants and small evergreens and (2) balling and burlapping for large evergreens and other plants which require considerable care in transplanting. Lifting may be done by hand with a sharp spade or by machine, and balling and burlapping are usually done by digging a trench at the required distance from the base and around the root system of the tree and enclosing the mass of soil and roots in burlap. In this way, the root system within the ball of soil supplies the leaves with the necessary water.

STORING. Storing consists in subjecting the plants to a set of environmental conditions which maintain life processes at a minimum. The fundamental processes concerned are respiration and transpiration; and, in general, the lower the respiration and transpiration rate, the longer is the storage life. Temperatures varying from 31 to 35°F, combined with relative humidity varying from 85 to 90 per cent and abundant ventilation, are usually used. Temperatures from 31 to 35°F not only permit a low rate of respiration, but also help bring woody plants out of the rest period; the high humidity permits a low rate of transpiration without excessive development of molds and fungi; and the abundant ventilation supplies sufficient oxygen and carries away the carbon dioxide and heat of respiration. In general, there are two types of storages for nursery stock: (1) inside and (2) outside, or heeling in. Inside storage requires the use of specially constructed houses usually with three parts: (1) work rooms, (2) packing rooms, and (3) storage rooms. For the most part, the storage rooms contain a series of deep shelves with vertical partitions. In this way stock of a given kind can be stored separately and maximum use of the storage house can be maintained. The use of storage houses permits grading, packing, and shipping during the winter, particularly in cold climates. Outdoor, or heeling-in, storage requires the use of well-drained sandy loam, preferably adjacent to an all-weather road and the packing shed. Sandy loams with adequately drained subsoils are ideal, since they do not become waterlogged in wet weather. Thus, nursery stock can be heeled-in or removed at any time the soil is not frozen. Because of the mild winters, outdoor storage is used more extensively in the South than in the North.

PACKING. Packing consists in preparing the nursery stock for shipment. The type of package varies greatly depending largely on the kind of plant, whether deciduous or evergreen, and on the size of the stock. In general, nursery stock is shipped according to the recommendations of the American Nurserymen's Association. Evergreens are usually shipped individually because of the necessity of balling and burlapping, and deciduous stock is usually shipped "bare-rooted" with the roots packed in moist sphagnum moss, peat, or shingle tow and with the top either covered with dried stalks or rushes and the entire plant wrapped in burlap or placed in a box lined with waterproof paper. Because parcel post shipments are

Fig. 24.2. A block of young peach trees. (Courtesy, Bountiful Ridge Nurseries, Princess Anne, Md.)

Fig. 24.3. An attractive, well-laid-out field of azaleas. (Courtesy, Howell Nursery, Semmes, Ala.)

frequently mailed in airtight containers, shipments by express are usually preferred. Note the block of young peach trees in Fig. 24.2 and the blocks of azaleas in Fig. 24.3.

The Sales Unit. The object of the sales unit is to market nursery products effectively. In other words, the sales area is located, designed, and maintained to attract the largest number of potential customers. Thus, the sales unit is usually located on a well-traveled highway and may be operated as a separate self-contained unit or in conjunction with the propagation or production units. In general, a well-developed sales unit contains (1) a display or show area, (2) a sales area, (3) a parking area and drives, and (4) a service section. These areas are usually arranged in proper proportion and balance in order to provide an attractive landscape atmosphere.

DISPLAY, OR SHOW, AREA. The display, or show, area contains plants that are usually not for sale, and they are arranged to show the effective use of landscape materials. Thus, the display area may show foundation plantings for small homes, pleasing combinations of trees and shrubs, or various kinds of gardens, such as the informal, formal, rose, azalea, camellia, or bulb.

SALES AREA. The sales area presents the materials that are for sale. In general, this area contains the business office, with at least three essential features: the reception and display room for materials that should be kept dry, such as seeds, bulbs, spray materials, catalogs, and books; the landscape or drafting room and wrapping, storing, and toilet facilities; and greenhouses for house plants, lathhouses, vents or terraces for potted plants, and pergolas for vines.

PARKING AREA AND DRIVES. The parking area and drives provide ample space for customers' cars and free access to all parts of the sales and display areas. In this way the loading of bought materials is facilitated.

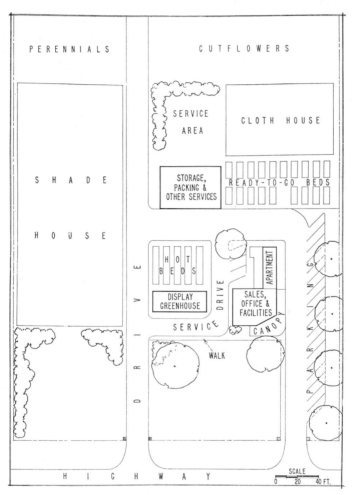

Fig. 24.4. Arrangement of a sales unit in south Mississippi. (Courtesy, F. S. Batson, Wiggins, Miss.)

SERVICE AREA. The service area contains facilities for the maintenance of display and sales areas. Principal features are workrooms for potting plants and other garden operations; storage bins for soil, peat moss, manure, and sand; storage space for pots, labels, commercial fertilizers, pest-control materials, and wrapping materials; garage and parking space for employees; and heeling-in space. Note the arrangement of various areas in Fig. 24.4.

OPPORTUNITIES IN NURSERY STOCK PRODUCTION

In Colonial times industry was largely agricultural in nature and fruit trees were in great demand. However, with the growth of nonagricultural industry and the development of large centers of population, the demand for fruit trees has declined and that for ornamentals has markedly increased. In fact, as previously stated, at least 80 per cent of all nursery stock at present consists of ornamental plants. In other words, most of the opportunities in the nursery business consist in the production and selling of ornamental plants.

What are the opportunities in the production of ornamental plants? To what extent are homes, private buildings and grounds, public buildings and grounds, highways, and industrial areas adequately landscaped? Although accurate information is unavailable, casual observation indicates that some homes are overlandscaped, that most homes are not landscaped at all, and that, in general, many highways are laid down and factories and industrial areas established with no attention to adequate beautification. Thus, the beautification and ultimate value of many homes and private and public areas have not been fully realized.

PLANT PATENTS

In 1930 the Congress of the United States passed a plant patent law. This law provides for the granting of patents to new and distinct varieties of asexually propagated crops only, provided the part used for propagation is not used for human consumption. Thus, new varieties of such crops as potato, Jerusalem artichoke, and sweetpotato are excluded.

The new and distinct varieties may be classified as follows: (1) sports due to bud variation, (2) mutations due to self-pollination within a species, and (3) hybrids due to crossing between plants of two species, two varieties, or a species and a variety. The prime advantage of the law is the provision for specific monetary return to the originator for his efforts in developing new sorts. For example, the Joseph H. Hill Co., Richmond, Indiana, growers and breeders of greenhouse roses, developed and patented a new variety of rose called Better Times. Under the law the originator receives 8 cents for each plant that he sells and the buyer agrees to maintain no more than the original number of plants that he bought. In other words, if a buyer bought 1,000 plants of Better Times, he would agree to maintain no more than 1,000 plants. In this way the originator has some control of the parent stock of new varieties. The plant patents are secured through and are administered by the Office of Commissioner of Patents, Washington, D.C.

QUESTIONS

1. What are nursery plants? What is the relative importance of the two groups?
2. Name the three phases of the nursery business.
3. State the objectives of the propagation unit, the production unit, and the sales unit.
4. The alley house of the greenhouse range should be wide enough to permit the use of a truck. Explain.
5. Water in which seed is soaked should be changed daily. Explain.
6. In your opinion, how does temperature of 32 to 40°F, combined with stratification, shorten the rest period of seeds which have a rest period?
7. What does the nurseryman mean by the term well-ripened stock?
8. Applications of nitrogenous fertilizers, if made in late summer, prolong vegetative growth, delay maturity of the tissues, and make plants susceptible to winter injury. Explain.
9. A warm, rainy fall followed by a sudden killing frost usually results in marked injury to nursery stock. Explain.
10. A warm, sunny fall is most favorable for the conditioning of nursery plants for the winter. Explain.
11. In general, top pruning should be avoided in late summer. Explain.
12. Deciduous trees for the lawn and for street planting are pruned to branch at different heights. Explain.
13. Show how root pruning favors carbohydrate accumulation.
14. In general, nursery plants are removed in the fall, winter, or early spring. Explain.
15. What is meant by balling and burlapping?
16. Why are balling and burlapping necessary for evergreen stock?
17. Earth fills over the original soil of a tree are likely to kill the tree. Explain.
18. How can the bad effects of a fill be overcome?
19. The roots of wrapped nursery stock require air. Explain.
20. Many districts of the southern region are favorable for the production of nursery stock. Explain.
21. The sales area should provide an attractive landscaped atmosphere. Explain.
22. In general, which crops are excluded from the plant patent law?
23. How does a breeder benefit by securing a plant patent?

25

HORTICULTURE
AND THE HOME

Plan your work and work your plan.

Just as there are certain principles of plant growth which lead to a knowledge of how plants grow and develop, so there are certain principles of landscape design which lead to a knowledge of how best to beautify the home grounds. In order to utilize these principles fully, the making of a landscape plan is very helpful. There is nothing unusual about this. Teachers develop lesson plans; research workers develop project outlines; dressmakers use patterns; architects develop designs for buildings, bridges, and so forth, from which blueprints are made to be followed by the engineer, carpenter, plumber, or bricklayer. In fact, all worthwhile activities require the development of plans for their effective and efficient operation.

THE DEVELOPMENT OF THE
LANDSCAPE PLAN

Objectives. To landscape the home effectively certain objectives should be clear before the landscape plan is made. These objectives are (1) to secure attractive grounds; (2) to provide natural, easy, and safe approaches; (3) to obtain privacy for the family; (4) to provide for the recreational needs of the family; (5) to provide a convenient, well-arranged, attractive service area; and (6) to harmonize the home, buildings, various areas, walks, drives, garden, and orchard into one complete unit.

In the development of the landscape plan the following steps are essential.

Preparation of a Map of the Entire Property. In general, the map should include the boundary lines; the location of the home with its windows, doors, porches, and rooms; the location of other buildings; the walks and drives; the direction of water flow. As with all maps, the drawing should be done to a definite scale, as for example 1 inch equals 10 feet, and the direction of north should be indicated. To save time most authorities recommend the use of cross-section or coordinate paper. In this way, the right angles are readily available and distances can readily be ascertained.

Saving Topsoil and Placing Guards around the Trunks of Valuable Trees. The topsoil, particularly that of the area to be occupied by the house and the lawns, should be placed in a pile on one side of the property, and guards should be placed around the base of valuable trees. In the first case the valuable topsoil will not be covered by subsoil due to excavations for the cellar or to grading, and in the second case stripping of the bark and partial girdling of the trees will be avoided.

Control of Water. The water supply is controlled by adequate grading and drainage. In general, if the property is located on the same level or below that of adjacent property, drainage is likely to be a problem. On the other hand, if the property is located on a hill or a slope, soil erosion is likely to be a problem. In either case, the area adjacent to the home should slope slightly away from the side of the building. If the home is located on a level lower than that of the adjacent property, the excess water can be drained away by means of a turf gutter or a retaining wall or both, by using drain tile under the foundation, and if necessary by waterproofing the basement floor. If the home is located on a hill or on a slope, the flow of the excess water can be reduced by using a gradual slope on a wide terrace with or without retaining walls.

Division of Property into Its Three Main Areas: (1) the Front, or Public, (2) the Private, or Family, and (3) the Service. The front, or public, area includes the front lawn, the base planting, and the trees which frame the home. It is developed primarily to serve as an attractive foreground and frame for the house and property. The following guides are suggested for use in the development of the public area: (1) Make the lawn open and spacious in proper proportion; (2) confine shrubs to the borders, corners, and base of the buildings; (3) balance the plantings, both trees and shrubs, about an imaginary line through the entrance of the house or property; and (4) use only those trees and shrubs which will compliment the house to best advantage.

As stated previously, the lawn should be open and spacious. In general, for small properties the width preferably should be greater than the depth, and for large properties the depth may or may not exceed the width. In all cases a smooth-surface, grass-sodded lawn is very essential. Important factors in obtaining a satisfactory lawn are (1) thoroughly prepared, well-drained, fertile soil, (2) use of well-adapted seed or lawn plants, (3) application of an adequate supply of fertilizers and water, and (4) suitable maintenance practices. Lawns have many functions. They markedly reduce erosion; they reduce glare and cool the immediate surroundings; and they serve as an outdoor carpet. Lawn plants may be placed in two groups: (1) warm-season and (2) cool-season. Some of the most common are presented in Table 25.1. What kind of lawn plants are used in your community?

Table 25.1.   WARM-SEASON AND COOL-SEASON LAWN PLANTS

Kind of plant	Leaf		Plant height, in.	Sod‡	Ability to maintain itself	How propagated
	Width*	Color†				
Warm-season Plants						
Bermuda	n.	d.g.	2–3	d.	Low	Sod, sprigs, seed
Fine-leaved Bermuda	n.	d.g.	2–3	d.	Low	Sod, sprigs
St. Augustine	m.b.	l.g.	3–4	m.d.	High	Sod, sprigs
Centipede	b.	l.g.	3–4	d.	High	Sod, sprigs
Carpet	b.	l.g.	2–3	d.	High	Seed
Zoysia	n.	d.g.	3–4	d.	High	Sod
Cool-season Plants						
Kentucky blue	n.	l.g.	3–4	m.d.	High	Seed
Italian rye	n.	g.	6–8	m.d.	High	Seed

* n., narrow; m.b., moderately broad; b., broad.
† l.g., light green; g., green; d.g., dark green.
‡ d., dense; m.d., moderately dense.

The base planting is the planting around the base of the house. Its function is to unite and harmonize the dwelling with the remainder of the grounds. The extensiveness of the planting depends on (1) the size of the house and grounds, (2) the height of the house, and (3) the prominence of various features of the house. In general, with a large house and spacious grounds, large groups of plants are used. On the other hand, with a small house and small grounds, small groups of plants or even single specimens are used. Similarly, tall shrubs are used at the corners or angles, and short plants at the steps or doorway. As a rule, shrubs are placed at least 3 feet from the building. Although some shrubs thrive best in shade and others thrive best in the sun, most shrubs grow satisfactorily in sun and partial shade.

The *private area* consists mainly of recreational areas for the family and includes such features as the barbecue pit, family area, children's playground, flower garden, specimen shrubs or flowers, birdbath, lily pond, or rock garden. It is sometimes called the outdoor living room. The following guides are suggested for use in the development of the private area: (1) Enclose the area to ensure privacy and to form a background for landscape features; (2) arrange flower beds, rock garden, barbecue pit, or other feature around the perimeter; (3) allow the center to remain open; and (4) make the area easily accessible to the house and to other parts of the property.

The *service area* includes the garage with its turning area, the parking area for guests, the laundry lines, the fuel tank, the greenhouses, hotbeds, or propagating frames, the vegetable garden, and the home fruit planting. Naturally, the kitchen door should be part of and contiguous with the service area.

Pinpointing or Locating, Selecting, and Naming the Trees and Shrubs. The primary objective is to place each tree or shrub in accordance with the specifications for any given location, e.g., planting short kinds under the windows and tall kinds at the corners of the house. Thus, a knowledge of the ultimate height and form of plants is essential. Other factors that should be considered are (1) adaptation to climate and soil, (2) relative freedom from insects and diseases, and (3) light intensity requirements. Obviously, plants which are adapted to any given climate and soil and are relatively free from insects and diseases are by far the most satisfactory. In general, the department of horticulture of the land-grant college or university of any given state maintains up-to-date lists of trees and shrubs which are recommended for landscape use. Finally, the trees and shrubs are named. This is usually done by using a key. This consists in making a list of the trees and shrubs, assigning each plant a number, and writing in the number at the place where the tree or shrub is located on the landscape plan.

ARRANGEMENT OF LANDSCAPE PLANTS

In general, trees are planted singly or in groups rather than in rows. For small properties, they are planted singly or in groups of two or three, and with large or spacious properties they are planted in groups of three or more. Trees at the rear of the house and on the rear and sides of the property provide an effective frame and background and balance the land-scape planting. In general, shrubs are planted in groups. Each group contains tall, moderately tall, and short kinds. These differences in ultimate height are necessary to provide balance at angles and corners and in mass plantings. For angles and corners the tall plants are placed at the junction of the two lines forming the angle, with medium plants next and the short plants on the outside. For mass effects, the tall plants are arranged in the middle, with medium and short plants on the sides. In either case, over-planting, a rather frequent occurrence, should be avoided. It results in shading the leaves and in severe competition for water and essential raw materials. This causes low rates of photosynthesis, poor growth, a sickly appearance, winter injury, and finally death.

CARE OF PLANTS IN THE HOME

Principal factors concerned are (1) relative humidity of the home, (2) type of container, (3) composition of the soil, (4) application of commercial fertilizers, and (5) control of pests.

Relative Humidity of the Home.   As stated in Chapter 4, the rate of water absorption should equal the rate of transpiration; and the principal factors influencing the rate of transpiration are the leaf area, temperature, light intensity, wind velocity, and relative humidity. Thus, with the environmental factors constant the amount of water lost per unit of time will be more or less proportional to the leaf area. In other words, plants of the same kind with a large number of leaves under the same environmental conditions will lose more water per unit time than plants with a small number of leaves. On the other hand, with the same kind of plant and with the leaf area constant, the amount of water lost will be determined largely by the environmental factor in the minimum. In the home the amount of moisture in the air or the relative humidity is likely to be the limiting factor. This is particularly true of non-air-conditioned homes in the winter and of homes during the time the air conditioning equipment is in operation. Since air conditioners take water out of the air, they lower the relative humidity.

According to authorities the optimum relative humidity for human comfort is between 50 and 60 per cent. Consequently, if the humidity is within or near this range, the use of pans of water to increase the relative humidity would seem to be impractical. Fortunately, under these conditions all that is necessary to avoid deficits of water within the tissues of plants is to maintain the soil in a moist condition. If, however, the air becomes exceedingly dry, the use of shallow pans of water would not only promote human comfort, but it would also lower the rate of transpiration.

Type of Container.   As previously pointed out, the living tissues of the root system are constantly respiring, and in respiration free oxygen is taken in and carbon dioxide is given off. This free oxygen flows from the outside air into the pore spaces of the soil, and the carbon dioxide flows from the pore spaces to the outside air. If the pore space becomes saturated because of overwatering and/or lack of drainage, the supply of oxygen becomes limiting and the concentration of carbon dioxide assumes toxic proportions. As a result, the respiration and growth of the root system are impaired, and the ability of the root-hair zone to absorb water and essential raw materials is reduced. Thus, adequate drainage of the soil is essential at all times.

From the standpoint of drainage and aeration, plant containers may be divided into two groups: (1) porous, or clay pots, and (2) nonporous, e.g., glazed, ceramic, rubber, glass, china, and plastic pots. With the porous pot, since water escapes through the pores, watering at frequent intervals is necessary and, unless extreme care is taken, the soil is likely to become dry. However, adequate aeration is likely to exist at all times. With the nonporous pot, watering at relatively wide intervals is necessary and, unless extreme care is taken, inadequate aeration is likely to be a problem. With both types provision for drainage of excess water is necessary. This is accomplished by placing coarse gravel, pebbles, or pieces of broken clay pot in the bottom and over the hole of the container. In this way, the drainage of excess water is facilitated and a continuous supply of oxygen is available for the respiration and growth of the root system.

Composition of the Soil.   As previously pointed out, the root system of plants in pots and similar containers is restricted, the volume of soil in the pot is low, and frequent watering is necessary. Thus, soils for plants in pots should retain large quantities of available water and essential raw materials and permit the rapid diffusion of carbon dioxide and oxygen in the respiration of the root system and the soil organisms. For these reasons, the soil should contain adequate quantities of highly decomposed organic matter, such as well-rotted manure, peat or leaf mold, fine to medium-coarse sand (usually builder's sand is satisfactory), and loam, such as sandy loam, silt loam, and clay loam. The highly decomposed organic matter forms humus which retains water; the sand promotes aeration and drainage; and the fine clay particles of the loam combine with the humus particles in the formation of a clay-humus complex which serves as a storehouse for the adsorption of essential cations. Although different species vary in their soil requirements, in general, the following mixtures on a volume basis should be satisfactory: (1) 1 part highly decomposed organic matter, 1 part builder's sand, and 2 parts well-drained silt loam or clay loam or (2) 1 part highly decomposed organic matter and 3 parts well-drained sandy loam.

Application of Commercial Fertilizers. When a seedling plant is placed in a finish pot, the amount of essential raw materials in the soil is usually sufficient for the initiation of growth. As the plant develops its root and top system, the essential raw materials are rapidly exhausted. As a result, applications of commercial fertilizers are necessary.

In general, commercial fertilizers may be applied in the liquid or dry form. However, applications in the liquid form are usually more satisfactory, since the essential elements are immediately available, and, if high-analysis mixtures are used, most of the ingredients will dissolve readily and more or less completely in water. To avoid possible harmful effects, the liquid fertilizer should be applied when the soil is moist at the recommended concentration. If the soil is dry or if concentrations above the recommended dose are used, plasmolysis of the absorbing system is likely to take place, which is manifested by drooping or wilting of the leaves and by a corresponding reduction in growth and in general health of the plant.

Control of Pests. Principal pests are aphids, mites, mealybugs, and scales. As stated in Chapter 15, all these pests have sucking or rasping mouth parts and their mode of feeding is quite similar. In general, they pierce the epidermis of the leaves and young stems and suck the manufactured compounds from the internal tissues and reduce the chlorophyll content of the photosynthetic surface. In this way the rate of photosynthesis is reduced.

Control measures are general and specific in nature. General methods consist in (1) carefully inspecting the plants before they are brought into the home and removing insect pests which may be present; (2) inspecting the plants at frequent intervals, particularly the underside of the leaves and young stems; and (3) supplying the plants with optimum moisture and essential elements. Specific measures vary with the nature of the pest. Spraying the tops with nicotine sulfate for aphids, syringing the leaves and stems with a fine mist of water for spider mites, and swabbing the bodies of mealybugs and scales with a ball of cotton soaked with rubbing alcohol are generally recommended.

QUESTIONS

1. The money used in landscaping the home is an excellent investment. Explain.

2. Landscaping the home grounds is more than merely planting "bushes" around the house. Explain.
3. What are the three areas of the home grounds? What is the purpose of each of these areas?
4. State the main features of the front or public area.
5. Groups of flowers, shrubs, and trees are undesirable in the center of the front lawn. Give reasons.
6. How does the lawn reduce glare and cool the immediate surroundings?
7. Whenever sodium nitrate or ammonium nitrate is broadcast on lawns, it should be done when the grass is dry and preferably watered into the soil. Give two reasons.
8. In general, the blade of the lawnmower should not be set lower than 1.5 to 2.5 inches. Explain.
9. If the lawn is cut regularly, the clippings should be allowed to remain. Explain.
10. When any given lawn is irrigated the zone of soil occupied by the plant's roots should be wetted, no more and no less. Explain.
11. What are the lawn plants recommended for your locality? Give reasons for this recommendation.
12. What is the base planting? What is its function?
13. What is the purpose of the private, or family, area? State four features of this area.
14. What is the purpose of the service area?
15. Diagram the arrangement of tall, medium, and low shrubs to be used at a corner and in mass plantings.
16. Name two locations where groups of shrubs may be placed to advantage.
17. Show how wide spacing of shrubs maintains a more desirable home landscape appearance than close spacing.
18. Make a complete plan for landscaping the grounds of your home, using a few well-chosen trees and shrubs.
19. Outline the characteristics a plant should possess to be adaptable to the relatively adverse conditions of the home.
20. Some housewives have difficulty in maintaining plants in the home in a healthy condition, others have no difficulty. Explain.

THE HOME VEGETABLE GARDEN

The value of vegetables in the diet has long been established. Vegetables are healthful. Certain sorts contain abundant minerals and vitamins and provide roughage; other sorts contain abundant carbohydrates and proteins. Since the health, development, and comfort of the family depend on an adequate diet, the best means of providing the necessary foods at the lowest possible cost should be considered.

The home vegetable garden can be made to provide an adequate supply of vegetables for the family during the growing season and for canning and storage for winter use. In many cases vegetables are not otherwise available because of the distance to markets or lack of purchasing power. Homegrown vegetables are higher in quality because they are consumed or preserved sooner after they are harvested. To a certain extent vegetables can be substituted for more costly food. Thus, the importance of the home vegetable garden is apparent.

If properly cared for and managed, a small plot of land is excellently productive. For example, garden authorities state that a properly managed half-acre garden will produce enough vegetables for the average farm family the year round. Because garden crops differ in their requirements and behavior, careful planning is essential. As previously stated, some mature in a relatively short time and make their best growth in the spring or fall. Others thrive best in the summer. Some require the entire growing season. Some are tall; others are relatively short.

The vegetable garden is an integral part of the landscape plan and should be planned and considered as such. Two rather distinct types of management are used: (1) as a distinct unit and (2) in combination with the flower garden and/or home orchard. Helpful rules in planning and operating are: (1) Plant in rows—100 feet of any crop is usually

Fig. 25.1. A summer home garden in Oktibbeha County, Miss. (Courtesy, K. H. Buckley, Mississippi Agricultural Extension Service.)

sufficient; (2) place the perennials—asparagus, rhubarb, and small fruits —on one side of the garden to avoid interference with the tillage operations of the annual crops; (3) plant crops together which have similar methods of culture; (4) rotate the crops; (5) use the wheel hoe wherever possible; (6) supply water during times of drought; and (7) keep the garden free from weeds.

Succession Cropping.   An important garden practice, succession cropping, is simply a short rotation which conserves space and labor, e.g., early maturing crops, such as spinach, lettuce, endive, green onion, or mustard, followed by bean, pea or tomato, pepper, and eggplant; cabbage, cauliflower, carrot, beet, pea, and kohlrabi followed by snap bean, cowpea, or corn; beans followed by late cabbage, cauliflower, or sweet corn; sweet corn followed by bean, beet, lettuce, turnip, carrot, mustard, or spinach.

In general, the soil of the garden should be deep, friable, high in organic matter, well drained, and slightly acid. Liberal supplies of barnyard manure, combined with deep plowing and thorough preparation of the seedbed, are essential in successful home or farm gardening. Note the summer home garden in Fig. 25.1.

QUESTIONS

1.   Enumerate the advantages of a home garden.
2.   Make a simple plan for a home garden showing the proper arrangement for perennials and long-season and short-season crops.
3.   Outline the steps in properly preparing a garden previous to planting.
4.   Make a list of vegetables which can be grown in your locality.
5.   How many kinds can be grown and during how many months of the year can at least one vegetable be harvested?
6.   What methods would you use to control the growth of vegetables?

THE HOME ORCHARD

Like the vegetable garden, the home orchard should be considered an integral part of the landscape plan. On relatively large properties, the trees are grown together as a unit and are grown primarily for their fruit. However, on small properties the trees may be grown for their landscape value as well as for their fruit. For example, peach trees are both useful and ornamental. They display flowers in the spring, produce fruit in the summer, and provide an attractive color in the fall, whereas flowering ornamentals, such as the redbud, flowering peach, or dogwood, display flowers and provide an attractive color only. Thus, fruit trees may be utilized for their landscape value as well as for their fruit.

Important factors in the selection of appropriate kinds and varieties of fruits are (1) resistance or susceptibility to pests and (2) adaptation to the local environment. As is well known, certain fruits are susceptible to many insects and diseases and others are relatively free. In general, fruits which are susceptible require the application of dusts and/or sprays which must be applied at the right time and in proper dose. This practice is relatively expensive and time-consuming and frequently requires special equipment. Thus, when facilities, time, or interest are limited, greater satisfaction is likely to be obtained with fruits which are relatively free from pests. Note the relative freedom from pests of the crops listed in Table 25.2.

Table 25.2. SUGGESTED FRUITS FOR A HOME ORCHARD

Fruit	Trees or plants	Number of varieties recommended	Planting distance, ft	Relative freedom from pests
Pecan	4	3	60 × 60	Free
Apple (on dwarf stock)	8	7	20 × 20	Not free
Peach	12	7	20 × 20	Not free
Plum	6	3	20 × 20	Not free
Cherry	3	3	20 × 20	Not free
Muscadine grape	4	2	10 × 30	Free
Other grapes	8	3	10 × 10	Not free
Brambles	40	2	5 × 5	Not free
Strawberry	400	2	3 × 1	Not free
Fig	4	2	15 × 15	Free

An important factor of the environment is temperature. As discussed in Chapter 5 horticultural crops may be divided into two groups: (1) cool-season and (2) warm-season. Thus, for the reasons given in Chapter 5 and with other factors favorable, cool-season fruits thrive best in the northern half or in the elevated sections of the southern half of the United States, and warm-season fruits thrive best in the southern half of the country. In other words, all the fruits listed in Table 25.2 will seldom be grown in any one home orchard. For example, in California the English walnut takes the place of the pecan. In the northern states, the apple, peach, cherry, and black grape take the place of the pecan, muscadine grape, and fig, and along the Gulf Coast and in many parts of Florida,

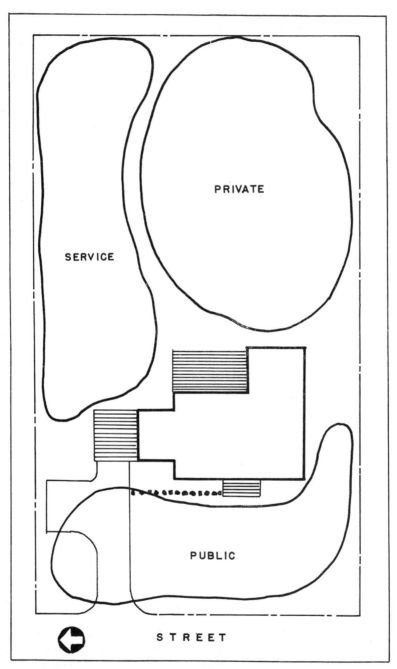

Fig. 25.2. *Principal areas of the home grounds.* (*Courtesy, Robert W. Gray, Virginia Polytechnic Institute.*)

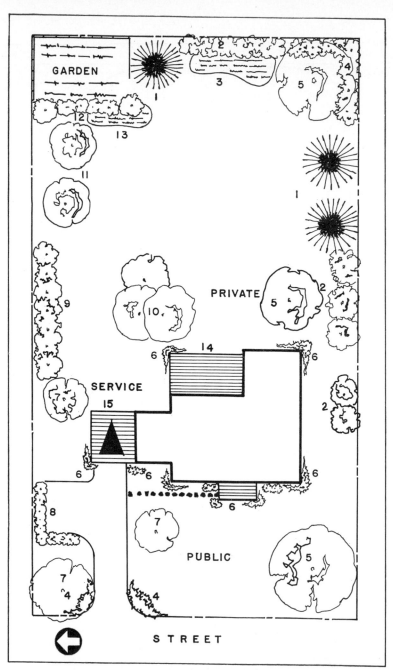

Fig. 25.3. *Beautification of the home grounds of Fig. 25.2. (Courtesy, Robert W. Gray, Virginia Polytechnic Institute.) 1. evergreen. 2. flowering shrubs for screen. 3. flower bed for annuals and perennials. 4. evergreen shrubs. 5. tree for shade and screen. 6. evergreen shrubs, foundation plants. 7. flowering tree. 8. flowering shrubs. 9. evergreen or deciduous shrubs for screen. 10. specimen tree for year-round interest. 11. dwarf fruit trees. 12. flowering shrubs for screen. 13. flower bed for bulbs. 14. patio. 15. carport with storage area.*

462

citrus fruits take the place of the apple and peach. Study the landscape plan and development of the home grounds in Figs. 25.2 and 25.3.

QUESTIONS

1. Contrast the peach and the redbud for use in landscaping small properties.
2. Show how fruit trees can be used to screen out undesirable views and to provide a background for the house.
3. In general, the average homemaker is more successful with bramble fruits, figs, and strawberries than with peaches, apples, and pears. Explain.

Page references followed by *t.* refer to tables